Physics of the
Earth's Interior

International Geophysics Series

Edited by

J. VAN MIEGHEM

Royal Belgian Meteorological Institute
Uccle, Belgium

Physics of the Earth's Interior

Beno Gutenberg

Seismological Laboratory
California Institute of Technology
Pasadena, California

Academic Press • New York and London • 1959

ACADEMIC PRESS INC.
111 Fifth Avenue
New York 3, N. Y.

United Kingdom Edition
Published by
ACADEMIC PRESS INC. (London) Ltd.
40 Pall Mall, London S.W. 1

Library of Congress Catalog Card Number 59-15508

PRINTED IN THE UNITED STATES OF AMERICA

Preface

"Physics of the Earth's Interior" embraces such a wide range of properties and processes that the space available in one volume imposes severe limitations on their discussion. Moreover, the uneven familiarity of any geophysicist with the many fields of natural science which are involved favors their uneven treatment. For these reasons, the author has limited discussions related to gravity, terrestrial magnetism, tectonic processes, and the history of the earth, to such problems which, if solved, may give information on the earth's interior. On the other hand, seismological investigations are discussed only insofar as they bear upon the structure of the earth and the physics of its interior; seismology is to be treated in detail in another monograph of this series.

Conclusions and hypotheses concerning the earth's interior are in a state of flux. Some basic conclusions which ten years ago were considered to be practically certain, in recent years have been found to be incorrect. Many other fundamental problems, such as the origin of the earth, its thermal history, the temperature, composition, and state of the core, or the so-called 20°-discontinuity in the mantle are just as controversial as they were one or two decades ago. Consequently, in many sections of the book the unsolved problems that are pointed out are more numerous than the reports of results which were apparently accomplished.

References follow each chapter. They have been selected with preference given to recent publications which either contain new results or more detailed observations or which include important additional references.

The author is grateful to Dr. H. Benioff for permission to use several unpublished illustrations which had been drafted by Mr. R. Gilman. Most of the other illustrations have been drafted or redrafted by Mr. L. Lenches, and a few by Mr. J. Nordquist.

BENO GUTENBERG

Seismological Laboratory, California Institute of Technology
Pasadena, California

September, 1959

Contents

7. Density, Pressure, Gravity, and Flattening in the Earth

8. Elastic Constants, and Elastic Processes in the Earth

9. Nonelastic Processes in the Earth

List of Frequently Used Symbols

(For symbols of waves through the earth, see Section 5.1).

a	Equatorial radius of the earth
a	Amplitudes
a,b	Various constants, defined in the text
c	Polar radius of the earth
c	Specific heat
d	Depth or thickness of a layer
f	Various functions and constants defined in the text
g	Gravity
h	Depth or elevation
h	One of "Love's numbers"
i	Angles of incidence
k	Bulk modulus
k	Heat conductivity
k	Coefficient of absorption
k^*	One of "Love's numbers"
l	One of "Love's numbers"
m	Mass
n	Number of data, etc.
n	Refractive index
o	The index zero refers to the earth's surface
p	Pressure
q	Various quantities defined in the text
r	Radius
r_0	Mean radius of the earth
s	Index related to deepest point of a ray
t	Time
u	Various quantities defined in the text
v	Velocity of transverse waves in km/sec
w	Volume
x,y	Horizontal components
z	Vertical component

A to G	Bullen's regions in the earth (Fig. 2.2)
$\left.\begin{array}{c} A \\ B \\ C \end{array}\right\}$	Various constants defined in the text
A	Moment of inertia corresponding to axis a
C	Moment of inertia corresponding to axis c
D	Specific depths, defined in the text
E	East
E	Young's modulus
F	Various factors, defined in the text
G	Constant of gravitation
H	Specific depths or elevations defined in the text
I	Longitudinal portion of seismic rays in the inner core
J	Energy
K	Longitudinal portion of rays in the outer core (or whole core)
K	Boltzmann constant
L	Wavelength
L	Heat of fusion
Lg	Channel wave in the granitic layer
M	Depth of the Mohorovičić discontinuity (thickness of the crust)
M	Magnitude of earthquakes
N	North
P	Rate of heat generation by radioactive material
P	Longitudinal waves in the mantle
Pa	Longitudinal channel wave below M
PcP	Longitudinal wave in the mantle, reflected at the core boundary
PP	Longitudinal wave in the mantle reflected at the surface

Q	Heat flux
Q	Various quantities, defined in the text
R	r/r_0
S	Stress
S	Strain rebound (Benioff)
S	Entropy
S	South
S	Transverse waves in the mantle
SH	Component of a transverse wave in a horizontal plane
SV	Component of a transverse wave in a vertical plane
Sa	Similar to Pa
ScS	Similar to PcP
SS	Similar to PP
T	Period
T	Temperature in degrees centigrade unless noted otherwise
T^*	Melting temperature
U	Group velocity in km/sec
V	Velocity of longitudinal waves in km/sec
$\overline{V}$	$= d\Delta/dt$, apparent velocity along the earth's surface in km/sec
W	West
W	Potential
Z	Elevation
α	Coefficient of thermal expansion
α	Flattening, $(a - c)/a$
α	Angles, defined in text
β	Volume thermal expansion
β	Various quantities defined in the text
γ	Gravity at sea level
γ	Shearing strain
γ	Grueneisen's ratio

γ	Combination of Love's numbers (Chapter 8)
δ	Combination of Love's numbers (Chapter 8)
δ	Logarithmic decrement
ϵ	Electronic charge
η	Radau's constant
η	Coefficient of viscosity
κ	Thermal diffusivity
λ	Electronic conductivity
λ	Lamé's constant
λ	Time of relaxation
λ_r	Time of retardation
μ	Coefficient of rigidity
μ	Coefficient of retarded elastic movement
ρ	Density
ρ	Radius of curvature
ρ_m	Mean density
σ	Electric conductivity
σ	Poisson's ratio
τ	Actual minus adiabatic temperature gradient
τ	Chandler period of nutation
φ	Latitude
ψ	Longitude
ω	Angular velocity
ω	Dip angle
ω	Opacity
Γ	$= 1 - (d\Phi/dr)/g$
Δ	Distance along earth's surface in km
Δ	Symbol for "change in"
Δg	Gravity anomaly
Θ	Angular distance in degrees
Λ	Combination of Love's numbers (Chapter 8)
Φ	$= V^2 - \frac{4}{3}v^2$
Ω	Operator (Eq. 9.3)

1. Fundamental Problems and Fundamental Data

1.1 Methods of Investigating the Earth's Interior, and the Accuracy of the Results

No direct observations exist of properties of the earth's interior below a depth of a few kilometers. Laboratory experiments may be used to investigate quantitatively the combined effects on rock samples of pressures and temperatures corresponding to those existing in the earth's crust, and some effects of higher temperatures and pressures have been studied qualitatively. However, the use of such results in investigations of processes and physical constants in the earth's mantle and core involves uncertainties which increase considerably with increasing depth. Especially, estimates of the temperature as well as of the composition of the earth's interior become more and more uncertain as the depth increases.

Most information on properties and processes below the uppermost portion of the earth's crust results from the application of theory to phenomena observed at the earth's surface. One example is the use of observed transmission times of elastic waves through the earth's interior to calculate the velocities of elastic waves as a function of depth. Another example is the investigation of the rigidity in the earth's interior on the basis of the observed tides of the earth's surface which are produced by the effects of tidal forces from sun and moon upon the whole earth.

In investigations of properties and processes at great depths in the earth, extrapolation of theoretical equations is frequently required extremely far beyond the range of conditions for which they have been developed. Similarly, numerical values of constants are sometimes used far beyond the range for which laboratory data on the one hand and theoretical information on the other hand exist. Examples of such investigations are the attempt to

1

calculate the coefficient of heat conductivity in the lower portion of the mantle, or to find the melting point of materials in the mantle and the core. Such difficulties arise frequently if depths are involved in which the pressure is on the one hand much greater than it is available for quantitative results in laboratories, but on the other hand much smaller than the minimum pressure which permits application of the Thomas–Dirac–Fermi model or other molecular models as a basis for theoretical calculations. The interpolation between results or equations for the two pressure ranges is required for many theories concerning the deep interior of the earth; however, extrapolations from either side are very difficult and usually contain theoretical as well as numerical assumptions which may lead to grave errors. Unfortunately, geophysicists are often not familiar enough with molecular theories to realize the underlying assumptions; frequently, results based on extrapolation of such theories far beyond the range, within which they are considered to be good approximations, are much less accurate than their users believe. Conclusions concerning the deep portion of the mantle and the core may, consequently, be subject to two major sources of error: those resulting from misinterpretation of observations, and those from application of theoretical equations which fit the problem only poorly or not at all and, in addition, may contain incorrectly estimated numerical factors. Frequently, the mathematical development of the equations is not the main source of errors, but the insufficiently known or incorrect solution of the physical side of the problem.

Most mathematical obstacles are encountered in attempted solutions of equations which have been set up in connection with problems concerning the upper portion of the earth, especially in seismology. In such instances we need frequently better approximations than those which are available, in order to get more accurate results on the basis of well known detailed observations. On the other hand, in problems related to the deep interior, the mathematical portion of the theory is frequently much more accurate than it is necessary, considering the inaccurate assumptions in connection with the physics of the processes, especially when molecular theories are involved.

Most of our conclusions about the earth's interior have been reached during the past fifty years. Many of them are still more or less doubtful. With the improvement of instruments and the increase in the number of observatories and of observations, it has been found repeatedly that conclusions which had been considered to be good approximations are far from correct.

Many results concerning the interior of the earth are based on observations of elastic waves which are produced by earthquakes or artificial explosions. Unfortunately, in many early investigations of the velocity of waves through the earth, inaccurate travel times had been used for these waves. This was partly a consequence of too low a magnification of seismographs for waves in the range of periods involved, usually between one and ten seconds, partly of too slow a speed of the drums used for recording and partly of uneven motion of these drums. Moreover, occasionally, misinterpretation of waves observed in seismograms or incorrect assumptions concerning the paths of such waves in the earth have resulted in relatively large errors concerning the structure of portions of the earth, and even in the reporting of discontinuities in the earth which do not exist.

Frequently, the method of least squares is very useful in investigations of properties of the earth's interior. However, sometimes small "probable errors" have been considered to be an indication of high accuracy of a conclusion, while actually they have been mainly an indication of good agreement between the observations. Systematic misinterpretation of seismograms, or use of incorrect assumptions in combining observations as a function of distance, may produce actual errors far in excess of the calculated "probable errors". Frequently, it is advisable to plot the observations in order to find out if there are different possibilities to combine them to curves. Travel time curves for longitudinal waves arriving at epicentral distances between about 200 and 1000 km are a case in point [Gutenberg, 1954, p. 341].

Geoscientists who in their research had to make use of findings in a field with which they are not familiar have occasionally quoted models, e.g., for the wave velocities as function of depth, as well established findings, although such models, sometimes a choice of several, had been proposed only as a working hypothesis. Occasionally, only a particular detail of such a model has been presented as a confirmed result. The "discontinuity at a depth of 413 km," which has been quoted repeatedly in the literature concerning the structure of the earth, is an example. It is usually called the "twenty degree discontinuity" and is discussed in more detail in Section 4.2. At the meeting of the *International Association of Seismology and Physics of the Earth's Interior* at Toronto in 1957 the question was raised, if there are indications for a discontinuity at a depth of the order of 400 km. Apparently, nobody believed that there is a discontinuity near 400 km, while depths near 200 km and near 500 km have been mentioned as a possible source for the observed complicated travel time curve near the twenty degree discontinuity. Others doubt the existence of any marked discontinuity at depths between 100 and at least 900 km.

Investigators agree very closely on some types of observational data, but as soon as such data are used for calculations the discrepancies may increase with the number of mathematical operations, especially if derivatives enter. For example, recent tables for the transmission times t of longitudinal waves through the earth as a function of the epicentral distance Δ (in km) along the earth's surface rarely deviate from each other as much as 3 sec in values up to over 1000 sec. However, frequently the "apparent velocity" $\bar{V} = d\Delta/dt$ along the earth's surface is needed as a function of Δ. The various curves for $\bar{V}$ as a function of Δ differ relatively more than those for $t(\Delta)$. If $\bar{V}^2$ enters, the relative errors are increased still more. In problems where differences between $\bar{V}^2$ for longitudinal waves and the corresponding $\bar{v}^2$ for transverse waves are involved, results based on nearly the same $t(\Delta)$ curves may differ by a factor of almost two at some distances.

A difficulty common to various types of problems is introduced by local differences in the structure of the earth's crust, especially between oceanic and continental areas. Usually, these differences do not seriously affect conclusions concerning the deep interior. But in many problems, for example in the determination of gravity at sea level, these differences may produce complications. While gravity at a given point of the earth's physical surface can be determined with high accuracy, the establishment of gravity at a common equipotential surface (usually sea level) requires assumptions concerning the crustal structure. As a consequence, corrected individual values of gravity at sea level, which are to be used as basis for equations for gravity at sea level as a function of the latitude, may locally have errors of an order of magnitude of a hundred times those of the original measurements.

There are many problems concerning the earth's interior about which opinions differ widely. For example, a rather wide range of figures is still being given for the temperature in the earth. One fundamental difficulty here, as in some other problems, is the fact that the history of the earth is unknown, although there seems now to be fair agreement that the age of the earth is about 4×10^9 years. In particular, there are still considerable differences in opinions concerning the question of whether the earth started as a cold body from relatively small solid particles, from a hot mass of gas, or in still another way. This has to be considered, if the temperature in the earth is calculated on the basis of an assumed history. Moreover, there is no full agreement about the amount of heat developed at various depths from radioactive sources inside the earth at different times, and still less about the heat conduction as a function of depth and time.

There is considerable disagreement about the density in the inner core of the earth; its composition; the question whether the inner core is solid or not; the reason for the relatively large increase in wave velocity in the outer portion of the mantle at a rate greater than that calculated from the effect of the increase in pressure; the problem, which, if any, discontinuities in the earth are caused by a change from one solid phase of a given material to another solid phase, or by a change in state, and which discontinuities are the result of chemical differences between two materials; there are many others.

Frequently, equations involved in theoretical research are rather complicated, and it may be necessary to use approximations. Specifically, in investigations of the earth's interior which are based on observations of seismic waves, equations frequently are applied which have been derived by neglecting terms of second (and higher) order. In using these equations, the assumptions made in their development are frequently overlooked. However, they imply, for example, that the energy flux is in the direction of the wave propagation. While this is correct for a homogeneous body, it does not generally hold if the wave velocity changes with depth. Equations have been formulated which avoid these approximations and could give a higher accuracy, but they are so complicated that they have not been used in investigations of the earth's interior. The application of the approximate equations may affect appreciably calculations of amplitudes of waves through the earth, but usually the errors resulting from their use in the calculation of wave velocities in the earth are relatively small.

In many problems, nonelastic behavior of materials in the earth plays an important role. Its introduction into theoretical research is needed, for example, in investigations of the propagation of elastic waves through the transition zone between the outer (liquid) and the inner (solid?) core. Moreover, it may enter the interpretation of observations connected with processes, in which friction plays a role. Theories of nonelastic behavior of materials are also important in the investigation of processes in which movements are involved lasting for hundreds of years or longer as in "subcrustal currents," or in movements of large blocks of the earth's outer portion relative to each other, or in "postglacial uplift". Usually, the theoretical treatment of such problems is made difficult by the necessary selection of assumptions, which, on the one hand, fit the process at least fairly well, and, on the other, lead to usable equations. Unfortunately, there is frequently no close agreement even among rheologists about the physics of such processes nor about their representation by equations.

As a result of the various types of errors which are made, frequently unconsciously, in theoretical assumptions concerning the physics of geophysical problems or the numerical constants involved in the theories, results of geophysical investigations are sometimes considered to be "certain" or "probable" by their authors, while actually they deserve a much lower degree of confidence. This has been pointed out especially by Birch [1952, p. 234]. Over-optimism about the accuracy of results is found more frequently when the deep interior of the earth with its poorly known physical conditions and the doubtful values of physical constants is concerned, than in connection with solutions referring to the upper portion of the earth. Here, effects of nonelastic processes may be a major source of unexpected errors.

Unfortunately, it is not possible to warn readers constantly not to rely too much on over-optimistic conclusions. To some extent, many scientists (including the author) have a tendency to overestimate occasionally the accuracy of their own findings and to pay too little attention to publications of scientists outside (and, sometimes, inside) their own special fields. On the other hand, it is nothing unusual that a tentative suggestion or "model" of a geophysicist is quoted by a writer in a different field as proof for one of his hypotheses. This is partly a consequence of the fact that no investigator of geophysical, geochemical, or geological problems is familiar with all fields of the earth sciences which are involved in his research. Moreover, for many problems concerning the earth's interior the observations do not permit a unique solution. This fact is usually pointed out by specialists who have arrived at certain probable solutions. However, others using such findings which have been published with certain limitations, create in their publications the impression that such solutions are definite unique results.

There are indications if the errors to be expected for a given solution are large or small. Great errors are unlikely if additional data, especially by use of new methods, confirm older conclusions. But there is good reason for doubt if more or improved data result in greater scattering of the deviations from the adopted conclusion, or if plotting of the residuals increases the deviations from an expected curve. "It is easy to draw a straight line through two points, but the problem may become difficult if there are three points."

The preceding discussion gives only a few points which have to be considered in judging the expected accuracy of findings concerning the interior of the earth. In many instances, we believed at an earlier date, say ten years ago that we knew much more about the earth than we believe we know at present. The history of our fundamental theories for the cause of terrestrial magnetism or of our hypotheses concerning the earth's core are excellent examples that Goethe's *"Es irrt der Mensch so lang er strebt"* (humans are erring as long as they seek the truth) applies to many of our conclusions about the earth's interior.

1.2 The Figure of the Earth and Related Constants

The most useful approximation to the complicated physical surface of the earth is an *ellipsoid* of rotation around the short polar axis. At Madrid, 1924, a set of quantities were internationally adopted which are internally consistent. They include the equatorial radius, $a = 6378.388$ km and the polar radius $c = 6356.912$ km; $a - c = 21.476$ km; the *flattening*, $\alpha = (a - c)/a$, is assumed to be exactly $\alpha = 1/297 = 0.00336700$ [for details, see, e.g., Landolt-Börnstein, 1952, p. 259; or Heiskanen and Meinesz, 1958, Chapter 3]. Most recent determinations of the equatorial radius give less than the internationally adopted value; Jeffreys [1948] found $a = 6378.099 \pm 0.116$ km; Jones [1954, p. 17] included gravity observations and calculated $a = 6378.084 \pm 0.078$ km; Chovitz and Fischer [1956] found $a = 6378.260 \pm 0.100$ km. Results for the flattening have changed relatively little. Since about 1830, values near $1/\alpha = 297$ have been preferred, e.g. by Darwin and by Helmert. Jones [1954] found $1/\alpha = 297.300 \pm 0.065$, Jeffreys [1948] calculated $1/\alpha = 297.10 \pm 0.36$, while Kaula [1958] considers $1/\alpha = 298.15 \pm 0.26$ to be the best approximation on the basis of gravity observations.

In problems in which it is sufficiently accurate to consider the earth to be a *sphere*, usually the earth's radius r_0 is assumed to be equal to r_V, the radius of a sphere with a volume equal to that of the ellipsoid, but neither the radius for a sphere of equal surface (r_S) nor the mean radius $r_m = (2a + c)/3$ differ much from r_V. The data for the international ellipsoid give

$$r_V = 6371.221 \text{ km} \qquad r_S = 6371.228 \text{ km} \qquad r_m = 6371.229 \text{ km.}$$

For finding distances on the earth it is frequently necessary to assume that it is a sphere to avoid tedious calculations. To achieve sufficient accuracy, e.g. for calculation of distances in seismology, it may be necessary to use geocentric latitudes φ' instead of geographic latitudes φ:

$$\tan \varphi' = (1 - \alpha^2) \tan \varphi = 0.993277 \tan \varphi \tag{1.1}$$

if $1/\alpha = 297$. Tables for $\sin \varphi'$ and $\cos \varphi'$ may be found in Anonymous [1951]. The error in calculating distances by use of geographic latitudes may exceed 40 km.

The following are quantities derived from the data for the international ellipsoid. A mean degree of a meridian is 111.137 km, that of the equator 111.324 km. On a sphere with a volume equal to that of the international ellipsoid, 1 degree is 111. 199 km. The surface of the *ellipsoid* is 5.101×10^{18} cm^2, its volume 1.083×10^{27} cm^3.

The calculation of the *mass* of the earth depends on the calculation of the mean density ρ_m of the earth (Section 7.1). The mass is found to be near 5.975×10^{27} g; the last decimal is not certain. The ratio of the mass of the earth to that of the sun is near 3.00×10^{-6}, its reciprocal is given by Jones [1954] as $333,422 \pm 114$, by Jung [1956] as 332,290.

According to Jung [1956, p. 637], the main *moments of inertia* A relative to the equatorial axes and C relative to the axis of rotation are $A = 8.092 \times 10^{44}$ g cm^2, $C = 8.118 \times 10^{44}$ g cm^2 on the assumption of the international ellipsoid. Bullard [1957, p. 25] uses 8.091×10^{44} g cm^2 for the mean moment of inertia. The most frequently needed combination of A and C is $(C - A)/C$, which is usually given as 0.003273, or its reciprocal as 305.5; Jung [1956, p. 637] gives 305.8 ± 0.8.

Attempts have been made to approximate the figure of the earth by a *triaxial ellipsoid*. Various investigators agree that on this assumption the long axis of the equator is within about 20° towards the meridians of Greenwich and of 180° longitude; the differences of the two equatorial axes have been found to be between about 150 and 350 m. Nevertheless, many (including the author) doubt that the equator is elliptic [e.g. Heiskanen and Meinesz, 1958, p. 79; Heiskanen and Uotila, 1958, p. 207]. The ellipticities which have been found for the equator may be mainly the effect of systematic errors in assumptions made in the calculations, especially considering the fact that two major blocks of continents are separated by two oceans; moreover the points of observations are distributed very unevenly over the earth.

For other approximations to the figure of the earth, *geoids* are used which are equipotential surfaces near mean sea level. They do not deviate by more than about ± 100 m from the nearest ellipsoid. A geoid may have local portions which are concave inward [for details, see e.g. Jung, 1956]. Among other approximations to the figure of the earth which have been used are various spheroids. There are differences of opinion about the use of some of them [e.g. Jeffreys, 1952, p. 183; Jung, 1956, pp. 555–557; Kaula, 1959].

1.3 Gravity at Sea Level

If the figure, mass distribution, and motion are given for a planet, we can calculate the gravitational acceleration on any equipotential surface in the planet. Calculations of gravity at the earth's surface are usually based on the internationally adopted ellipsoid (Section 1.2) with the flattening α. If γ_e is the gravity at sea level at the equator, the corresponding gravity γ_0 in the geographic latitude φ at sea level is given [e.g. Heiskanen and Meinesz, 1958, p. 52] by

$$\gamma_0 = \gamma_e \left[1 + \beta \sin^2 \varphi - \frac{\alpha}{8} (5F - \alpha) \sin^2 2\varphi + \cdots \right] \qquad (1.2)$$

where

$$\beta = \left(\frac{5}{2} - \frac{17}{14} \alpha \right) F \qquad \text{and} \qquad F = \frac{\omega^2 a}{\gamma_e} \qquad (1.3)$$

ω is the angular velocity of the earth's rotation, F the ratio of the centrifugal acceleration to the gravitational acceleration at the equator. If we introduce the internationally (Stockholm, 1930) adopted values for α, F, and γ_e we find the internationally adopted equation

$$\gamma_0 = 978.049 \ (1 + 0.0052884 \sin^2 \varphi - 0.0000059 \sin^2 2\varphi + \cdots) \ \text{gal.}$$
$$(1.4)$$

The neglected terms are believed to contribute less than $\frac{1}{4}$ mgal.

The value of γ_e was computed in 1928 by Heiskanen on the basis of gravity observations at several thousand stations for which he had reduced gravity isostatically (Section 3.7) to sea level. It is based on the gravity at a reference point at Potsdam. Unfortunately, a value has been assumed for this reference point which is too great by about 0.013 gal. The value of β follows from Eq. (1.3). It should be noted that Eq. (1.3) contains the adopted value for the flattening α so that any change in the assumed value of α results in a change of β, and vice versa. Table 1.1 gives selected recent determinations of γ_e and β. The third coefficient in Eq. (1.4) has been assumed since 1930 to be 59×10^{-7}. It depends on the distribution of density in the earth. Before 1930, its value had been taken as 70×10^{-7}. On the basis of Bullen's values for the density in the earth (Section 7.5) Bullard [1948] has calculated 78.7×10^{-7} for this numerical factor. Its effect on the resulting γ_0 is small.

There is no doubt that all numerical factors in Eq. (1.4) should be improved. Kaula [1958] has pointed out that systematic errors have resulted from neglecting the effect of elevation on gravity in areas which have not been surveyed. However, a change in one of the internationally adopted quantities requires changes in all others. Consequently, a revision of all has been postponed at recent international meetings until data for more locations have been calculated, and the value at the base in Potsdam is

TABLE 1.1. SELECTED VALUES OF THE CONSTANTS γ_e (GRAVITY AT THE EQUATOR AT SEA LEVEL) BASED ON $g = 981.247$ GAL AT THE BASE IN POTSDAM, AND IN β OF EQ. (1.2), AND VALUE OF THE GRAVITY γ_p AT THE POLES

Author	Year	γ_e gal	β	γ_p gal
Internationally adopted	1930	978.0490	0.0052884	983.221
Heiskanen	1938	.0451	53027	.231
Jeffreys	1949	.0544	52790	.218
Schütte	1950	.0520	52827	.219
Uotila	1957	.0496	52934	.227
Heiskanen and Uotila	1958	.0497	52902	.224
Kaula	1958	.0404	53014	.225

better known. Heiskanen and Meinesz [1958, p. 76] point out that no errors from incorrect coefficients in Eq. (1.4) or in the value at the base in Potsdam produce noticeable errors in conclusions concerning the crust or interior of the earth, as long as all observations and calculations are based on the same system. Most calculations require differences in gravity values, not the absolute values. However, "from a purely scientific point of view, it is best to have as correct a gravity system as possible" [Heiskanen and Meinesz, p. 76] and to avoid accumulation of even small errors.

1.4 Astronomical Data

The inclination of the ecliptic is $23° 27' 8''. 26 - 0.4684 \times (t - 1900)$ according to Jung [1956, p. 632]. Other astronomical figures concerning the earth are:

Solar day: 86,400 sec.

Sidereal day: 86,164.09 sec. For changes in the length of the day, see Jones [1954, pp. 32, 35; 1956, pp. 18–23]

Angular velocity of the earth: $7.29211508 \times 10^{-5}$ radians/sec = $15.0410683''$/sec.

Rotational energy: 2.160×10^{36} ergs
Velocity at the equator: 46,500 cm/sec
Centrifugal force at the equator: 3.392 cm/sec^2
Centrifugal force/gravity at the equator: 0.00346
Gravitational constant: $G = (6.67 \pm 0.01) \times 10^{-8}$ cm^3/g sec^2
Mean distance earth–sun: 149.504×10^6 km $= 24,439$ r_0
Present eccentricity of the earth's orbit: 0.01674
Average daily movement of the earth around the sun: 3548″.19
Average velocity around the sun: 29.8 km/sec; maximum, 30.8 km/sec;
    minimum, 29.3 km/sec
Perihelion: about January 2
Sidereal year: 365.2564 solar days $= 3.1558 \times 10^7$ sec
Period of the precession of the equinoxes: 25,735 years
Data for the moon:
    Distance moon–earth: mean, 384,400 km; maximum, 406,740 km;
    minimum, 356,410 km.
    Density of the moon: 3.335; radius 1738 km
    Ratio mass moon/mass earth 1:81.53

References

Anonymous [1951]. "The geocentric direction cosines of seismological observatories."
18 pp. Intern. Assoc. Seismol., Kew Observatory.

Birch, F. [1952]. Elasticity and constitution of the earth's interior. *J. Geophys. Research*
57, 227–286.

Bullard, E. C. [1948]. The figure of the earth. *Geophysics Suppl.* **5**, 186–192.

Bullard, E. C. [1957]. The density within the earth. *Verhandel. Ned. Geol. Mijnbouwk.*
Genoot. (*Geol. Ser.*, Gedenkboek V. Meinesz), **18**, 23–41.

Chovitz, B. and Fischer I. [1956]. A new determination of the figure of the earth from
arcs. *Trans. Am. Geophys. Union* **37**, 534–545. [1957]. Discussion. **38**, 579–580.

Gutenberg, B. [1954]. Low-velocity layers in the earth's mantle. *Bull. Geol. Soc. Am.*
65, 337–348.

Heiskanen, W. A., and Meinesz, F. A. V. [1958]. "The Earth and its Gravity Field," 478
pp. McGraw-Hill, New York.

Heiskanen, W. A., and Uotila, U. A. [1958]. Some recent studies of gravity formulas.
In "Contributions in Geophysics" (H. Benioff, M. Ewing, B. F. Howell, and F.
Press, eds.), Vol. **1**, pp. 200–209. Pergamon, New York.

Jeffreys, H. [1948]. The figures of the earth and moon. *Monthly Notices Roy. Astron. Soc.*
Geophys. Suppl. **5**, 219–247.

Jeffreys, H. [1952]. "The Earth," 3rd ed., 392 pp. Cambridge Univ. Press, London and
New York.

Jones, H. S. [1954]. Dimensions and rotation. *In* "The Earth as a Planet" (G. P. Kuiper,
ed.), pp. 1–41. Univ. Chicago Press, Chicago, Illinois.

Jones, H. S. [1956]. The rotation of the earth. *In* "Encyclopedia of Physics" (S. Flügge, ed.), Vol. **47**, pp. 1–23. Springer, Berlin.

Jung, K. [1956]. Figur der Erde. *In* "Encyclopedia of Physics" (S. Flügge, ed.), Vol. **47**, pp. 534–637. Springer, Berlin.

Kaula, W. M. [1958]. Gravity formulas utilizing correlation with elevation. *Trans. Am. Geophys. Union* **39**, 1027–1033.

Kaula, W. M. [1959]. Reconciliation of Stokes' function and astro-geodetic geoid determinations. *J. Geophys. Research* **64**, 61–71.

Landolt-Börnstein [1952]. Astronomie und Geophysik. *In* "Zahlenwerte und Funktionen" (A. Euken, ed.), 6th ed., Vol. **3**, 795 pp. Springer, Berlin.

2. The Structure of the Earth

2.1 Historical Review

As soon as the mean density of the earth had been found to be appreciably higher than the density in the crust, it was concluded that the material in the deep portions of the earth must have a relatively high density. Wiechert [1897] had made the first calculations on a theoretical basis. He had assumed that a metal core of practically constant density is surrounded by a rock mantle in which the density does not vary appreciably and has an average value between 3.0 and 3.4 g/cm³. Wiechert furthermore had supposed three values (296, 297, and 298) for the reciprocal of the flattening and he had taken 5.53 g/cm³ as the mean density of the earth. He had concluded that on these assumptions the ratio of the radius of the core to the thickness of the rock mantle is between 3.0 and 4.0, and that the mean density of the core is slightly greater than 8. Wiechert finally had pointed out that this density is of the order of magnitude of the density to be expected for compressed iron in the core, and he had inferred that the earth consists of an iron core with a radius of roughly 5000 km which is surrounded by an approximately 1400 km thick rock mantle.

The first attempt to find the structure of the whole earth from transmission times of earthquake waves through the earth had been made by Oldham [1906]. While he had not considered his data (Table 2.1) good enough for mathematical treatment, he had concluded that the crust consists of heterogeneous rock, that below this crust down to a depth corresponding to about 0.4 of the earth's radius (depth of roughly 3800 km) there is uniform material, while the core (radius about 2600 km) has radically different properties. On the basis of the transmission times for the earliest waves through the earth which had been reported by seismological stations after earthquakes, he had plotted one continuous curve which he had supposed to represent the transmission time curve (time as function of epicentral distance) for direct longitudinal waves through the earth. Actually, they belonged to various longitudinal phases. Oldham had concluded that the transition from the mantle to the core is rapid but not discontinuous. On the other hand, the travel time curve which he had assumed for transverse waves, was discontinuous.

After Wiechert [1907] had developed the theory of seismic waves, and Zoeppritz and Geiger [1909] had calculated velocities of longitudinal waves (Fig. 2.1) in the mantle, Oldham had modified his views. He then had concluded that below a roughly 30 km thick crust is "a shell of about half

TABLE 2.1. TRAVEL TIMES OF LONGITUDINAL WAVES (P) AND TRANSVERSE WAVES (S) ACROSS THE EARTH ACCORDING TO OLDHAM [1906], GUTENBERG [1914]. AND AVERAGE TIMES ASSUMED IN 1958. θ = EPICENTRAL DISTANCE IN DEGREES. A, TRAVEL TIMES OF P; B, TRAVEL TIMES OF S; C, TRAVEL TIMES OF SS.

θ	A			B		C
	Oldham [1906] min	Gutenberg [1914] min:sec	1958 min:sec	Oldham [1906] min	1958 min:sec	1958 min:sec
30	6	6:22	6:13	11	11:10	
60	11	10:20	10:09	19	18:23	
90	15	13:18	13:03	25	23:25	
120	18		15:10	29	28:08	36:45
			18:54			
150	21	20:00	19:50	45	—	42:45
180	22	20:24	20:14	50	—	47:50

to three fifths of the radius in depth, consisting of matter to which neither the term solid nor fluid can be applied. . . . While highly rigid as against stresses of short duration . . . it is capable of yielding to stresses of small amount if of secular duration. At its lower limit this passes somewhat rapidly, but more gradually than at the outer limit into a central nucleus. . . . Here the material may be described as fluid." Oldham had realized in 1919 that his "transverse waves through the core" of 1906 are actually transverse waves reflected at the earth's surface (SS) which have not entered the core (compare last column in Table 2.1).

Between 1907 and 1910, great progress had been achieved. Zoeppritz [1907] had made the first calculations of wave velocities inside the earth on the basis of approximate travel time curves (transmission time as function of epicentral distance) for longitudinal waves (P) and transverse waves (S). On the basis of theoretical developments by Herglotz, Wiechert

[Wiechert and Geiger, 1910] had worked out an accurate and fairly rapid method, to calculate the velocities of waves through the earth as a function of depth, if the travel time curve is continuous, and Geiger (loc cit.)

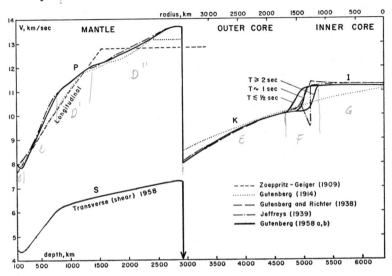

FIG. 2.1. Velocity V of longitudinal waves (P, K, I) and transverse waves (S) in the earth. T = period.

had applied this method to several travel time curves, including those of Oldham [1906]. If r_s is the radius to the deepest point of a ray arriving at an angular epicentral distance $\Theta = \Theta_s$ then

$$\log r_s = 3.80393 - 0.0024127 \int_0^{\Theta_s} q \, d\Theta \qquad (2.1)$$

where $\cosh q$ is the ratio of the fixed apparent velocity $(d\Theta/dt)_s$ in degrees/sec at the distance Θ_s on the earth's surface to the variable apparent velocity from $\Theta = 0$ to $\Theta = \Theta_s$. The velocity V_s at the depth r_s is found from

$$V_s = \frac{r_s}{r_0} \left(\frac{d\Delta}{dt}\right)_s \qquad (2.2)$$

where Δ is the epicentral distance measured along the surface in kilometers, corresponding to Θ in degrees; $(d\Delta/dt)_s$ is the apparent velocity at the distance Δ_s in km/sec; r_0 is the radius of the earth.

On the basis of Zoeppritz' [1907] curves for the velocity as a function of depth which are similar to those of Zoeppritz–Geiger [1909] in Fig. 2.1, Wiechert [1907] had concluded that the earth's core begins at a depth of roughly 1500 km. However, already in 1907 Wiechert [1907, footnote on p. 508; see also Wiechert, 1908] had pointed out that longitudinal waves from the neighborhood of Samoa, where he had installed seismographs, arrive at Göttingen with a delay of about 2 min, indicating that the velocity must decrease at some depth below 1500 km.

To improve the findings about the core, Gutenberg [1914] has studied records of earthquakes which had epicentral distances of over 80° from Göttingen. He has found that at a depth of 2900 km the velocity of longitudinal waves decreases from $13\frac{1}{4}$ to $8\frac{1}{2}$ km/sec (Fig. 2.1), and that the radius of the core is about 3500 km. Geiger and Gutenberg [1912] had found earlier that the constitution of the mantle changes irregularly but not discontinuously at three depths. The major of these "discontinuities of second order" is the one which Wiechert and Zoeppritz had located at a depth of 1500 km. As a consequence of better travel time data and more accurate methods of calculation, the depth of this boundary, which originally had been considered by Wiechert to indicate the surface of the core, has been found at smaller and smaller depths and is considered now to be at a depth of about 950 km (Fig. 2.1).

If the epicentral distances Θ increase beyond 103°, the amplitudes of direct longitudinal waves P (through the crust and mantle only) decrease rapidly with distance, and gradually direct short-period P-waves disappear on seismograms. However, P-waves having periods exceeding about 10 sec are frequently observed as far as $\Theta = 140°$ in major earthquakes, and even farther on records on some great earthquakes. These waves are considered to be diffracted in the mantle along the core boundary.

At distances between about 100° and 140°, longitudinal waves with periods of the order of magnitude of 1 sec are observed. They follow the diffracted P-waves after several minutes. On records of earthquakes originating at distances exceeding 140°, the seismograms usually begin with relatively large impulses which are produced by longitudinal waves through the outer portion of the core.

The short-period waves which follow the diffracted P-waves at epicentral distances between about 100° and 140° after a few minutes, had been believed originally to be diffracted inside the core. However, Lehmann [1936] has pointed out, that the range of over 40° in angular distance over which they are observed is too great for this explanation. She has suggested that the core consists of two portions, the outer and the inner core, and that the wave velocity in the inner core is higher than that in the outer core. Gutenberg and Richter [1938] have tried to calculate the radius of the boundary between the two portions of the core and have concluded that

the transition from the outer to the inner core begins about 1500 km from
the earth's center and covers a zone about 300 km wide (Fig. 2.1). On the
other hand, Jeffreys [1939, 1952] assumes that the velocity decreases in a
layer between the outer and the inner core, and that at the bottom of this
layer there is a discontinuity between this layer, belonging to the outer
core, and the inner core (Fig. 2.1). There seems to be general agreement
that the observed travel times do not fit a sudden increase in velocity between the outer and inner core, unless one *assumes* a preceding decrease in
velocity, for which, however, there is no direct indication.

Finally, Gutenberg [1957, 1958b] has concluded that in the transition
zone from the outer to the inner core short waves seem to travel faster than
long waves (Fig. 2.1) and that this probably indicates a zone of transition
from liquid to solid material of the same kind. Similar conclusions, based on
nonseismological reasoning, had been drawn earlier by others [e.g., Bullen,
1953, p. 225].

2.2 The Boundaries of the Major Units of the Earth

On the basis of findings from elastic waves, the earth has been divided
into the *crust*, the outer and inner *mantle* and the *outer* and the *inner core*
(Fig. 2.2). The *Mohorovičić discontinuity* at which the velocity of longitu-

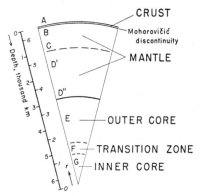

Fig. 2.2. Layers in the earth. The letters A to G correspond to subdivisions of Bullen
[1956] after revision [Gutenberg, 1958a].

dinal waves jumps to over 8 km/sec from a smaller value (frequently 6 to
7 km/sec) above it, is usually taken as the boundary between the crust and
the mantle. For other definitions of "crust", see Section 3.1.

The German expressions *Steinmantel*, which has later been condensed to *Mantel*, and *Kern* have been used since Wiechert [1896, 1897]. The English designations "crust," "mantle," and "core" have been in general use at least since 1940 [e.g. Daly, 1940, p. 1], after originally the expression "shell" had been preferred to "mantle." The corresponding French terms are *écorce* (or *croûte terrestre*), *manteau*, and *noyau*. A more detailed subdivision into regions, marked by the letters A to G has been suggested by Bullen [1953]. Fig. 2.2 shows his revised subdivisions [Bullen, 1956, p. 104]. Gutenberg [1958a] has suggested revision of the boundary between B and C. A revised definition of F will become necessary as soon as more definite data become available for the travel times of the waves through the transition zone between outer and inner core [Gutenberg, 1958b].

2.3 Causes for Discontinuities in the Earth

Discontinuities in the earth may be caused either by changes in the chemical composition of the material in the earth or by changes in phase of a given material. Phase changes may occur between a solid and a liquid phase (change in state) or between two different solid phases.

The discontinuities between the various layers in the uppermost 100 km below the sediments are caused mainly by differences in silica content between distinct layers. For the corresponding major divisions, Adams [1951, p. 72] has proposed the terms *sialic layer*, *simatic layer*, and *ultra-simatic layer*. "The simatic layer is arbitrarily defined as a layer in which the chemical composition of the rock is intermediate in silica content, i.e., corresponds to a gabbro, while the sialic and the ultra-simatic layers are defined, respectively, as ones in which the rocks are significantly more siliceous and less siliceous in chemical composition." The crust is then composed of sialic and simatic layers, while at least the upper portion of the mantle is formed by ultrasimatic rocks.

For practical purposes, the boundaries between the layers of the crust below the sediments are drawn on the basis of the velocities of seismic waves. In the sediments, these velocities depend appreciably on the age of the sediments and on their depth, that is on pressure and temperature. Both affect the velocities in the sialic and simatic layers, too.

The Mohorovičić discontinuity is usually considered to correspond to the boundary between simatic and chemically different ultrasimatic material. However, Lees [1953] has come to the conclusion that "geological evidence shows the extreme improbability that there can be a layered arrangement of this type. . . . An alternative explanation of the seismic facts, more acceptable geologically, is that the discontinuities result from phase modification."

The mantle is generally believed to consist of ultrabasic rock. The relatively small change in velocity in its upper 200 km (Fig. 2.1)—apparently including a slight decrease in wave velocity at least under most continents—is probably the effect of changes in pressure and temperature. At depths between 200 and 950 km, there is a faster increase in the wave velocities than could be produced by the pressure. Gradual changes in composition or in phases have been suggested as cause. Below a depth of about 950 km, the increase in velocity corresponds approximately to the rate to be expected as a consequence of the increase in pressure.

There is general agreement that the outer core is liquid and does not transmit transverse waves; the inner core is being considered to be solid by many, but there is no proof. It is widely believed that the whole core consists mainly of an iron–nickel alloy. However, some consider the possibility of a phase change at the boundary between the mantle and the core, and they assume the same chemical composition for both. On the other hand, higher content of hydrogen in the core than in the mantle has been considered by a few to be the reason for the sudden decrease in wave velocity at the core boundary.

References

Adams, L. H. [1951]. Elastic properties of materials of the earth's crust. *In* "Internal Constitution of the Earth" (B. Gutenberg, ed.), 2nd ed., pp. 50–80. Dover, New York.

Bullen, K. E. [1953]. "Introduction to the Theory of Seismology," 2nd ed., 296 pp. Cambridge Univ. Press, London and New York.

Bullen, K. E. [1956]. Seismic wave transmission. *In* "Encyclopedia of Physics" (S. Flügge, ed.), Vol. **47**, pp. 75–118. Springer, Berlin.

Daly, R. A. [1940]. "Strength and Structure of the Earth," 434 pp. Prentice Hall, New York.

Geiger, L., and B. Gutenberg [1912]. Ueber Erdbebenwellen. VB. Konstitution des Erdinnern, erschlossen aus dem Bodenverückungsverhältnis der einmal reflektierten zu den direkten longitudinalen Erdbebenwellen. *Nachr. Ges. Wiss. Göttingen Math. physik. Kl.* **1912,** 144–206.

Gutenberg, B. [1914]. Über Erdbebenwellen VIIA. Beobachtungen an Registrierungen von Fernbeben in Göttingen und Folgerungen über die Konstitution des Erdkörpers. *Nachr. Ges. Wiss. Göttingen Math. physik. Kl.* **1914,** 166–218.

Gutenberg, B. [1957]. The "boundary" of the earth's inner core. *Trans. Am. Geophys. Union* **38,** 750–753.

Gutenberg, B. [1958a]. Velocity of seismic waves in the earth's mantle. *Trans. Am. Geophys. Union* **39**, 486–489.

Gutenberg, B. [1958b]. Caustics produced by waves through the earth's core. *Geophys. J.* **1**, 238–248.

Gutenberg, B., and Richter, C. F. [1938]. P' and the earth's core. *Monthly Notices Roy. Astron. Soc. Geophys. Suppl.* **4**, 363–372.

Jeffreys, H. [1939]. The times of the core waves (second paper). *Monthly Notices Roy. Astron. Soc. Geophys. Suppl.* **4**, 594–615.

Jeffreys, H. [1952]. "The Earth." 3rd ed., 392 pp. Cambridge Univ. Press, London and New York.

Lees, G. M. [1953]. The evolution of a shrinking earth. *Quart. J. Geol. Soc. London* **109**, 217–257.

Lehmann, I. [1936]. P'. *Publs. Bur. Central Seismol. Intern. Trav. Sci.* (A) **14**, 87–115.

Oldham, R. D. [1906]. The constitution of the earth as revealed by earthquakes, *Quart. J. Geol. Soc.* London, **62**, 456–475.

Oldham, R. D. [1919]. The interior of the earth. *Geol. Mag.* **6**, 18–27.

Wiechert, E. [1896]. Ueber die Beschaffenheit des Erdinnern, *Sitzber. Physik.-ökonom. Ges. Königsberg* **37**, 4–5.

Wiechert, E. [1897]. Ueber die Massenverteilung im Innern der Erde, *Nachr. Ges. Wiss. Göttingen Math. physik. Kl.* **1897**, 221–243.

Wiechert, E. [1907]. Ueber Erdbebenwellen. I. Theoretisches über die Ausbreitung der Erdbebenwellen. *Nachr. Ges. Wiss. Göttingen Math. physik. Kl.* **1907**, 415–529.

Wiechert, E. [1908]. Die Erdbebenforschung, ihre Hilfsmittel und ihre Resultate für die Geophysik. *Physik. Z.* **9**, 36–47.

Wiechert, E., and Geiger, L. [1910]. Bestimmung des Weges der Erdbebenwellen im Erdinnern. *Physik. Z.* **11**, 294–311.

Zoeppritz, K. [1907]. Ueber Erdbebenwellen. II. Laufzeitkurven. *Nachr. Ges. Wiss. Göttingen Math. physik. Kl.* **1907**, 529–549.

Zoeppritz, K., and Geiger, L. [1909]. Ueber Erdbebenwellen. III. Berechnung von Weg und Geschwindigkeit der Vorläufer. Die Poisson'sche Konstante in Erdinnern. *Nachr. Ges. Wiss. Göttingen, Math. physik. Kl.* **1909**, 400–429.

3. The Earth's Crust

3.1 Definitions

The word "crust" indicates a hard external covering of an object in contrast to a softer interior. Correspondingly, the expression "earth's crust" was originally used for a crystalline shell of the earth in contrast to a supposedly vitreous "substratum" [Fisher, 1889]. Later, "crust" was considered synonymous with *lithosphere* (outer shell having a yield strength supposedly of the order of 10^9 dynes/cm^2) in contrast to the *asthenosphere* at greater depth (with much smaller yield strength, permitting viscous or plastic flow under relatively small stresses). This definition has the disadvantage that the transition from the lithosphere to the asthenosphere is gradual, without a definite boundary. Partly for this reason most geophysicists now define the Mohorovičić discontinuity as the crust's lower boundary. The author follows this definition of crust.

The layer immediately above the Mohorovičić discontinuity is frequently the sima (or gabbro-type) layer of the geologists, the material below is probably ultrasima (see definitions in Section 2.3). Expressions such as sialic, granitic, basaltic, ultrabasic layers are used by most geophysicists to indicate the velocities of elastic waves in the respective layers above and below the Mohorovičić discontinuity without reference to their composition. This may vary appreciably from place to place in a given layer, although frequently there is no great discrepancy between the geological and the geophysical use of the terms. Other definitions of the word crust include that by Benioff [1954] as the roughly 700 km thick shell in which earthquakes are known to occur. It is important that the word crust be defined by every author using it.

21

3.2 Methods of Determining Velocities in Layers and Their Thickness

The most important methods of determining properties of layers in the crust are based on the investigation of *elastic waves* produced either by earthquakes or by artificial explosions. Earthquake waves have the advantage of greater energy and larger amplitudes, but their use requires the cal-

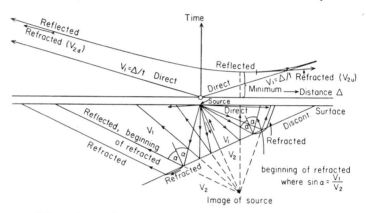

FIG. 3.1. Schematic travel time curves (top) and wave paths (below) of direct, reflected, and refracted waves in a crust consisting of two homogeneous layers with velocities V_1 and V_2 respectively, if the layers are separated by a dipping discontinuity.

culation of four unknown quantities: the origin time, the focal depth, and the two coordinates of the epicenter. The last three or all of them are usually known in artificial explosions. A detailed description of the methods used to find the crustal structure by artificial explosions in oceanic areas has been given, e.g., by Gaskell and associates [1958].

Methods of locating earthquakes are described in modern textbooks of seismology [e.g., Richter, 1958]. Methods of calculating the thickness of crustal layers and the wave velocities as function of depth are discussed in detail in textbooks on seismic exploration [e.g., Dix, 1952]. These or similar equations are used to find the corresponding properties of the crustal layers from earthquake records, considering, however, the effect of the focal depth.

There are two different types of such methods, one using refracted waves and another based on reflected waves (Fig. 3.1). The following are some of the equations which are used if it can be assumed that the layers are horizontal, that the velocity is constant within each layer, and that the curvature of the earth can be neglected. If t is the travel time (time of transmission from the source to the point of observation), Δ the distance in kilometers from the epicenter (point vertically above the starting point of motion), V_1 the velocity in km/sec in the upper layer, V_2 in the second layer, V_3 in the third layer, then

$$V_1 = \left(\frac{d\Delta}{dt}\right)_1, \quad V_2 = \left(\frac{d\Delta}{dt}\right)_2, \quad V_3 = \left(\frac{d\Delta}{dt}\right)_3. \qquad (3.1)$$

The values of $(d\Delta/dt)_1$, $(d\Delta/dt)_2$, $(d\Delta/dt)_3$ have to be found for the branch of the time–distance curve which represents transmission times or arrival times of the waves which have their deepest point respectively in the first, second, and third layer.

If the source is in the surface, the travel time t_f of the waves refracted through the second layer is given by

$$t_f = \frac{2h_1 \sqrt{V_2^2 - V_1^2}}{V_1 V_2} + \frac{|\Delta|}{V_2}. \qquad (3.2)$$

The thickness h_1 of the first layer is given by

$$h_1 = \frac{V_2 t_f - \Delta}{2 \sqrt{(V_2/V_1)^2 - 1}}. \qquad (3.3)$$

The transmission time t_r of waves reflected at the bottom of the first layer is given by

$$t_r = \frac{\sqrt{4h^2 + \Delta^2}}{V_1}. \qquad (3.4)$$

If waves reflected at the bottom of the first layer, and waves refracted through the second layer arrive simultaneously at the distance Δ^*, then

$$h_1 = \frac{\Delta^*}{2} \sqrt{\frac{V_2 - V_1}{V_2 + V_1}}. \qquad (3.5)$$

If the discontinuity between the first and second layers is dipping and forms the angle ω with the horizontal, the transmission time of the refracted wave is given by

$$t_f = \frac{1}{V_1} [\Delta \sin (i_1 \pm \omega) + 2d \cos i_1 \cos \omega] \qquad (3.6)$$

where d is the depth of the discontinuity under the source, which again is assumed to be in the surface; the minus sign is to be used in the direction of decreasing d; i_1 is the angle of incidence at the discontinuity in layer 1:

$$\sin i_1 = V_1/V_2. \qquad (3.7)$$

For the reflected waves in the direction of down-dip of the discontinuity

$$t_r = \frac{1}{V_1} \sqrt{a^2 + (\Delta - \Delta^*)^2} \tag{3.8}$$

where

$$a = \Delta^* \cot \omega = 2d \cos^2 \omega.$$

The equations are more complicated if more layers are involved, or if a gradual change of velocity with depth in a layer is assumed, or if the curvature of the earth is considered, or if the source is not in the surface.

If there are n horizontal homogeneous layers, and the source is in the surface, the thickness h_{n-1} of the layer with the velocity V_{n-1} below which the velocity is V_n, is given by

$$h_{n-1} = \frac{(V_n Y_n - X_n) \cos i_{n-1}}{2[(V_n/V_{n-1}) - (V_{n-1}/V_n)]} \tag{3.9}$$

where i_{n-1} is the angle of incidence in the layer $n - 1$, and

$$X_n = \Delta - \sum_1^{n-2} 2h_n \tan i_n \tag{3.10}$$

$$Y_n = t - \sum_1^{n-2} \frac{2h_n}{V_n \cos i_n} \tag{3.11}$$

$$\sin i_1 : \sin i_2 : \ldots : \sin i_n = V_1 : V_2 : \ldots : V_n \tag{3.12}$$

where still the curvature of the earth is neglected. The thickness of the first layer is found from Eq. (3.3).

If the curvature of the earth is considered, the *ray equation* is given by

$$\frac{r}{V_r} \sin i_r = \text{const} = \frac{r_0}{V_0} \sin i_0 = \frac{r_s}{V_s} \tag{3.13}$$

where i_r is the angle of incidence at the distance r from the earth's center and V_r the velocity, assumed to depend on r only; r_0, V_0, i_0 refer to the earth's surface, r_s and V_s to the deepest point of the ray, where $i_s = 90°$.

Among the sources of errors is the use of too much simplified assumption, for the earth's crust, for example, that each layer is homogeneous so that neither the velocity of longitudinal nor that of transverse waves changes in any direction in the layer. This is often assumed, though frequently incorrectly, for the layers below the sediments. Moreover, there are indications from field observations as well as from laboratory experiments that below a certain depth in the crust the effect of increase in temperature with depth may decrease the wave velocity more than the increase in pressure increases it. Consequently, there may be layers or portions of layers in which one or both wave velocities decrease with depth. If it is assumed in such instances that the velocity increases with depth, gross errors may result.

At a depth h below the surface the radius ρ of the curvature of a ray is given by

$$\frac{1}{\rho} = \frac{\sin i}{V}\left|\frac{dV}{dh}\right| \tag{3.14}$$

where i is the angle of incidence at the depth h and V the velocity. If dV/dh is positive, the ray is convex downward (Fig. 3.2(a)), otherwise it is

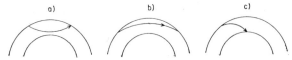

FIG. 3.2. Ray paths (schematic) if (a) the wave velocity increases with depth; (b) decreases with depth and $dV/dr < V/r$; (c) decreases with depth, but $dV/dr > V/r$.

convex upward. If the velocity V decreases downward at a depth $h = r_0 - r$ ($r_0 = $ radius of the earth) at the critical rate

$$\frac{dV}{dh} = \frac{V}{r} \tag{3.15}$$

it follows from Eq. (3.14) that $\rho = r/\sin i$ so that a horizontal ray ($\sin i = 1$) has the same curvature downward as the sphere at the depth h. If the velocity decreases with depth more rapidly than given by Eq. (3.15) no ray can have its deepest point at this level (Fig. 3.2(c)), but must continue downward until a layer is reached in which the velocity decreases with depth less than at the rate V/r (Fig. 3.2(b)), or one in which the velocity increases with depth. Consequently, the travel time curve is interrupted and no portion of the curve exists for waves with their deepest point in such a "low-velocity" layer. Consequently, for a layer with greater decrease in velocity with depth than given by Eq. (3.15) the velocity cannot be found from travel times of refracted waves arriving at the surface. If it is assumed erroneously that a travel time curve exists in such instances, all conclusions may be completely misleading [Gutenberg, 1954]. It is nothing unusual that in such instances small diffracted waves are misinterpreted as direct waves, and continuous travel time curves are plotted. As near the earth's surface V/r is about 0.001 km/sec per km, Eq. (3.15) shows that practically any decrease in velocity with depth leads to "shadow zones" at the surface for the respective waves.

Laboratory experiments [Hughes and Maurette, 1957] indicate that in the deep portions of the crust and immediately below the Mohorovičić discontinuity layers may exist in which the velocity decreases with depth as a consequence of the increase in temperature and pressure with depth. In such laboratory tests, wave velocities are determined for each rock sam-

TABLE 3.1. VELOCITIES V OF LONGITUDINAL WAVES AND v OF TRANSVERSE WAVES IN KM/SEC FOUND FROM LABORATORY EXPERIMENTS (a) BY HUGHES AND MAURETTE [1957] AND (b) BY BIRCH [1958] IN ROCKS, ASSUMING THE LISTED TEMPERATURES T IN °C AND PRESSURES p IN BARS AT THE DEPTHS h IN KM IN THE EARTH'S CRUST.

	(a)						(b)		
h, km	1	5	10	15	20	25	11	23	32
T, °C	45	135	225	290	350	400	220	420	520
p, bars	260	1300	2600	3900	5300	6700			
V, km/sec									
Granite	5.96	6.16	6.15	6.11			6.22	6.26	6.27
Gabbro	6.70	6.90	6.96	6.95	6.88	6.80	6.85	6.84	6.83
Basalt	5.44	5.68	5.74	5.79					
Dunite	7.35	7.50	7.22						
v, km/sec									
Granite	3.36	3.48	3.50	(3.49)					
Gabbro	3.47	3.51	3.52	3.51	3.47	3.44			
Basalt	3.21	3.22	3.23	3.23					
Dunite	3.77	3.90	3.68						

ple at various pressures and at various temperatures. Then assumptions are made for the pressure and temperature at a few depths in the earth. While only small errors are to be expected for the assumed pressure, the temperature at a given depth may differ appreciably from place to place depending on the structure of the crust, especially its thickness. Thus, the assumed "average" temperatures may introduce noticeable errors for the calculated wave velocities. Moreover, there are doubts how far the properties of samples in experiments correspond to those *in situ* [Birch, 1958]. Some characteristic results of experiments are listed in Table 3.1.

Birch [1958] finds that the maximum temperature gradient at the depth z, $(dT/dz)_m$, for which in a homogeneous layer of rock the rays are curved upward, is approximately given by

$$\left(\frac{dT}{dz}\right)_m = \frac{1}{V}\left(\frac{dV}{dT}\right)_p \qquad (3.16)$$

where T = temperature, V = velocity, p = pressure. Calculated values for $(dT/dz)_m$ are listed in Table 3.2. Unfortunately, estimates for the temperature gradient dT/dz in and below the earth's crust vary considerably. However, Table 3.2 indicates that a downward curvature of rays of

TABLE 3.2. MAXIMUM GRADIENTS $(dT/dz)_m$ OF TEMPERATURE FOR UPWARD CURVATURE OF RAYS OF LONGITUDINAL WAVES IN AVERAGE GRANITE AND GABBRO AFTER BIRCH [1958] AND BELOW THE CRUST ACCORDING TO VALLE [1956], AND ESTIMATED TEMPERATURE GRADIENTS dT/dz IN THE EARTH. ALL DATA ARE APPROXIMATE.

Pressure interval 10^3 kg/cm^2	Average depth km	$(dT/dz)_m$		Estimated dT/dz in the earth, °C/km		
		Granite °C/km	Gabbro °C/km	Birch [1958]	Wolff [1943]	Jeffreys [1952]
2–4	10	48	21	18	30	30
4–6	17	24	14	16	30	25
6–10	30	19	10	12	26	22
		Below crust ultrabasic rock				
		longit. waves	transv. waves			
—	(40)	14	11	—	21	(7)

longitudinal waves can be expected in deep portions of granitic layers under some areas. Downward curvature should occur fairly frequently in the gabbro layers which, under continents, extend usually from roughly 20 to 40 km depth. Tables 3.1 and 3.2 indicate that in the gabbro layers under continents the velocity decrease possibly starts already at the top of a gabbro layer. Estimates for the corresponding critical gradient in ultrasimatic rock have been made by Valle [1956].

Reliable information about velocities and depths of layers require data about the dip of the discontinuities. If one or more layers are dipping, the travel time curves of corresponding refracted waves in opposite direction from the source have different slopes (Fig. 3.1). The dip can be calculated. All these problems are discussed in detail in textbooks on exploration geophysics. If we use the symbols of Eqs. (3.5) to (3.8) in connection with a source in the surface, and if t_0 is the travel time of the reflected wave returning to the source, then, for example,

$$\sin \omega = \frac{\Delta}{t_0 V_1} - \frac{tV_1}{t_0}\left(\frac{dt}{d\Delta}\right)_\Delta. \qquad (3.17)$$

If in a two-layer medium with constant velocities of respectively V_1 and $V_2 > V_1$ the discontinuity forms an angle ω with the horizontal, and if at the surface the observed apparent velocities of the refracted waves are $\bar{V}_{2u}$ "up-dip" and $\bar{V}_{2d}$ "down-dip" (Fig. 3.1), the true velocity V_2 below the discontinuity is given by

$$V_2 = \frac{2 \cos \omega}{1/\bar{V}_{2d} + 1/\bar{V}_{2u}} \tag{3.18}$$

and the apparent velocities are

$$\bar{V}_{2d} = \frac{V_1}{\sin (i_1 + \omega)} \qquad \bar{V}_{2u} = \frac{V_1}{\sin (i_1 - \omega)}. \tag{3.19}$$

It is obvious from Fig. 3.1 and Eqs. (3.19) that from observation of arrival times in one direction only and assuming that V_2 equals $\bar{V}_{2u}$ or $\bar{V}_{2d}$, appreciable errors in the calculated velocity below the discontinuity may result, even, if this velocity is constant. These errors are frequently underestimated, especially in investigations related to the Mohorovičić discontinuity. Among other errors is the reading of the arrival times too late if the record is so small that the first wave or waves are not found on the seismogram.

If reflected waves are used (Fig. 3.1), dipping layers may be found from the fact that the shortest travel times of the reflected waves are not observed at the source but on the "up-dip" side (Fig. 3.1). If the dip of a layer changes, the correlation of reflections may become difficult. In working with crystalline layers in the crust it is frequently easier to record refracted than reflected waves. Moreover, it is more difficult to find the velocity as function of depth from reflected than from refracted waves. Consequently, it is more frequently necessary to make assumptions about the change of velocity with depth if reflections are used than if records of clear refracted waves are available. Incorrect assumptions or incorrect interpretations may be a source of relatively large errors, especially if a (usually deep) layer is missed in which the velocity decreases with depth. In such instances, even spurious discontinuities may be found, if the refraction method is used, and considerable errors may result in the investigation of the structure of the crust (or any deeper layer), even if this research is undertaken by experts.

3.3 Velocities in Crustal Layers and Depths of Discontinuities Based on Observation of Elastic Waves

Almost three quarters of the earth's surface is covered by water with maximum depths exceeding 10 km, and about 4% of the surface is covered by ice. In most continents and ocean bottoms the uppermost layers are formed by unconsolidated and consolidated sediments. The greatest portion of the crust consists of igneous rocks which have solidified from a nonsolid state.

Information about the layers consisting of igneous rocks is usually based on determination of the velocities of longitudinal and transverse waves as a function of depth. The interpretation of the observed velocities in terms of rock types requires data from laboratory experiments on the range of velocities in various rock samples which should be investigated under con-

TABLE 3.3. VELOCITIES V OF LONGITUDINAL WAVES AND v OF TRANSVERSE WAVES IN KM/SEC IN VARIOUS ROCK TYPES AT 1 ATM PRESSURE AND ROOM TEMPERATURE, FROM LABORATORY EXPERIMENTS AND FROM DETERMINATIONS IN THE FIELD AT OUTCROPS. (a) FROM LEET AND BIRCH [1942]; (b) MACELWANE [1951, PP. 233, 237]; (c) BAULE AND MÜLLER [1956, p. 195]; (d) BIRCH [1958]; (e) HUGHES AND MAURETTE [1957].

Rock type	(a)		(b)	(c)		(d)	(e)	
	V	v	V	V	v	V	V	v
Granite	4.0–5.7	2.1–3.3	4.5–5.6	5.2	3.0	5.2		3.4
Basalt	5.6		5.6	6.4	3.2		5.4	3.2
Gabbro						6.3	6.4–6.7	3.5
Dunite							7.4	3.8
Eclogite				8.0	4.3			

ditions as close as possible to those at the depths involved. Results of field observation as well as of laboratory experiments are affected by systematic errors. Moreover, properties of two rocks of the same type may differ appreciably, and there are many instances where there is no full agreement about the classification of a given rock.

Velocities V of longitudinal waves and v of transverse waves in rocks are summarized in Table 3.3. Some of them are based on laboratory experiments, others on determination *in situ* in a well identified rock layer, or they are averages based on various published data.

The increase in pressure with depth in the earth's crust increases the velocities V of longitudinal waves and v of transverse waves appreciably in the first few kilometers. This is mainly an effect of the closing of the pores in the rock. At greater depth, the effect of the increasing temperature, which decreases the velocities, approaches more and more the effect of the increasing pressure. At least in some areas, this effect of the increase in temperature may surpass the effect of the increase in pressure, as discussed above.

With still further increasing depth, the rate of temperature increase and therefore its effect per kilometer of depth becomes smaller while the effect of the increase in pressure continues at an almost constant rate down to much greater depths. This results in a renewed increase in wave velocities with depth, but probably rather far below the crust (Section 4.2).

Effects of pressure and temperature on the velocities combine with effects of change in material. Chemical and physical processes, especially tectonic movements, have resulted in appreciable local differences in the structure of the crust, and have even affected the upper portion of the mantle.

The sedimentary layers are investigated mainly by geologists and exploration geophysicists. The earth's crust below the sediments is usually divided by geophysicists into the so-called *granitic* layer and the *basaltic* or *gabbro* layer since it has been found that two discontinuities play a greater role than others: the *Conrad discontinuity* between the "granitic" and the "basaltic" layers, and the *Mohorovičić discontinuity* (condensed to *"Moho"* or even *"M"*-discontinuity by some) between crust and mantle.

In a study of records of an earthquake about 25 miles from Zagreb, Yugoslavia, A. Mohorovičić [1910] observed that a different type of longitudinal wave arrives first beyond about 200 km distance from the source than arrives first closer to the source. He has interpreted this fact as the result of a discontinuity in the earth at a depth of the order of 50 km, at which the wave velocity increases suddenly. This research has been continued by his son, S. Mohorovičić [1927], after Conrad [1925] had found an additional longitudinal phase, P*, in an investigation of waves from an earthquake in the eastern Alps. The corresponding transverse phase, S*, was identified later. The P* and S* waves indicate the existence of at least one discontinuity, the "Conrad discontinuity," between the bottom of the sediments and the Mohorovičić discontinuity.

Waves produced by earthquakes and artificial explosions which have traveled through the earth's crust have been studied extensively in recent years. The refraction as well as the reflection methods have been used. Selected results are summarized in Table 3.4. The velocities listed in the first two columns for continental areas are in the range found for granite (Tables 3.1 and 3.3) and have been attributed to the so-called granitic layer, although the composition of the material in this layer differs from region to region. Moreover, in several areas indications of waves with additional velocities and discontinuities within the granitic layer [Bederke, 1957, p. 234] have been found. On the other hand, there is no indication of the granitic layer below ocean bottoms beyond the shelves. In many continental regions the bottom of the granitic layer is the Conrad discontinuity. It is marked by C in Table 3.4 where, under the oceans, the Conrad discontinuity is taken as the bottom of the sedimentary layer.

It is frequently difficult to establish the Conrad discontinuity by the refraction method (including travel times of waves from earthquakes), since in many regions there are no distances where the P* waves with their deepest point in the "basaltic layer" arrive earlier than either longitudinal waves through the granitic layer only, or the waves which have entered the ultrasima. Consequently, in several continental areas the Conrad discontinuity has not been found (though it may exist).

There are indications of additional well defined discontinuities between the Conrad and Mohorovičić discontinuities; especially in several continental areas, layers with velocities of $6\frac{1}{2}$ to 7 and of 7 to $7\frac{1}{2}$ km/sec for longitudinal waves are indicated. In Table 3.4 all layers between the Conrad and the Mohorovičić discontinuities are combined as "gabbro" or "basaltic" layers, and only the lowest velocities found in a given region for this layer are listed. Caloi [1958] suggests that there may be a "diorite" layer ($V = 6.1$ km/sec) and a "gabbro" layer ($V = 7$ km/sec). Many velocities listed in Table 3.4 for the "gabbro" layers are higher than those found from samples of basalt (Tables 3.1, 3.3), but are within reasonable limits of those obtained from gabbro samples. This is also true for the layer on top of the Mohorovičić discontinuity in oceanic areas. However, there are probably appreciable differences in the composition of these "gabbro" layers under various areas and at different depths.

In many oceanic areas, the depth of the Mohorovičić discontinuity is less than 10 km under the ocean bottom. In most continents its depth increases with increasing distance from the coasts and may reach over 50 km under high mountain areas. These "roots of mountains" have been found first from gravity data and are discussed in Section 3.8.1.

In most portions of the earth the material below the Mohorovičić discontinuity shows the same velocities of 8.1 to 8.2 km/sec for longitudinal waves and about 4.7 km/sec for transverse waves. Originally, lower values of about 7.8 and 4.4 km/sec respectively had been reported for many regions, but with the increase in sensitivity of the instruments, the calculated velocities have gradually approached the higher values, and seem to agree now much better. Some of the remaining differences may result from sources of error discussed in Section 3.2, especially from the assumption of horizontal layers, where actually the discontinuities are dipping. However, there is no reason why the ultrabasic material below the Mohorovičić discontinuity should be exactly the same everywhere. Moreover, differences

TABLE 3.4. RECENT DATA ON VELOCITIES V OF LONGITUDINAL AND v OF TRANSVERSE WAVES IN KM/SEC IN AND IMMEDIATELY BELOW THE EARTH'S CRUST. C = DEPTH OF THE CONRAD DISCONTINUITY (UNDER OCEANS: BOTTOM OF SEDIMENTS), M = DEPTH OF THE MOHOROVIČIĆ DISCONTINUITY; a INDICATES REFLECTION, b REFRACTION METHOD, A USE OF ARTIFICIAL EXPLOSIONS, E OF EARTHQUAKES. MOST VALUES ARE APPROXIMATE ONLY. AN ASTERISK (*) IN THE LAST COLUMN INDICATES THAT THE REFERENCE IS NOT TO THE AUTHOR OF THE RESULTS, AND MAY COMBINE DATA OF SEVERAL PUBLICATIONS.

"Granitic" layers		C	"Gabbro" layers		M	Ultrabasic layer		Region	Method	Reference* or author
V	v	km	V	v	km	V	v			
								Europe		
6.0	3.7	14	6.6	3.9	27	8.2	—	NW Germany	Ab	Gutenberg* [1955a]
6.0	3.4	20	6.6	3.7	31	8.2	4.8	Black Forest	Ab	Gutenberg* [1955a]
5.9	3.4	20	6.5	3.7	30	8.2	4.4	Black Forest	Ab	Rothé [1958]
—	—	—	—	—	30	—	—	Champagne	Aa	Geneslay et al. [1956]
—	—	17	—	—	37	—	—	Rochilles (Rhone)	Aa	Bernard [1956]
5.6	3.3	15	6.4	3.7	30	8.1	4.7	SW Germany	Eb	Hiller [1953]
—	—	20	—	—	28	—	—	Ulm (Germany)	Aa	Reich [1953]
6.1	3.5	25	6.7	—	—	—	—	Western Alps	Aab	Tardi* [1957]
5.6	—	20	6.5	—	30	8.2	—	Northern Alps	Aab	Reich [1957]
5.9	3.4	20	6.5	3.7	30	8.2	4.4	Bavarian Alps	Aa	Reich [1958]
5.7	3.4	(35)	6.6	3.6	45	8.0	4.4	Southern Alps	Eb	Caloi [1957a,b; 1958]
5.5	3.0	24	6.4	3.6	60	8.2	—	Abruzzi, Italy	Eb	Di Filippo and Marcelli [1952]
5.1	3.1	14	6.1; 6.9	4.2	32	8.2	4.5	Po Valley, Italy	Eb	Caloi [1958]
—	—	19	—	—	24	—	—	Debrecin, Hungary	Aa	Gálfi and Stegena [1957]
—	—	20	—	—	25	—	—	Pécs, Hungary	Aa	Stegena [1958]
5.6	3.3	11	6.4	3.7	31	8.2	—	Bohemia	Ab	Kárník [1956]
5.6	3.4	9	6.2	3.8	35	8.1	4.5	Hungary and S.Slov.	Eb	Vanek [1955]

TABLE 3.4. *Continued*

"Granitic" layers V	v	C km	"Gabbro" layers V	v	M km	Ultrabasic layer V	v	Region	Method	Reference* or author
								Continental Asia		
—	—	—	—	—	40	—	—	Korkin (Ural)	Ab	Riznichenko [1957]
5.6; 6.0	3.2; 3.4	15±	6.7	4.0	49	8.0	4.7	Kura depression, Caucasus	Ab	Balavadze and Tvaltvadze [1957]
—	—	—	—	—	50–67	—	—	Central Caucasus	Ab	
5.6	3.4	25	6.6	3.9	46	7.9	4.5	NE India	Eb	Anonymous [1955]
5.7	3.4	20	6.2	3.6	50	8.0	—	Central Asia	Ab	Bune and Butovskaya [1955]
5.5	—	15	6.4	—	55	8.1	—	Lake Issyk-Kul	Ab, Eb	Gamburtsev and Veytsman [1956]
5.5	—	20	6.4	—	35	8.1	—	S of eastern Lake Balkash		
5.5	—	16	6.4	—	38	8.1	—	200 km NW of Issyk-Kul	Ab	
5.5	—	18	6.4	—	40	8.1	—	S of western Lake Balkash		
—	—	45	—	—	60±	—	—	N. Pamir	Ab	Veytsman et al. [1957]
								North America		
6.1	—	—	—	—	33	8.1	—	Central Atl. Coast	Ab	Adams et al. [1952]
6.0	—	15	≥6½	—	40	8.1	—	Centr. Appalachians	Ab	Tatel et al. [1953]
6.3	3.6	35	—	—	36	8.1	4.7	New York	Ab	Katz [1953]
6.1	3.6	32	—	—	34	8.2	4.7	Pennsylvania	Ab	Katz [1953]
6.2	3.5	30	7.1	3.9	37	8.2	4.8	Canadian Shield	Ab	Hodgson [1953]
6.0	—	—	(7.0)	—	40	8.2	—	Wisconsin	Ab	Slichter [1951]
5.9	—	10	6.8	—	37	8.2	—	Southern California Valleys	Ab	Gutenberg [1952]
—	—	26	—	—	32	—	—	Southern California Valleys	Aa	Shor [1955]
6.4	3.8	28	7.1	4.1	35	8.1	4.5	Southern California Valleys	Eab	Gutenberg [1951]

TABLE 3.4. *Continued*

"Granitic" layers		C	"Gabbro" layers		M	Ultrabasic layer		Region	Method	Reference* or author
V	v	km	V	v	km	V	v			
North America (Continued)										
5.6	—	13	6.6	—	31	8.0	—	Centr. California	Eb	Byerly and Wilson [1935]
6.0	—	25	7.2	—	43±	8.2	—	Alberta, Canada, plains	Ab	Richards [1958]
6.1	—	—	—	—	31	8.1	—	Alaska	Ab	Aldrich et al. [1957]
South America										
—	—	—	—	—	34	—	—	Arequipa, Peru	Ab	Tatel and Tuve [1958]
—	—	—	—	—	55	8.0	—	Andes, Chile	Ab	Tatel and Tuve [1958]
Africa										
6.2	3.7	—	—	—	34	8.2	4.7	Johannesburg	Ab	Gane et al. [1956]
Australia, New Zealand										
6.1	3.7	—	—	—	37	8.2	4.7	West Australia	Ab	Doyle [1957]
6.0	3.6	—	—	—	35	8.2	4.7	West Australia	Ab	Bolt et al. [1958]
6.1	3.6	no	no	no	35	8.2	4.7	West Australia	Ab	Bullen [1958]
6.0	—	9	6.3	—	20	8.1	—	New Zealand	Aab	Eiby [1957, p. 26]
Japan										
6.1	3.4	24	7.4	—	32	8.2	—	NE Honshu	Ab	Research Group [1951, 1952, 1954]
5.8	3.4	22	7.0	4.0	32	8.1	4.7	Kyoto	Eb	Kishimoto [1955]

TABLE 3.4. *Continued*

Water depth km	C km	"Gabbro" layers V	v	M km	Ultrabasic layer V	v	Region	Method	Reference* or author
							Atlantic Ocean		
1½–4	5½	6.6	—	14	7.9	—	E. Atlantic	Ab	Hill* [1957]
4–5	7	6.6	—	10	7.9	—	E. Atlantic	Ab	Hill* [1957]
4–5	7½	6.8	—	13	8.1	—	W. Atlantic	Ab	Hill* [1957]
>5	8	6.7	—	11	8.0	—	W. Atlantic	Ab	Hill* [1957]
5	7	6.6	—	10	7.9	—	N. American Basin	Ab	M. Ewing et al. [1954]
5	8	6.7	—	13	8.1	—	E. of Barbados	Ab	J. I. Ewing et al. [1957]
>5	8	6.3	—	12	8.0	—	Puerto Rico Trench	Ab	Officer et al. [1957]
							Pacific Ocean		
3½	4	6.5	—	9	8.0	—	Off San Diego, Calif.	Ab	Raitt [1949]
4	5	7.0	—	9	8.4	—	Off Lower California	Ab	Raitt [1956]
1½–4	6	6.7	—	12	7.9	—	Pacific Ocean	Ab	Hill* [1957]
4–5	7	6.8	—	12	8.3	—	Pacific Ocean	Ab	Hill* [1957]
>5	7	6.6	—	12	8.2	—	Pacific Ocean	Ab	Hill* [1957]
4–5	7	6.8	—	12	8.2	—	15° ± N, 160° E–120° E	Ab	Raitt [1956]
4–5	6	6.8	—	12	8.2	—	15° ± S, 170° E–110° E	Ab	Raitt [1956]
6	8	6.5	—	12	8.2	—	60 km E of Tonga Trench	Ab	Raitt et al. [1955]
9	12	6.5	—	20	8.1	—	Tonga Trench	Ab	Raitt et al. [1955]
—	10	6.9	—	17	8.1	—	Eniwetok	Ab	Raitt [1957]

in the velocities may result from the fact that under deep oceans not only
the ocean bottom is appreciably colder (order of magnitude 30°C/km)
than that under the continents, but that the Mohorovičić discontinuity
is also appreciably closer to the surface, so that the top of the ultrasima
may well be many hundred degrees colder under deep oceans than under
mountain areas in the continents. This could well result in measurable
differences in the wave velocities.

3.4 Effects of the Crust on Amplitudes of Reflected Waves PP

In an investigation of longitudinal waves PP reflected at the earth's
surface about half way between source and station, Gutenberg and Richter
[1935, pp. 305–324] have found that the ratio of the amplitudes of PP to
those of direct longitudinal waves P is noticeably smaller if PP is reflected

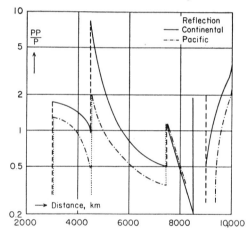

Fig. 3.3. Amplitude ratio PP/P for Continental and Pacific reflections after Gutenberg and Richter [1935].

under the Pacific Basin than in instances when it is reflected under continents or under other oceans (Fig. 3.3). The PP-waves are also relatively
large if they have been reflected under certain portions of the Pacific Ocean
outside the deep basin, for example near the coast of the United States or
south of the Galapagos Islands. Relatively large reflections seem to occur
in areas between coasts and the andesite line (Section 3.8.2). On the other
hand, relatively small PP-waves are also found if the reflection occurs
under the deep portion of the Arctic Basin.

Gutenberg and Richter [1935] have discussed possible reasons for the differences. The theory is complicated by the fact that the wavelengths of PP (roughly 40 km in the crust for waves having periods of 6 sec) are of the same order of magnitude as the thickness of the crustal layers in the continents, and possibly greater than the thickness of the crust under oceans. If a longitudinal wave is reflected at the top of a homogeneous half space, a portion of energy is reflected into a longitudinal wave (PP) and the remainder into a transverse wave (PS) vibrating in the plane of the ray. The division of the energy into these two waves depends only on Poisson's ratio σ in the material and on the angle of incidence i_0 of the ray at the surface. In Fig. 3.4 these ratios are plotted as a function of i_0 which decreases

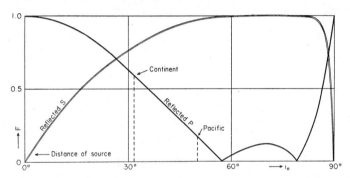

Fig. 3.4. Square root F of reflected to incident energy at the surface of a homogeneous half space, if the velocity ratio of longitudinal to that of transverse waves is 1.711 (Poisson's ratio 0.239), as function of the angle of incidence i_0 at the surface. The angles i_0 marked by "Pacific" and "Continent" respectively correspond to earthquake waves arriving at the same distance of roughly 3000 km, if the wave velocities V_0 at the surface are 8.2 and 5.7 km/sec respectively.

with increasing distance if the source is in the surface. As $\sin i_0$ is proportional to the velocity V_0 at the surface, i_0 is smaller, if at a given distance the reflection occurs in a region with a lower velocity near the surface than in a region with higher velocity. Fig. 3.4 shows extreme effects; for the continental reflection it is assumed that the reflection takes place at the top of the very thick granitic layer, for the pacific reflections it is assumed that the effect of the crustal layers (less than 10 km thick including several kilometers of water) can be neglected.

Other complications arise from the existence of several discontinuities, especially in the continental crust, at which reflections may occur. Again, the fact that the respective layers between the discontinuities are usually smaller than the wavelengths, prevents accurate calculations of the amplitudes of these various reflected waves. For reflection at the ocean bottoms, differences in the thickness of the layer of water may also play a role. Moreover, the PP-waves reflected at the surface do not necessarily have the largest amplitudes. Jeffreys [1926] has concluded that at short epicentral distances the PP-waves reflected at the base of the continental layers could be larger than those reflected at the surface.

In using the amplitude ratio PP/P, errors are introduced by the fact that the energies radiated into P and into PP depend on the angle between the ray leaving the source and the direction of movement at the source. However, PP and P leave the source in the same azimuth and at the epicentral distances involved their angles of incidence differ usually not by more than 20°. This may explain why it is not difficult to separate areas in which reflections produce relatively small amplitudes of PP, from others with relatively large amplitudes of PP. However, much more research is required in connection with the whole problem. Especially, more theoretical investigations are needed concerning the propagation of waves with lengths of the same order as that of the thickness of the layers through which they travel, and their reflection from such layers.

3.5 Conclusions from Channel Waves and Microseisms

When it appeared that records of artificial explosions at the surface indicate higher velocities for longitudinal as well as transverse waves in the "granitic layer" of the crust than records of earthquakes originating at depths of 15 km or more in the layer, Gutenberg [1951] tried to explain this difference on the assumption that the wave velocities decrease in the deep portion of the granitic layer. He also pointed out that the amplitudes of longitudinal waves which travel only through the granitic layer decrease much more rapidly with distance than it can be expected, unless the wave velocity decreases in the lower portion of the granitic layer. The fact that the direct longitudinal waves from artificial explosions near the surface are relatively better observed at distances of the order of 100 km, than those from earthquakes, indicates that absorption is not the cause for this rapid decrease in amplitudes with distance. Moreover, laboratory experiments (Section 3.2, Table 3.1) confirm the possibility that the wave velocities may decrease slightly with depth in the deepest portion of the granitic layer.

If the velocity decreases in a layer with increasing depth, an appreciable portion of the energy radiated by earthquakes may be trapped in this "low velocity layer," especially if the source of the energy is in the low-velocity layer. A channel may be formed in which energy is propagated with relatively little loss [Press and Ewing, 1952; Gutenberg, 1955a; Båth 1956, 1957]. Such *"channel waves"* through the granitic layer (Fig. 3.5) were first observed by Press and Ewing [1952] who designated them "Lg-" and "Rg-waves." Originally they suggested that Lg-waves consist of SH-waves (transverse waves vibrating horizontally) "multiply reflected within a superficial sialic layer." They found that the period of Lg-waves is $\frac{1}{2}$ to 6 sec, their velocity 3.5 km/sec, and that they are propagated across continents to distances up to 6000 km. The Rg-waves exhibit motion primarily similar to that in Rayleigh-wave type waves, with periods of about 8 to 12

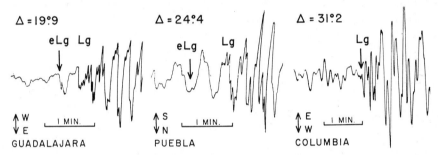

FIG. 3.5. Portions of records of the main Kern County, California, earthquake of July 21, 1952. Δ = distance in degrees. Arrows indicate direction of ground motion. Rearranged from Gutenberg [1955a].

sec and a velocity of about 3.1 km/sec. Båth [1957] described an additional channel wave, "Li," which is propagated with a velocity of 3.8 km/sec, probably through a deeper layer of the crust than Lg. He also reported first, that there are apparently two phases connected with Lg which he called Lg1 and Lg2. Since he found 3.54 and 3.37 km/sec respectively for the velocities of Lg1 and Lg2, and about 3.8 km/sec for Li, the average wavelengths of Lg1 and Lg2 are roughly 20 km and about 27 km for Li. Selected findings concerning the channel waves in the crust are listed in Table 3.5.

Ewing and Press [1956a, p. 133] have extended their original explanation that these waves are multiply reflected at the earth's surface and have pointed to their similarity to sound waves in a "whispering gallery," following Rayleigh [1945]. While most of the energy of longitudinal waves reflected at the earth's surface at angles of incidence between 40° and 80° goes into the reflected transverse waves (compare Fig. 3.4), the energy of transverse waves arriving at angles of incidence greater than about 40° is totally reflected. For the horizontal component of transverse waves (SH) there is always total reflection at the earth's surface, while for their component SV there is total reflection, if the angle of incidence is greater than roughly 40° [see, e.g., Gutenberg, 1944].

Press and Gutenberg [1956] have investigated the longitudinal channel wave IIg in the crust. "It is characterized by small amplitudes and erratic occurrence." Its average velocity of about 6.1 km/sec is slightly smaller than that of P waves below the sedimentary layers of the crust as observed in blasts. It corresponds approximately to the velocity of the beginning of the P-group in near earthquakes.

Gutenberg [1954] pointed out the similarity of low-velocity layers in the solid earth, the ocean, and the atmosphere. In all three media, they confine a portion of the energy radiating from a source and traveling in three

TABLE 3.5. SELECTED VALUES OF THE AVERAGE GROUP VELOCITY V (PROBABLE ERRORS ABOUT ± 0.1 KM/SEC) AND AVERAGE PERIODS T OF CHANNEL WAVES THROUGH THE EARTH'S CRUST

Author	Region	V, km/sec				T, sec	
		Li	Lg1	Lg2	Rg	Lg, Li	Rg
Press and Ewing [1952]	N. America		3.51		3.05	$\frac{1}{2}$–6	8–12
Lehmann [1953]	N. America		3.57			$\frac{1}{2}$–6	
Lehmann [1957]	N. America		3.5–3.6			$\frac{1}{2}$–3	
Gutenberg [1955a]	California		3.58	3.4		$\frac{1}{2}$–7	
Press [1956a]	California		3.54			$\frac{1}{2}$–5	
Båth [1953]	Scandinavia		3.5	(3.35)	3.0	4–10	
Båth [1954]	Scandinavia		3.54	3.37	3.1	3–8	3–14
Båth [1957]	Scandinavia	3.8				4–12	

dimensions to a limited channel. Gutenberg [1955a] suggested a tentative model for the major layers in the earth's crust (Fig. 3.6) which would explain the observed channel phases. The details differ for longitudinal and transverse waves; especially the decrease in velocity may begin at different depths for the two wave types. Båth [1956, 1957] has modified this model. Small changes in the velocity distribution may lead to noticeably different paths. The details of the actual velocity–depth curves are not known. However, the author believes that the combined evidence from travel times, laboratory experiments, and data on channel waves in the crust favors the hypothesis that below a locally variable depth, probably roughly 10 km, but different for longitudinal and transverse waves and for different materials, the wave velocities begin to decrease with increasing depth, as it is *sketched* in Fig. 3.6 at left. This is only a model and can *not* be used for quantitative conclusions.

Regardless of the explanation of Lg- and Rg-waves they permit some important inferences. Båth [1954] found that Lg-waves cross most of Eurasia, but are only poorly or not at all observed, if they had to pass under the mountain ranges in Southern Asia. They do not cross the Mediterranean, but they may be propagated across the crust under shallow portions of the Arctic Ocean near Scandinavia. Similarly, Oliver and associates

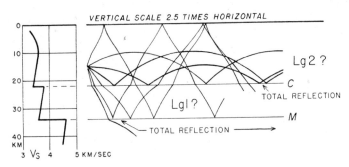

Fig. 3.6. Schematic paths of channel waves in the earth's crust, suggested by Gutenberg [1955a]. C = Conrad discontinuity, M = Mohorovičić discontinuity. At left: assumed velocity V_s of transverse waves as function of depth.

[1955] found that they travel in the granitic layer across the whole North American continent and also under shallow portions of the Arctic Ocean, but not under deep portions of the Arctic Ocean. It follows that the channel in the granitic layer is disturbed under high mountain ranges, and that it does not continue under oceans beyond some shallow coastal portions.

The propagation of microseisms with periods of 4 to 10 sec shows properties similar to those of Lg-waves. *Microseisms* are more or less continuous elastic waves in the crust which get their energy from ocean waves [e.g., Gutenberg, 1958]. They are considered by various seismologists to be channel waves, and they too lose much of their energy in passing under mountain ranges and ocean bottoms. The paths along which they travel with relatively small loss of energy indicate about the same areas with nearly undisturbed channels as the paths of the Lg-earthquake waves.

3.6 Conclusions from Dispersion and Extinction of Surface Waves

If the velocity of elastic waves changes with the depth d in the earth, surface waves must show dispersion, since the velocity of surface waves of the length L depends on L/d. Detailed theories for the dispersions belong to the fundamental problems of seismology and, therefore, should be discussed in the forthcoming volume on seismology.

Frequently, not the phase velocity V, but the *group velocity* U of surface waves is observed, where

$$U = V - L(dV/dL).   \tag{3.20}$$

There are two fundamental types of surface waves: (1) Rayleigh waves, in which the particles move retrograde in ellipses in the plane of wave propagation; the ratio of the vertical to the horizontal axis depends on Poisson's ratio σ and is theoretically close to 1.5 in the earth's crust. The velocity of Rayleigh waves in a homogeneous medium depends also on σ and is about $0.92\,v$, where v is the velocity of transverse waves. (2) Surface-shear or Love waves, in which the particles move perpendicular to the plane of propagation. Their velocity in a homogeneous medium equals the velocity v of transverse waves.

The theory of seismic surface waves has been investigated extensively. Already Love [1911] had discussed the theory of surface wave propagation in a two-layered earth. Among others, Meissner [1927] and Jeffreys [1935] have worked out equations for the velocity of surface waves as a function of the period in specific nonhomogeneous models on a variety of assumptions. Stoneley has done extensive research on surface wave dispersion in many models [e.g., Stoneley, 1948, 1953 with references to earlier publications]. Many of his results have been quoted by W. M. Ewing and associates [1957], who have extended the theory of surface waves in various respects; their book is indispensable to anyone working on the propagation of surface waves. One of the main problems in using surface waves for the determination of crustal structure, is to select one of the many models for the structure for which equations for the velocity of surface waves as function of the wave periods have been developed. On nearly all assumptions the effects of approximations in the theory are smaller than the effects of the deviations of the assumed model from the actual structure of the upper portion of the earth.

The first attempt to use the observed dispersion of surface waves in the investigation of crustal structure was made by Gutenberg [1924a,b] after Tams [1921] and others had found that the velocity of average surface waves (periods roughly 20 sec) is different for continental and for oceanic paths. In 1924 Gutenberg found that the group velocity of short Love as well as Rayleigh waves (periods smaller than about 30 sec) is noticeably higher through the crust under the Atlantic and Pacific Oceans than under Eurasia, while the velocities of long surface waves of a given period are nearly the same everywhere. Figure 3.7 includes observed group velocities after Gutenberg [1926], and various old and recent calculated curves of the group velocity for Eurasia and the Pacific.

Observations of the dispersion of surface waves and respective conclusions concerning the thickness of the crust in various regions have been improved in many investigations, partly by the use of improved theoretical equations. Results by Ewing and Press [1956a] for the dispersion of surface

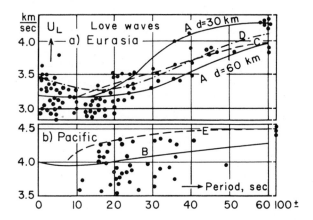

FIG. 3.7. Group velocity U_L of Love waves. Observations are from Gutenberg [1926]. Calculated curves A are based on Meissner [1927] for a homogeneous crust of thickness d and velocity of transverse waves $v = 3.2$ km/sec, overlying a half space with $v = 4.0$ km/sec. Curve B is based on Meissner's theory for a medium in which v increases from 4.0 km/sec at the surface to 7.0 at a depth of 1200 km. Curve C is observed between Nevada and New York, D is calculated for a homogeneous 35-km thick crust with $v = 3.51$ km/sec, below which $v = 4.7$; the ratio of the rigidities is assumed to be 2.22; E is observed, and also calculated assuming a 6-km thick layer under the ocean with $v = 3.77$ km/sec, below which $v = 4.5$ km/sec; ratio of rigidities 1.76. A and B after Gutenberg [1926]; C, D and E after Ewing and Press [1956a].

shear waves through Eurasia as well as through the bottom of the Pacific Ocean are included in Fig. 3.7. Press et al. [1956] have found good agreement between theoretical and observed dispersion for Rayleigh waves through Africa. They have based their calculated dispersion curve on the theoretical equations of Jeffreys [1935] on the assumption of a "35 km thick homogeneous crust with a shear velocity 3.51 km/sec overlying a homogeneous mantle with shear velocity 4.68 km/sec and density 1.25 times that of the crust." This may serve as an example for the assumptions made in such theoretical calculations. On similar assumptions, Press and

Ewing [1955] have found good agreement between theoretical and observed dispersion through North America.

Press [1956b] has assumed that the average group velocity of Rayleigh waves in the continents may be found from a standard distribution of velocity with depth, and that, with a good approximation, only the thickness of the continental crust may be taken as variable. It is then possible to draw standard curves for the group velocity U of Rayleigh waves with periods of 10–40 sec; these curves are based on the dispersion curves observed for Africa by using the theoretical relationship between Rayleigh-wave velocities and crustal thickness. Press has based his calculations on

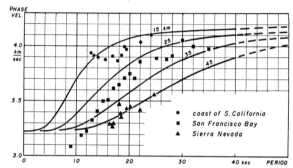

Fig. 3.8. Mean velocity of Rayleigh waves observed in three portions of California, and calculated curves for crustal thickness of 15, 25, 35, and 45 km, based on Press [1956b].

equations which have been discussed e.g. by Lee [1932, p. 89; see also Jeffreys, 1935] which give the velocity of Rayleigh waves if a superficial layer covers a half space with greater velocity, and on Eq. (3.20). For waves with periods of over 40 sec Press has followed Press and Ewing [1955, p. 59] in calculating V on the assumption of a crustal layer with a shear velocity $v = 3.51$ km/sec, overlying a mantle in which $v = 4.68$ km/sec.

Figure 3.8 shows such standard dispersion curves for the phase velocity V in an average continental crust on the assumption of four different thicknesses; included are observations in three portions of California [Press, 1956b, 1957]. The calculated thicknesses of the crust are averages for the area across which V has been observed. Press uses arrays of three stations, forming triangles. If these triangles are small, they give averages for smaller areas than if the triangles are large; however, the sides of the triangles must be large enough (order of 100 km) to permit sufficiently accurate determination of the differences in arrival times of the troughs or crests of the surface waves at the three stations forming the triangle.

Press has found the following approximate crustal thicknesses in Southern and Central California by this method: near the coast, 19 km; south of Pasadena, 31 km; east of Pasadena, 35 km; south and south-west of the Sierra Nevada, 43 km; under the southern Sierra Nevada, 48 km; and under the southern San Francisco Bay area, 30 km. Ewing and Press [1957, 1959] have then applied the same method to larger triangles, formed by seismological stations across North America, and have found the following crustal thicknesses: Rocky Mountain region, 50–55 km; western Great Plains, 40–45 km; central Interior Plains, 35 km; Canadian Shield, 35 km. On the basis of similar methods, Båth and Vogel [1958] have concluded that the average thickness of the oceanic crust is about 15 km in the Norwegian Sea and 10 km under the Mid-Atlantic Ridge southwest of Rykjavik.

Stoneley [1948, 1953] has investigated solutions of equations for Love waves and Rayleigh waves respectively in a two-layered crust (thicknesses of layers respectively d_1 and d_2) and has found consistent solutions of the form $2d_1 + d_2 = 65$ km. This has to be combined with other information to give d_1 and d_2 separately. Various results [Stoneley, 1957] are of the same order of magnitude as the findings listed in Table 3.4 from body waves.

The propagation of surface waves across oceanic portions of the crust is affected by the water layer. Long trains of Rayleigh waves are characteristic of the corresponding seismograms [Ewing and Press, 1956a; p. 128]. Stoneley [1926] has studied effects of the water layer in oceans on Rayleigh waves, and Jeffreys has shown in an added note, that in this case a minimum group velocity must exist for certain small periods. Ewing and Press [1956a, p. 129] have pointed out that the observed Rayleigh wave dispersion along oceanic paths agrees with the theoretical expectation (Fig. 3.9 curve B). Contrasting with findings from continental surface waves, second and higher modes of Rayleigh waves along oceanic paths have not been found thus far.

Surface waves traveling along the boundary of the Pacific Basin or crossing this boundary repeatedly show appreciably smaller amplitudes than surface waves traveling under otherwise similar conditions, especially for about the same distance, along paths not crossing the Pacific boundary. In investigating the relationship between amplitudes of surface waves and the magnitude of shallow earthquakes, Gutenberg [1945] found that surface waves which arrive at Pasadena from northwest have amplitudes between $\frac{1}{3}$ and $\frac{1}{4}$ of the average, after having followed closely the boundary of the Pacific Ocean off Japan, the Kuriles, and the Aleutian Islands. Surface waves from northern South America, arriving from southeast and following the Pacific coasts to the southeast of Pasadena show similar reduction in

amplitudes. Many additional observations of such instances have been
made since of relative small amplitudes of surface waves from shallow earthquakes after the waves had traveled for long distances along the Pacific

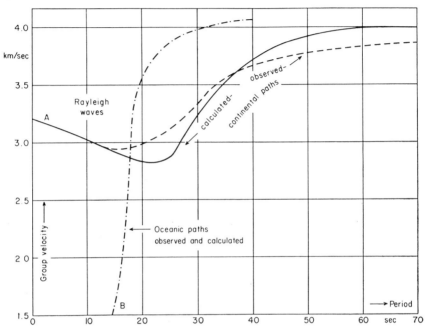

FIG. 3.9. Group velocity of Rayleigh waves after Ewing and Press [1956a]. (A)
Assumed: 35-km thick crust with transverse wave velocity $v = 3.57$ km/sec, below the
crust $v = 4.68$ km/sec.; density below the crust $1\frac{1}{4}$ times the density in the crust. (B)
$V = 1.52$ km/sec in 5.57 km deep water, below which longitudinal velocity $V = 7.95$
km/sec, $v = 4.56$ km/sec, density 3 g/cm³.

boundary. No similar observations of energy loss in surface waves following
or crossing the boundaries of the Atlantic or Indian Oceans have been
reported.

3.7 Gravity Anomalies and the Structure of the Earth's Crust

Gravity is observed at points of the earth's surface by various methods
described in modern textbooks on geodesy and gravity [Heiskanen and
Meinesz, 1958] and on exploration geophysics. To find comparable gravity
data, the gravity values g found at an elevation h above sea level must be

reduced to values at sea level. The main corrections which must be applied are: (1) A correction for the change in distance from the earth's center from h to sea level, neglecting the effect of matter between the two levels. (2) A correction for the effect of the surrounding terrain (valley, mountains) at the point of observation. (3) A correction for the effect of the mass in the layer between h and sea level.

The first correction is made as if the point of observation was moved from the elevation h (positive above sea level, negative below) to sea level through air. This "free air reduction" is given with sufficient approximation by $-h(dg/dr)_0$, where h is measured in meters and

$$(dg/dr)_0 = -0.30855 - 0.00023 \cos 2\varphi + 0.000144 \, H \text{ mgal/m} \quad (3.21)$$

if H is the height above sea level measured in km. For most purposes the whole correction for elevations h in meters above sea level is given with sufficient accuracy by $+0.3086 \, h$ mgal. For points below sea level, the correction is negative.

The second correction is the "terrain correction," which is always positive. If mass is missing around the station (e.g. on a mountain top) the attraction downward is too small; if there is too much mass around the station (valley), the attraction upward is too great. To correct for this deficit, tables for standard zones have been introduced [Garland, 1956, p. 224]. As the distance of the zones from the point of observation increases, their width also increases; the correction necessitated by the terrain in each section of each zone has to be considered.

The calculation of the third correction, that for the mass between the point of observation and sea level, is still a controversial problem. Various methods are in use. In one, first suggested by Bouguer and therefore called the "Bouguer correction," it is assumed that the mass between h and sea level has to be depressed below sea level. This correction is $-2\pi G\rho h$, where ρ is the density of the mass (assumed to be constant), G is the gravitational constant (about 6.673×10^{-8} cm^3/g sec), h is the elevation. Assumptions for the density must consider the type of surface layers (recent sediments, old sediments, water, etc.). This correction is frequently combined with the free air correction.

Some geodesists and especially geophysicists working in exploration geophysics prefer the use of Bouguer corrections to other corresponding types of correction after they have familiarized themselves with the interpretation of the results. However, many are afraid to introduce systematic errors through the use of Bouguer corrections and prefer to suppose that the crustal layers have a tendency to gradually approach a position of hydrostatic equilibrium with a time constant of the order of 1000 or 10,000 years. Unfortunately, there are different possibilities how this may be achieved. Pratt [1855] and Airy [1855] had found independently that the deviation of the plumb line south of the Himalaya as a consequence of the mass of the mountains is smaller than it had been calculated. Pratt had assumed that this indicated smaller density of the rock in the mountains than average, while Airy had suggested that the mountains have "roots," and that the lighter surface material with the same density everywhere extends deeper into the heavier material below the mountains than below

TABLE 3.6. AVERAGE DENSITIES OF IGNEOUS ROCK, (a) WITHOUT, (b) WITH WATER CONTENT, IN SELECTED REGIONS ACCORDING TO WASHINGTON [1922]. h = AVERAGE ELEVATION IN METERS, n = NUMBER OF ANALYSES

Region	h	(a)	(b)	n
Colorado, U.S.A.	2134	2.76	2.71	171
Mexico, Central America	2000	2.79	2.74	47
Atlantic Islands	1830	2.89	2.81	34
Andes	1820	2.81	2.75	39
Alps	1550	2.78	2.70	161
British Columbia	1100	2.81	2.75	49
United States	760	2.78	2.73	295
Australia	350	2.81	2.72	238
Germany	300	2.81	2.74	252
Great Britain	100	2.83	2.76	57
Atlantic Ridge	−1830	2.89	2.81	56
Atlantic Basin	−4116	2.89	2.81	56
Pacific	−4520	3.09	3.04	72

lowlands; the crustal layer "floats" in the deeper material similar to icebergs floating in water. Dutton [1892] proposed the term "isostasy" for this tendency of the earth's crust to approach hydrostatic equilibrium. Neither the Airy nor the Pratt explanation is satisfactory, but even at present geodesists, geophysicists, and geologists frequently do not agree about how much of isostasy in a given region is a consequence of "roots" following Airy, and how much a consequence of different densities, following Pratt.

From determinations of the average rock densities in various regions (Table 3.6) Washington [1922] concluded that "the average density of the igneous rocks of a region varies in the opposite sense as the average altitude." This would indicate that compensation following the Pratt hypothesis prevails. Washington's research should be repeated with modern means.

Unfortunately, gravity anomalies do not permit the decision as to what extent the Pratt and the Airy hypotheses represent the conditions which are responsible for isostatic equilibrium in a given region [Heiskanen, 1936]. One difficulty arises from the fact that the reduction of gravity to sea level must be made by assuming one of the hypotheses which are to be tested, and then some criterion has to be adopted to decide which hypothesis approaches most closely the facts.

There are various variables in all methods by which the values of gravity observed at a given elevation at the earth's surface are reduced to gravity values at sea level. The main unknown quantities for the reduction supposing the Airy hypothesis are the supposedly constant density in the upper layer, the constant density below this layer, and the locally variable depth to which the upper layer extends. In the Pratt reduction method the major unknown quantities are the "depth of compensation," which is the same below sea level everywhere, and below which a constant density is to be assumed everywhere, while the density above the depth of compensation varies from place to place; this depth is to be estimated, if possible, on the basis of observations.

A more preferable method would be to assume for calculations of gravity at sea level the number and thickness of the crustal layers inferred from other, especially seismic, methods and to combine them with any data which are available for the densities in these layers. This method had been suggested and used originally by Heiskanen [1927; 1936, p. 915] but was later abandoned by him on account of the relatively great time which is needed for reduction of each single observation. Among other suggested reduction methods is that of Hayford [1910] who has modified the Pratt method by assuming that the depth of compensation has to be taken from the earth's physical surface and not from sea level. His method was used in early calculations in the United States.

It is almost generally believed that isostasy exists. This means that, except in recently or presently disturbed regions, the masses in columns with equal cross section, resting at a depth H below sea level are approximately equal. H must be taken greater than the deepest portion of the earth's crust (say, at least 70 km). If ρ is the density at the elevation z above H, and h the elevation of the column above sea level, then

$$\int_0^{H+h} \rho \, dz = \text{const.} \tag{3.22}$$

For the generalized Airy hypothesis we may assume n homogeneous layers with the thicknesses d_n and the densities ρ_n; we have to include the portion of the mantle between H and the Mohorovičić discontinuity as well as any layer of water in oceans, and may write

$$\sum_{1}^{n} \rho_n d_n = \text{const.} \tag{3.23}$$

In the original Airy hypothesis, only one discontinuity is assumed in continental areas, so that

$$\rho_m d_m + \rho_c d_c = \text{const.} \tag{3.24}$$

where the index m refers to the layer in the mantle between H and the Mohorovičić discontinuity, c to the crust. In oceanic areas the water has to be considered, in addition. In world-wide calculations, a density of $\rho_c = 2.67$ is used at present as average for the whole crust, and $\rho_m = 3.27$ g/cm³ below the Mohorovičić discontinuity. The author believes that a greater value should be assumed for ρ_c (see below).

If in the Pratt hypothesis D is the depth of compensation below sea level (the same everywhere), h_D the local elevation of the earth's surface above D, and ρ_D the density in a given column above D, $\rho_D h_D$ is the same everywhere. It is assumed that ρ_D is constant in each column from bottom to top but varies from column to column.

In the generalized method of Heiskanen, Eq. (3.23) holds; the density is assumed to be constant in each layer at a given location, but to increase from layer to layer with depth, and it may vary from column to column. This is assumed in some research in the U.S.S.R. For example, for a profile between Lake Issyk-Kul and Lake Balkash, Gamburtsev and Veytsman [1956] assume for the top layer a constant density of 2.65 g/cm³ everywhere, locally variable densities between 2.78 and 2.87 in the basaltic layer, and everywhere 3.52 g/cm³ below the Mohorovičić discontinuity.

There is no general agreement about the minimum area which may be assumed to be compensated as a unit. Meinesz [1931, and in later publications] and others have discussed this problem in detail. Probably the minimum radius (of the order of 10 km?) of areas compensated as a whole depends on local structure. Probably in most regions the processes (secular flow) which lead to isostasy act mainly in the deep portions of the crust and in the upper portion of the mantle, where the temperature is relatively close to the melting point of the material (Fig. 6.1).

Thus, with some oversimplification, we may say that a "static" portion of isostasy results from differences in the thickness of the crustal layers, especially the depths of the Conrad and Mohorovičić discontinuities, while a "dynamic" portion is mainly the effect of flow processes in the upper-most portion of the mantle.

The difference between the gravity observed at a specific point and reduced to sea level, and the average gravity at sea level for this point, calculated from Eq. (1.4), is called "gravity anomaly." Depending on the method of reduction, we find "free air anomalies," "Bouguer anomalies," isostatic anomalies, etc. Some of the assumptions made in the calculations of gravity anomalies have been discussed by Gutenberg [1955b]. First of all, a criterion has to be assumed, somewhat arbitrarily, to decide which reduction method makes assumptions closest to the facts for a given area. At present, that method of reduction is preferred in a given region, which leads to the smallest variations of the anomalies as a function of the station height [Heiskanen, 1951]. Until several years ago, that reduction method had been preferred which gave the smallest residuals, but this procedure leads almost to a vicious circle.

The thickness of the crust is now taken as $30 + aH$ km, where H is the height of the station above sea level; a is calculated on the assumption that the density in the crust is 2.67 g/cm³ everywhere, and 3.27 g/cm³ everywhere below the crust. Thus, it is assumed that the average density of the combined "granitic" and "basaltic" layers is the same everywhere. Considering the effect of pressure on the density and the higher density in the "basaltic" layer than in the "granitic" layer, Gutenberg [1955b] believes that the "average" density in the crust varies locally, that the assumed "average density of the crust" of 2.67 g/cm³ is too small by roughly 0.1 g/cm³ and that in most regions the difference in average densities above and below the Mohorovičić discontinuity is probably closer to 0.5 than to 0.6 g/cm³.

The usefulness of the Bouguer anomalies for finding of the crustal structure is open to doubts. Heiskanen [1953] points out that Bouguer anomalies frequently give valuable information for local exploration. The fact that they are usually positive over ocean basins, increasing with the depth of the water, and negative in continents, with increasing absolute amounts corresponding to the height of the area (Table 3.7) shows "qualitatively that isostatic equilibrium prevails. However, we cannot use these [Bouguer] anomalies for quantitative investigation" [Heiskanen, 1953, p. 11]. On the other hand, Tsuboi [1957] has based a method to calculate the thickness of the crust on Bouguer anomalies. He has assumed that the crust is homogeneous and rests on a homogeneous substratum. Some methods by others are based on a two-layered crust. The uncertainty, which method of reduction gives the best approximation to the actual values of gravity at sea

TABLE 3.7. GRAVITY ANOMALIES IN MILLIGALS; SOURCES (s IN LAST COLUMN): (a) WOOLARD [1952], (b) HEISKANEN [1936]; h = ELEVATION (OR DEPTH) IN METERS; ASSUMED DEPTH OF COMPENSATION ACCORDING TO PRATT T = 85.3 KM; D = ASSUMED THICKNESS OF THE LIGHTER UPPER LAYER (AIRY) IN KILOMETERS. FOR THE ASSUMED DENSITIES, SEE TEXT

Region	h	Free air	Bouguer	Isost.	Pratt	Airy $D=77$	Airy $D=64$	Airy $D=40$	s
Alexandria, La.	24	−1	−4	−9	—	—	—	—	a
Wien, Austria	183	0	−19	—	+25	+17	+21	+29	b
München, Germany	525	−15	−62	—	+2	+8	+8	+6	b
Grand Canyon	849	−108	−184	−12	—	—	—	—	a
Bridgeport, Nebr.	1114	−14	−139	−9	—	—	—	—	a
Zermatt, Alps	1606	+28	−118	—	+52	−16	−2	+31	b
Gornergrat, Alps	3016	+217	−120	—	+62	−9	+4	+36	b
Pikes Peak, Col.	4293	+206	−139	−9	—	—	—	—	a
Atlantic Ocean	−5880	−15	+389	+7	—	—	—	—	b
W. Pacific Ocean	−5840	+15	+330	+18	—	—	—	—	b
E. Pacific Ocean	−5910	−27	+379	−21	—	—	—	—	b
Indian Ocean	−4389	−11	—	+2	—	—	—	—	b
Nares Deep	−7860	−239	—	−103	—	—	—	—	b
North of Deep	−5570	−14	—	+3	—	—	—	—	b
Marianne Deep	−8740	−244	—	−90	—	—	—	—	b

level, introduces systematic errors which may reach or even exceed 10 mgal (compare Table 3.8).

A great amount of theoretical work has been done to permit finding of the crustal structure from gravity anomalies [Ansel, 1936; Heiskanen, 1936; Heiskanen and Meinesz, 1958] but as a consequence of the infinite number of possible solutions in a given instance, and the errors involved in

TABLE 3.8. ISOSTATIC GRAVITY ANOMALIES Δg IN MILLIGALS AFTER HEISKANEN [1936], USING: (a) PRATT'S REDUCTION METHOD, DEPTH OF COMPENSATION T KM; (b) AIRY'S METHOD, "THICKNESS OF THE CRUST" D KM; (c) HEISKANEN'S METHOD, ON THE BASIS OF GEOPHYSICALLY DETERMINED DATA FOR THE CRUSTAL LAYERS.

Region	Method of reduction								
	(a)		(a)		(b)		(b)		(c)
	Δg	T	Δg	T	Δg	D	Δg	D	Δg
87 stations in plains, USA	+8	85.3	+7	113.7	+6	60	+4	40	+4
20 mountain stations, USA	+18	85.3	+9	113.7	−10	77	+11	40	+6
27 coastal stations, USA	+3	85.3	−1	113.7	−4	77	+4	40	−1
23 coastal stations, Pacific, USA	—	—	−20	113.7	−20	60	−18	40	−15
12 stations, Caucasus	+47	156.3	+61	113.7	+28	77	+38	64	—
10 stations, Alps	+31	85.3	+81	113.7	−14	77	+19	40	—

the reduction of the observations, other information should be combined with the gravity data to find reliable results for the structure and thickness of the crust. However, a few general conclusions which are based on gravity observations alone, are beyond the limits of probable errors.

The fundamental result which has been derived from gravity observations is the confirmation that isostatic equilibrium exists over most of the earth. The absolute values of the greatest negative isostatic gravity anomalies which have been calculated on the basis of our present knowledge of the structure of the earth's crust occur in belts over ocean deeps which surround the Pacific Ocean. In some instances they exceed 200 mgal. The earliest detailed investigation of one of these belts with negative gravity anomalies was carried out by Meinesz [1933, 1934, 1948]; this belt parallels approximately the ocean deeps, usually slightly on the land side, to the east, south, (Fig. 3.10(a)) and west of the East Indies. Other belts with similarly great negative anomalies have been found slightly west of the ocean deeps to the east of the Philippine Islands; from the Marianne Islands to Japan (Fig. 3.10(b)); south of the Aleutian Islands; west of South America; and east of the Tonga Islands.

Extended zones of positive isostatic gravity anomalies usually exist on both sides of the belts of negative anomalies, especially on the side towards the continents. Many of these belts with positive anomalies are wider than the negative zones, but their maximum deviation from zero is smaller than

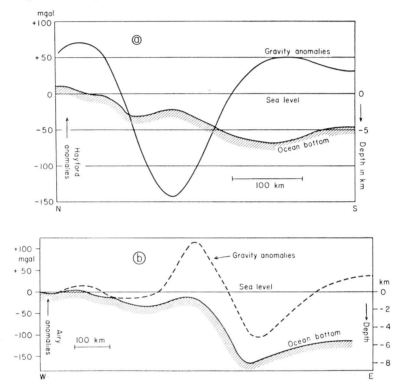

FIG. 3.10. Gravity anomalies over profiles perpendicular to great ocean deeps. (a) Java Sea to Indian Ocean near Djakarta; regional isostatic Hayford–Pratt anomalies for depth of compensation at $H = 30$ km; after Meinesz [1948]. (b) East of southern Honshu, Japan; Airy anomalies for $D = 40$ km; after Heiskanen [1945].

that in the negative zones. Elsewhere, there seem to be no extended zones of large positive isostatic anomalies. Limited areas with relatively great positive isostatic anomalies are, e.g., near Cyprus (over 150 mgal) and in Armenia (over 100 mgal).

Until recently, it had been generally assumed that the belts of negative isostatic anomalies near the ocean deeps indicate zones in which convection currents, perhaps in the upper portion of the mantle, move material gradually downward along extended narrow zones and thus, in course of long times, produce and maintain the narrow belts of great ocean deeps. As the material in the upper portion of the crust is colder than in the deeper portions, the movements proceed more slowly near the surface, so that rupture, producing earthquakes, is relatively frequent. However, Ewing and Heezen [1955] have pointed to the findings of their group that deep sediments of relatively small density (8 km thick in one place) fill the bottom of the Puerto Rico trough, and they have constructed a profile showing that the deep sediments there could explain the apparent anomalies which had been calculated on the basis of incorrect assumptions. Thus, caution is necessary in drawing conclusions about the structures and processes in and below the crust from gravity observations alone. Here is another field where more investigations are needed. Moreover, data from various branches of geophysics have to be combined before a more extended theoretical treatment is possible.

3.8 Results Based on Several Methods

3.8.1 The "Roots of Mountains"

According to the Airy hypothesis, the earth's crust should be thickest under mountains, about average under lowlands in continents, and thinnest under oceans. Mountains should have "roots" where either the granitic layer protrudes into the basaltic layer, or the basaltic layer into the mantle, or both, while under oceans there should be "antiroots" where the ultrasima protrudes upward into the crust. First, the antiroots under the oceans have been confirmed by gradually improved data from earthquake surface waves (Section 3.6), starting with the findings by Tams [1921]. Body waves have given the first confirmation for the "roots of mountains," when Gutenberg [1933, p. 456] had concluded on the basis of travel times of longitudinal waves over short distances, that there is a thickening of the crustal layers in Europe under the Alps, and when Byerly [1938] had reported a delay of a few seconds for longitudinal waves which have traveled under the Sierra Nevada from earthquake foci to the east of the mountains to nearby stations to the west. Byerly has interpreted this delay as a consequence of the root of the Sierra Nevada.

These roots have been confirmed by later investigations, for example, by Caloi [1958, p. 66] for the Alps, and by Gutenberg (see Fig. 3.11(b)), and by Byerly [1956] for the Sierra Nevada. Combinations of recent results for the thickness of the crust in Southern California based on various

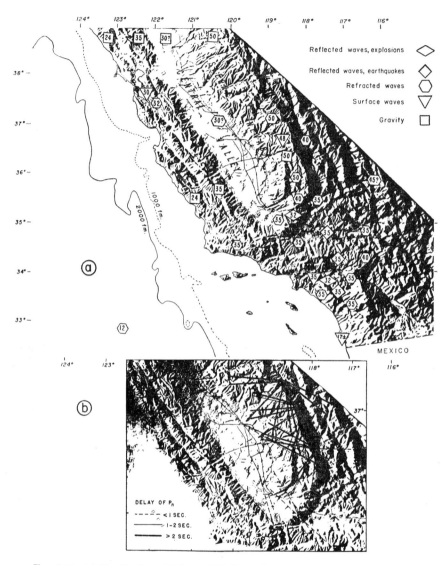

FIG. 3.11. (a) Depth of the Mohorovičić discontinuity in Southern California on the basis of various methods after Gutenberg [1957]. (b) Delay of longitudinal waves in the Sierra Nevada region after Gutenberg [1943]. Base map of N. F. Drake, Dept. of Geology, Stanford University, 1896.

methods (Fig. 3.11(a)) show good agreement between the results of these methods and leave no doubt about the root of the Sierra Nevada, nor about the decrease in crustal thickness towards the ocean. It seems that the roots of the Sierra Nevada are mainly a consequence of a thickening of the basaltic layer, while neither data from body waves nor those from Lg-waves [Press, 1956a] indicate appreciable changes in the thickness of the granitic layer there. The depth of the Conrad discontinuity between the granitic and basaltic layers is about 25 km in the few portions of Southern California for which we have data.

Tatel [in Aldrich et al., 1957, p. 96] points out that results of seismic and gravity data do not lead necessarily to the same conclusion, and "that high land areas and thick crustal regions do not necessarily go together. The question arises whether or not there is disagreement between the two sets of measurements, gravity and seismic." As it has been pointed out in Section 3.7, the assumption that the densities are constant in the crustal layers is incorrect, and the variations in the ratio between the thickness of the granitic and basaltic layers have to be considered. Tatel comes to a similar conclusion: the residuals "indicate wide-scale crustal inhomogeneities, or perhaps a horizontal distribution of inhomogeneities in density in the upper mantle rocks."

In the U.S.S.R., data for gravity anomalies are frequently combined with results of density determinations of rocks and of seismic investigations along a given profile to find the most probable crustal structure. This procedure permits the finding of a solution which fits all data within the limits of error. Riznichenko [1957] points out that these results in the U.S.S.R. are possible only if one permits the existence of appreciable differences in the structure of the crust from place to place. There, too, in some areas, the base of the granitic layer has a downward profile, which, with distortions and increased amplitudes, repeats the upward relief of the surface, while in others a root is not formed by changes of the thickness of the granitic, but of the basaltic layer. Similarly, Veytsman and associates [1957] point out that comparison of data obtained by the seismic method "with gravimetric data makes it possible to select regional gravity anomalies due to the masses of granite and basalt layers and of the upper part of the mantle." "A large variety of relations between the thickness of the granite and basalt layers was found. The relief of the basalt layers' surface was in most regions considerably more complex than that of the Mohorovičić discontinuity."

It seems that in most regions the shape and depth of the Mohorovičić discontinuity is the main controlling factor for the gravity anomalies, but that in some areas the thickness of the granitic layer is of major importance.

In the U.S.S.R. a special seismograph is being used to record reflections for the determination of the layering of the crust. Riznichenko [1958; see also Conference, 1958, p. 85] has described some of the results. In the

Tien-Shan Hercynian belt the roots of mountains are mainly the effect of thicker basaltic layers; the granitic layers there are roughly 20 km thick, the basaltic layers an additional 30 km. On the other hand, in the Alpide belt of the U.S.S.R. the root is mainly in the granitic layer, which extends to 30 km in portions of West Turkmenia and to 40 km in North Pamir. The corresponding thickness of the basaltic layer is respectively about 20 and 30 km.

Balavadze and Tvaltvadze [1957] have used seismic, gravimetric, magnetic, and density data for Georgia and the adjoining regions of the Caucasus to study the crustal structure. They have found that in the mountain regions which they have investigated the gravity anomalies are determined mostly by the depth of the Mohorovičić discontinuity, but "in intermountain and foothill regions chiefly by a change in the surfaces of granite and substratum."

Finally, Ewing and Ewing [1959] have investigated the root of the Mid-Atlantic Ridge. This follows roughly the center of the Atlantic Ocean from north to south. South of the Azores, it is about 1000 km wide and rises up to about 4 km above the ocean bottom to the west and east of it. From seismic and gravity data, Ewing and Ewing [1959, p. 308] conclude that under its center its root extends up to at least 30 km into the mantle. This ridge and the frequently wide shelf areas on both sides of the Atlantic Ocean have contributed to the differences found from surface wave velocities for the "average" structure of the Atlantic and Pacific Oceans.

The variety of conditions which lead to isostasy, including local differences in the density of the crustal material and the number and depths of discontinuities, have resulted in contradictory hypotheses about isostasy, whenever the assumptions for conditions, by which isostasy is achieved, have been oversimplified. This has led in some instances to doubts about the existence of mountain roots. For example, Bucher [1957, pp. 40–43, 470] is very skeptical about the existence of mountain roots, although he admits the existence of antiroots under the oceans [Bucher, 1957, p. 48]. The differences in the densities in the various crustal layers as well as in the thickness of the crust in continental and oceanic areas indicate beyond reasonable doubt that isostasy is achieved following varying combinations of the generalized Airy and Pratt hypotheses.

In many regions, the thickness of the crust changes gradually if the equilibrium is disturbed by erosion, sedimentation, or slowly progressing tectonic movements. Processes which tend to restore the equilibrium in such areas do not act necessarily in the crust alone, but frequently also in the upper portion of the mantle. Nonelastic processes at depths of the order of 100 to 200 km, where the high temperature seems to lead to a somewhat smaller viscosity and a lower yield point than in the crust (Section 9.4) may play an important role. At these depths, slow "subcrustal currents" seem to be able to reduce stresses to one half during periods of the order of 1000 years. Deep below a region in which mass is removed at the surface, such subcrustal currents probably move mass from the outside towards the area with reduced mass. The crust may bend passively at first, but some kind of flow is possible in the crust, too, though probably more slowly than in the upper mantle. Thus, in areas of disturbed equilibrium, processes with a tendency to restore the equilibrium probably act mainly at depths which are appreciably greater than the depths of the Conrad and the Mohorovičić discontinuities, where the fixed increases in density with depth are essential in the accomplishment of isostatic equilibrium.

Processes which are connected with the restoration of equilibrium affect much larger areas than those where the equilibrium had been disturbed originally. An example, the "postglacial uplift," is discussed in Section 9.4. The density of the material which, in instances of erosion, is added at depth, but during sedimentation is removed at depth, is greater than the density of the material which respectively is removed or added at the surface. Consequently, the elevation of the earth's surface in such regions changes permanently during the processes.

3.8.2 The "Boundary" of the Pacific Basin; the "Andesite Line"

Suess [1892] has pointed out with details that there are two major types of oceanic areas, those with "Atlantic structure" (including the Indian Ocean) with coasts traversed obliquely by mountain ranges, and those with "Pacific structure" with coasts paralleling mountain chains. He also has discussed a line which separates structures of two different types of material in the western Pacific Ocean. Marshall [1912] has pointed out that west of this line (Fig. 3.12) young eruptive magmas are predominantly andesitic, east of it principally basaltic. Born [1933] and others call it the "andesite line," but others prefer the expression "Marshall line."

Turner and Verhoogen [1951, p. 124] point out that there is a relatively sharp boundary between the andesite dacite rhyolite kinds of volcanic rocks "of the Pacific margin (the circum-Pacific province) and the olivine-basalt trachite association of the island groups scattered within the Pacific basin." This boundary (the andesite line) "is defined purely in terms of petrographic data. It should not be used synonymously with any 'Pacific Ocean boundary' . . . even though some degree of correlation between seismic and petrographic provinces may prove possible." As Fig. 3.12 shows, there is a fairly good correlation between the andesite line and the earthquake belts, especially if it is considered that the andesite line can be located only where sufficient evidence of the composition of volcanic rocks is available, that is, mainly where there are islands. The scanty data from the

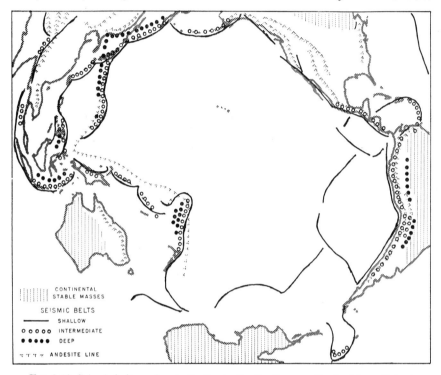

FIG. 3.12. Seismic belts and andesite line in the Pacific area. Revised from Gutenberg and Richter [1954].

eastern Pacific do not permit us to draw with any confidence the corresponding line which must exist there. Hess [1955a] believes that "andesite will be produced where deformation is sufficiently strong to bulge the basaltic layer down to sufficient depth to cause partial fusion." This would limit the andesitic rocks to narrow belts along the andesite line. Problems connected with the andesite line contain various controversial hypotheses.

3.8.3 The Earthquake Belts

The Pacific Basin is surrounded by arcuate structures (Fig. 3.12); nearly all are convex towards the basin. Gutenberg and Richter [1954, p. 28] have

described them as follows, beginning on the convex side of the arc (compare
Fig. 3.13): "(A) an oceanic trench, trough or foredeep. (B) shallow earthquakes and negative gravity anomalies, occurring in a narrow belt on the

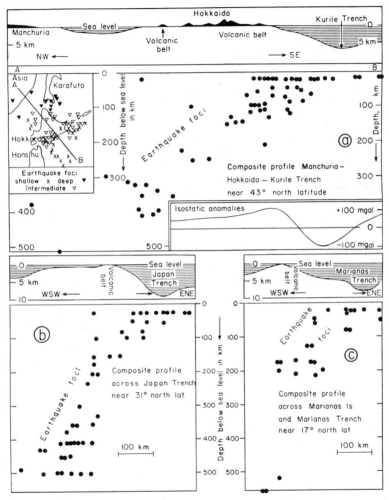

FIG. 3.13. Three composite profiles in the western Pacific, showing earthquake foci,
ocean trenches, and volcanoes.

concave side of the submarine trough. Frequently the ocean bottom here
rises in a ridge, which may emerge into small non-volcanic islands. (C)
Maximum of positive gravity anomalies. Earthquakes at depths near 60

km, frequently large. (D) The principal structure arc, of Late Cretaceous
or of Tertiary age, with active or recently extinct volcanoes. Shocks at
depths of the order of 100 km. Gravity anomalies decreasing. (E) A second
structural arc. Volcanism older and usually in a late stage. Shocks at depths
of 200–300 km. (F) a belt of shocks at depths of 300–700 km. . . . The
details vary widely from region to region; often one or more features are
poorly represented or unknown."

These sequences of phenomena follow extended belts surrounding the
Pacific Basin. They are best developed off Central and South America, from
New Zealand to Samoa, from the New-Hebrides to New Guinea, from the
Marianas Islands to Kamtchatka and along the Aleutian Islands. Except

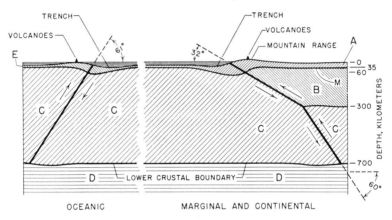

Fig. 3.14. Generalized oceanic and continental sections with orogenic fault types
after Benioff [1954]. Surface relief is exaggerated.

for relatively minor earthquake belts and ridges, the characteristic phenomena have not been found along the southern boundary of the Pacific Basin
and, except for earthquake belts, are poorly developed along the Pacific
coast of the United States and Canada. On the other hand, similar belts
extend from the Pacific Ocean along the East Indies into the coastal areas
of the north-eastern Indian Ocean, and indications of them can be found in
southern Asia and in the Mediterranean.

Benioff [1955] has divided the deep faults, indicated by the earthquake
foci (Fig. 3.13) in these belts, into two groups. "Dual faults" (Fig. 3.14)
usually have a "shallow member extending from the surface to a depth of
60 km and an intermediate member extending to a depth of approximately
300 km with an average dip of 33°. The triple form has a third component
extending down to a depth of approximately 650 km with a dip of 60°.

In the continental domain, the 300-km level appears to represent a tectonic discontinuity which may be the lower boundary of the continents." The boundary of the crust is by his definition at a depth of about 700 km.

Raitt and associates [1955] have investigated a profile across the Tonga Ridge and the Tonga Trench by seismic and magnetic methods. This profile crosses one of the arcuate structures described above, with earthquake foci at depths of about 25 km near the trench which is up to 10 km deep, foci at depths of 100 to 200 km under the volcanic ridge and increasing to about 650 km about 500 km farther west. Raitt, Fisher, and Mason have found the Mohorovičić discontinuity (bottom of the crust in our definition) at a depth of about 12 km below sea level in the basin about 50 km east of the Tonga Trench, at a depth of about 20 km below sea level under the trench, and no indication of a change in depth from there to the ridge. While the sediments under the Tonga Trench are very thin, contrasting with the Puerto Rico Trench (Section 3.7) they are about 2 km thick under the Tofua Trough next to the ridge.

There are many controversial hypotheses involved in explanations of the phenomena discussed in this section. These include hypotheses about the processes which have produced the present conditions during the earth's history. Hess [1955a,b] has pointed to the possible importance of serpentinization.

3.8.4 Transition from Oceanic to Continental Crust

The crustal structure under continents and under oceans is only tentatively known, but there is even more doubt about the transition from one to the other. While the crust under oceans is usually much thinner than under continents and the "granitic layer" is missing under the oceans outside the shelves, there is doubt whether or not the seismically determined "gabbro" layers under ocean bottoms and continents consist of the same type of rock, and if the "ultrabasic layer" is formed by the same type of material under both units. In each of these layers the velocities of elastic waves, where they have been observed, are the same within the limits of error under both units, and there is no indication of a change in the transition zones from continents to oceans. Observed local differences in the velocities (Table 3.4) are relatively small. They may correspond to actual differences in the material or may be the result of inaccurate assumptions. As it has been pointed out repeatedly, the determinations of wave velocities are frequently based on travel times obtained in one direction only, and the assumption has been made that the layers are strictly horizontal. Consequently, a very small dip of the discontinuity is sufficient to explain any observed difference in velocities in a given layer.

The best observations in the transition zone between ocean and continent by the seismic as well as the gravity methods are for the border-land between North America and the Atlantic Ocean [Worzel and Shurbet, 1955; Ewing and Press, 1955]. Figure 3.15 is a sketch, modified from Ewing

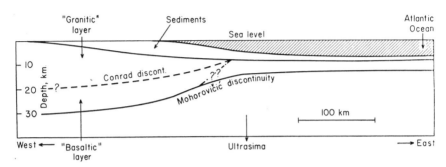

FIG. 3.15. Profile of hypothetical crustal structure from New Jersey to the Atlantic Ocean, modified from Ewing and Press [1955, p. 5].

and Press who consider the possibility of a change in material of the "basaltic layer" near the coast. Their original figure does not show the Conrad discontinuity under eastern North America, where thus far there are few indications for it, most of which are not definite.

There is no reason to expect appreciable differences for the corresponding transition zones at other oceanic coasts, except for the neighborhood of ocean deeps for which hypothetical profiles have been discussed in Section 3.8.3. On the other hand, Benioff [1955] has suggested possible differences in structure along Pacific coasts down to depths of several hundred kilometers (Fig. 3.14).

3.8.5 Disturbance of Isostasy by Removal or Addition of Loads at the Surface

There are several types of processes which disturb more or less continuously the equilibrium in the earth's crust, such as volcanic activity, melting or forming of ice, erosion, and sedimentation.

Gravity observations [Heiskanen, 1936, p. 941] show that isostatic anomalies are strongly positive in some regions of present volcanic activity, for example, over 100 mgal over portions of Hawaii, especially near the volcanoes, but that in others isostatic equilibrium seems to have been nearly reached. Similarly, in areas where ice is added relatively rapidly during increase in glaciation, or later removed (Section 9.4) one half of the sinking or uplift which is necessary to restore equilibrium occurs in time intervals of the order of 1000 years. Water masses added to the oceans during extended melting of ice, and water removed from the oceans by increase of the polar ice masses, should also disturb the equilibrium. However, the areas involved are much larger than those affected by the ice load.

In regions of sedimentation, the gravity anomalies do not seem to differ beyond the limits of error from those in the neighborhood. Apparently, sedimentation, and probably erosion, proceed at such a slow speed that the compensating sinking of the areas where the rivers deposit their sediments, respectively the rising of the eroded areas, proceed fast enough to prevent the forming of gravity anomalies which are great enough for definite verification.

3.9 Causes for Discontinuities in the Crust

There had been little doubt that all discontinuities in the crust of the earth are boundaries between material of different chemical composition until Lees [1953] proposed the hypothesis that the Mohorovičić discontinuity separates two different phases of rocks of the same chemical composition. Subsequently, this possibility has been considered by a few others. Unfortunately, experimental data are still very scanty on the temperature and pressure at which phase changes occur in the minerals which are possibly involved. Moreover, it is not known which specific rock types form the material on either side of the discontinuities, especially the Mohorovičić discontinuity. For several mineral systems the curves for phase changes as function of pressure and temperature intersect the curves which are assumed for pressure and temperature as function of depth in the earth at very small angles. Consequently, small differences in the temperature and pressure under various regions, especially between oceanic and continental areas, may result in relatively great differences in the depth at which a given phase change may occur. Among the few laboratory data which have been reported and may concern the earth's crust are experiments leading to curves for phase changes in nepheline by Boyd and England [1956]. They have discussed the possible importance of such phase changes in minerals existing in the crust and upper portion of the mantle. Moreover, Lovering [1958] considers the possibility that the Mohorovičić discontinuity corresponds to a transition of basalt into a high-pressure modification, possibly represented by eclogites. Similar suggestions for phase changes in the lower mantle are discussed in Sec. 4.3.

There is no agreement about the mineral systems making up the rocks immediately below the Mohorovičić discontinuity. Olivines, especially dunite, as well as pyroxenite and eclogite have been suggested as representatives of the rocks in question. However, while these exhibit the wave velocities observed in the upper mantle, they are relatively rare in the crust, although they are supposed to form the layers only about 10 km below the oceans, and about 30 km below the continental crust in low areas. Their scarcity in the crust is an argument in favor of the hypothesis that the boundary between mantle and crust corresponds to a phase change; the phase existing in the upper mantle should be unstable in the crust. However, at present the assumption of a different composition of the lower crust and the upper mantle is preferred. A trustworthy decision requires much more data on phase changes, or drilling of bore holes down below the Mohorovičić discontinuity. The details of such an experiment are being studied after a corresponding resolution (No. 3) has been adopted by the International Union of Geodesy and Geophysics at its meeting in Toronto, 1957 [Conference, 1958, p. 210]. The results of such an experiment could change considerably many of our ideas about the structure of the lower portion of the crust and the upper portion of the mantle.

References

Adams, L. H., Tuve, M. A., and Tatel, H. [1952]. Seismic exploration of the earth's crust. *Compt. rend. assoc. intern. séismol.* **10,** 113–114.

Airy, B. G. [1855]. On the computation of the effect of the attraction of mountain masses disturbing the apparent astronomical latitude of stations in geodetic surveys. *Phil. Trans. Roy. Soc. (London)* **145,** 101–104.

Aldrich, L. T., Graham, J. W., Tatel, H. E., Tuve, M. A., Wetherill, G. W. [1957]. The earth's crust. *Carnegie Inst. Wash. Yearbook for 1956/1957.* **56,** 94–96.

Anonymous [1955]. National report on seismology (1951–53), India. *Compt. rend. assoc. intern. séismol.* **11,** 239–244.

Ansel, E. A. [1936]. Zur Theorie des irdischen Schwerefeldes. *In* "Handbuch der Geophysik" (B. Gutenberg, ed.), Vol. 1, pp. 536–730. Borntraeger, Berlin.

Balavadze, B. K., and Tvaltvadze, G. K. [1957]. Structure of the earth's crust in Georgia from geophysical evidence. *Abstr. Repts. 9th Assembly IGGU, Intern. Assoc. Seismol. Acad. U.S.S.R. Moscow* pp. 16–18.

Båth, M. [1953]. Discussion [to Lehmann, 1953]. *Bull. inform. Union Géodésie Geophys. Intern.* **2,** 251.

Båth, M. [1954]. The elastic waves Lg and Rg along Euroasiatic paths. *Arkiv Geofysik* **2,** 295–342.

Båth, M. [1956]. Some consequences of the existence of low-velocity layers. *Ann. geofis.* **9**, 411–450.

Båth, M. [1957]. A continental channel wave, guided by the intermediate layer in the crust. *Geofis. pura e appl.* **38**, 19–31.

Båth, M., and Vogel, A. [1958]. Surface waves from earthquakes in northern Atlantic-Arctic Ocean. *Geofis. pura e appl.* **39**, 35–54.

Baule, H., and Müller, E. [1956]. Messung elastischer Eigenschaften von Gesteinen. *In* "Encyclopedia of Physics" (S. Flügge, ed.), Vol. **47**, pp. 169–201. Springer, Berlin.

Bederke, E. [1957]. Zur Geologie und Geophysik der Tiefen. *Geol. Rundschau* **46**, 229–245.

Benioff, H. [1954]. Orogenesis and deep crustal structure. *Bull. Geol. Soc. Am.* **65**, 385–400.

Benioff, H. [1955]. Seismic evidence for crustal structure and tectonic activity. *Geol. Soc. Am. Spec. Papers* **62**, 61–74.

Bernard, P. [1956]. Interprétation des ondes séismiques des explosions des Rochilles. *Compt. rend.* **243**, 2115–2118.

Birch, F. [1958]. Interpretation of the seismic structure of the crust in the light of experimental studies of wave velocities in rocks. *In* "Contributions in Geophysics" (H. Benioff, M. Ewing, B. F. Howell, and F. Press, eds.), Vol. **1**, pp. 158–170. Pergamon, New York.

Bolt, B. A., Doyle, H. A., and Sutton, D. J. [1958]. Seismic observations from the 1956 atomic explosions in Australia. *Geophys. J.* **1**, 135–145.

Born, A. [1933]. Der geologische Aufbau der Erde. *In* "Handbuch der Geophysik" (B. Gutenberg, ed.), Vol. **2**, pp. 565–867. Borntraeger, Berlin.

Boyd, F. R., and England, J. L. [1956]. Phase equilibria at high pressure. *Carnegie Inst. Wash. Yearbook* **55**, 154–157.

Bucher, W. H. [1957]. "The Deformation of the Earth's Crust." Reprinted (1933, Princeton Univ. Press), 518 pp. With a new foreword. Hafner, New York.

Bullen, K. E. [1958]. Seismology in our atom age. *Compt. rend. assoc. intern. séismol. et phys. intérieur de la terre, Toronto, 1957*, No. **12**, 19–35.

Bune, V. I., and Butovskaya, E. M. [1955]. Travel time curves and the earth's crustal structure in central Asia according to recordings of powerful explosions. *Trudy Geofiz. Inst. Akad. Nauk. S.S.S.R. No. 30*, (157), 142–156 (in Russian).

Byerly, P. [1938]. The Sierra Nevada in the light of isostasy. *Bull. Geol. Soc. Am.* **48**, 2025–2031.

Byerly, P. [1956]. Subcontinental structure in the light of seismological evidence. *Advances in Geophys.* **3**, 106–152.

Byerly, P., and Wilson, J. T. [1935]. The Central California earthquakes of May 16, 1933 and June 7, 1934. *Bull. Seismol. Soc. Am.* **25**, 223–246.

Caloi, P. [1957a]. La struttura della crosta terrestre, con particolare riguardo alle zolle continentali, quale risulta dallo studio dei terremoti e delle grandi esplosioni (Eurasia). *Ann. Geofis.* **10**, 183–188.

Caloi, P. [1957b]. Caratteristiche della crosta terrestre dalle Alpi agli Appennini. *Ann. geofis.* **10**, 189–192.

Caloi, P. [1958]. The crust of the earth, from the Apennines to the Atlantic, reconstructed in accordance with the data supplied by seismic surveys. *Z. Geophys.* **24**, 65–95.

Conference [1958]. *Compt. rend. assoc. intern. séismol. et phys. intérieur de la terre, Toronto, 1957, No. 12*, 301 pp. and appendixes.

Conrad, V. [1925]. Laufzeitkurven des Tauernbebens vom 28. November 1923. *Mitt. Erdbeben-Komm. Akad. Wiss. Wien* [N.F.] **59**, 23 pp.

Di Filippo, D., and Marcelli, L. [1952]. Struttura della crosta terrestre in corrispondenza dell'Italia Centrale (Gran Sasso). *Ann. geofis.* **5**, 569–579.

Dix, C. H. [1952]. "Seismic Prospecting for Oil," 414 pp. Harper, New York.

Doyle, H. A. [1957]. Seismic recordings of atomic explosions in Australia. *Nature* **180**, 132–134.

Dutton, C. E. [1892]. On some of the greater problems of physical geology. *Bull. Phil. Soc. Wash.* **9**, 51–64; Reprinted in "Physics of the Earth," Vol. **2**, Natl. Research Council [1931] no. 78, 201–211.

Eiby, G. A. [1957]. Crustal structure project. The Wellington profile. *New Zealand Dept. Sci. Ind. Research Geophys. Mem.* **5**, 5–31.

Ewing, J., and Ewing, M. [1959]. Seismic refraction measurements in the Atlantic Ocean basins, in the Mediterranean Sea, on the Mid-Atlantic Ridge, and in the Norwegian Sea. *Bull. Geol. Soc. Am.* **70**, 291–318.

Ewing, J. I., Officer, C. B., Johnson, H. R., and Edwards, R. S. [1957]. Geophysical investigations in the eastern Caribbean: Trinidad Shelf, Tobaggo Trough, Barbados Ridge, Atlantic Ocean. *Bull. Geol. Soc. Am.* **68**, 897–912.

Ewing, M., and Heezen, B. C. [1955]. Puerto Rico Trench topography and geophysical data. *Geol. Soc. Am. Spec. Papers* **62**, 255–268.

Ewing, M., and Press F. [1955]. Geophysical contrasts between continents and ocean basins. *Geol. Soc. Am. Spec. Papers* **62**, 1–6.

Ewing, M., and Press, F. [1956a]. Surface waves and guided waves. *In* "Encyclopedia of Physics" (S. Flügge, ed.), Vol. 47, pp. 119–139. Springer, Berlin.

Ewing, M., and Press, F. [1956b]. Structure of the earth's crust. *In* "Encyclopedia of Physics" (S. Flügge, ed.), Vol. 47, 246–257. Springer, Berlin.

Ewing, M., and Press, F. [1957]. Regional measurements of crustal thickness (abstr.). *Bull. Geol. Soc. Am.* **68**, 1725.

Ewing, M., and Press, F. [1959]. Determination of crustal structure from phase velocities of Rayleigh waves, pt. III, the United States. *Bull. Geol. Soc. Am.* **70**, 229–244.

Ewing, M., Sutton, G. H., and Officer, C. B. [1954]. Seismic refraction measurements in the Atlantic Ocean, *VI:* Typical deep stations, North American Basin. *Bull. Seismol. Soc. Am.* **44**, 21–38.

Ewing, W. M., Jardetzky, W. S., and Press, F. [1957]. "Elastic Waves in Layered Media," 380 pp. McGraw-Hill, New York.

Fisher, O. [1889]. "Physics of the Earth's Crust," 2nd ed., 2 Vols. Macmillan, London.

Gálfi, J., and Stegena, L. [1957]. Tiefenreflexionsversuche in Ungarn zum Studium der kontinentalen Aufbauung. *Geol. Rundschau* **46**, 26–29.

Gamburtsev, G. A., and Veytsman, P. S. [1956]. Comparison of deep seismic sounding data on the earth's crustal structure in the region of the northern Tien-Shan mountains with data from seismology and gravimetry. *Izvest. Akad. Nauk S.S.S.R. Ser. Geofiz.* **9**, 1036–1043 (in Russian).

Gane, P. G., Atkins, A. R., Sellschap, J. P. F., and Seligman, P. [1956]. Crustal structure in the Transvaal. *Bull. Seismol. Soc. Am.* **46**, 293–316.

Garland, G. D. [1956]. Gravity and isostasy. *In* "Encyclopedia of Physics" (S. Flügge, ed.), Vol. 47, pp. 202–245. Springer, Berlin.

Gaskell, T. F., Hill, M. N., and Swallow, J. C. [1958]. Seismic measurements made by

H. M. S. Challenger in the Atlantic, Pacific and Indian Oceans and in the Mediterranean Sea, 1950–53. *Phil. Trans. Roy. Soc. London* **A251**, 23–83.

Geneslay, R., Labrouste, Y., and Rothé, J.-P. [1956]. Réflexions à grande profondeur dans les grosses explosions (Champagne, Octobre 1952). *Publs. Bur. Central Séismol. Intern. Trav. Sci (A)* **19**, 331–334.

Gutenberg, B. [1924a]. Das Erdbeben in der chilenischen Provinz Atacama am 10. November 1922, 2. Teil. Die Bearbeitung der instrumentellen Aufzeichnungen. *Veröffentl. Reichsanstalt Erdbebenforsch.* **3**, 29–48, and Addendum, 8 pp.

Gutenberg, B. [1924b]. Der Aufbau der Erdkruste auf Grund geophysikalischer Betrachtungen. *Z. Geophys.* **1**, 94–108.

Gutenberg, B. [1926]. Ueber Gruppengeschwindigkeit bei Erdbebenwellen. *Physik. Z.* **27**, 111–114.

Gutenberg, B. [1933]. Der physikalische Aufbau der Erde. *In* "Handbuch der Geophysik" (B. Gutenberg, ed.), Vol. 2, pp. 440–564. Borntraeger, Berlin.

Gutenberg, B. [1943]. Seismological evidence for roots of mountains. *Bull. Geol. Soc. Am.* **54**, 473–478.

Gutenberg, B. [1944]. Energy ratio of reflected and refracted seismic waves. *Bull. Seismol. Soc. Am.* **34**, 85–102.

Gutenberg, B. [1945]. Amplitudes of surface waves and magnitudes of shallow earthquakes. *Bull. Seismol. Soc. Am.* **35**, 3–12.

Gutenberg, B. [1951]. Revised travel times in Southern California. *Bull. Seismol. Soc. Am.* **41**, 143–163.

Gutenberg, B. [1952]. Waves from blasts recorded in Southern California. *Trans. Am. Geophys. Union* **33**, 427–431.

Gutenberg, B. [1954]. Effects of low velocity layers. *Geofis. pura e appl.* **28**, 1–10.

Gutenberg, B. [1955a]. Channel waves in the earth's crust. *Geophysics* **20**, 283–294.

Gutenberg, B. [1955b]. Geophysical data implied in isostatic calculation. Publ. dedicated to W. A. Heiskanen. *Veröffentl. Finnish Geodetic Inst.* **46**, 43–50.

Gutenberg, B. [1957]. Zur Frage der Gebirgswurzeln. *Geol. Rundschau* **46**, 30–38.

Gutenberg, B. [1958]. Microseisms. *Advances in Geophys* **5**, 54–92.

Gutenberg, B., and Richter, C. F. [1935]. On seismic waves, II. *Gerlands Beitr. Geophys.* **45**, 280–360.

Gutenberg, B., and Richter, C. F. [1954]. "Seismicity of the Earth," 2nd ed., 308 pp. Princeton Univ. Press, Princeton, New Jersey.

Hayford, J. F. [1910]. Supplementary investigation in 1909 of the figure of the earth and isostasy. U.S. Coast and Geodetic Survey. 80 pp.

Heiskanen, W. [1927]. Die Erdkrustendicke nach den Schwereanomalien. *Z. Geophys.* **3**, 217–221.

Heiskanen, W. [1936]. Das Problem der Isostasie. *In* "Handbuch der Geophysik" (B. Gutenberg, ed.), Vol. 1, pp. 878–951. Borntraeger, Berlin.

Heiskanen, W. [1945]. The gravity anomalies on the Japanese islands and in the waters east of them. *Publ. Isostatic Inst. Intern. Assoc. Geodesy No.* **13**, 22 pp.

Heiskanen, W. [1951] Report on isostasy. 1. Isostatic theories. *Trav. Assoc. intern. geodesie Rappts. 8ᵉ et 9ᵉ, Bruxelles*, **1951**.

Heiskanen, W. [1953]. The geophysical applications of gravity anomalies. *Trans. Am. Geophys. Union* **34**, 11–15.

Heiskanen, W. A., and Meinesz, F. A. V. [1958]. "The Earth and its Gravity Field," 478 pp. McGraw-Hill, New York.

Hess, H. H. [1955a]. Serpentines, orogeny, and epeirogeny. *Geol. Soc. Am. Spec. Papers* **62**, 391–408.

Hess, H. H. [1955b]. The oceanic crust. *J. Marine Research (Sears Foundation)* **14**, 432–439.

Hill, M. N. [1957]. Recent geophysical exploration of the ocean floor. *In* "Physics and Chemistry of the Earth" (L. H. Ahrens, K. Rankana, and S. K. Runcorn, eds.), Vol. 2, pp. 129–163. Pergamon Press, New York.

Hiller, W. [1953]. Erdbebenherde, Tektonik, Herdtiefe, Herdmechanismus und Schichtung der Erdkruste in Südwestdeutschland. *Bull. inform. Union Geodésie Geophys. Intern.* **2**, 232–236.

Hodgson, J. H. [1953]. A seismic survey in the Canadian Shield. *Publs. Dominion Astrophys. Observatory Ottawa*, **16**, 133–163, 169–171.

Hughes, D. S., and Maurette, C. [1957]. Variation of elastic wave velocities in basic igneous rocks with pressure and temperature. *Geophysics* **22**, 23–31.

Jeffreys, H. [1926]. The reflexion and refraction of elastic waves. *Monthly Notices Roy. Astron. Soc. Geophys. Suppl.* **1**, 321–334.

Jeffreys, H. [1935]. Surface waves of earthquakes. *Monthly Notices Roy. Astron. Soc. Geophys. Suppl.* **3**, 253–261.

Jeffreys, H. [1952]. "The Earth," 3rd ed., 392 pp. Cambridge Univ. Press, London and New York.

Kárnik, V. [1956]. Les vitesses des ondes séismiques excitées par les explosions industrielles en Bohême. *Publs. Bur. Central Seismol. Intern. Trav. Sci. (A)* **19**, 319–324.

Katz, S. [1953]. Seismic Study of Crustal Structure in Pennsylvania and New York. Lamont Geol. Observatory Palisades, Tech. Rept. 32, 23 pp.

Kishimoto, Y. [1955]. Seismometric investigation of the earth's interior. Pt. II. *Mem. Coll. Sci. Univ. Kyoto* **A27**, 243–288.

Lee, A. W. [1932]. The effect of geological structure upon microseismic disturbance. *Monthly Notices Roy. Astron. Soc. Geophys. Suppl.* **3**, 83–105.

Lees, G. M. [1953]. The evolution of a shrinking earth. *Quart. J. Geol. Soc. London* **109**, 217–257.

Leet, L. D., and Birch, F. [1942]. Seismic velocities. "Handbook of physical constants," *Geol. Soc. Am. Spec. Papers* **36**, 93–101.

Lehmann, I. [1953]. On the short-period surface wave "Lg" and crustal structure. *Bull. inform. Union Géodésie Geophys. Intern.* **2**, 248–251.

Lehmann, I. [1957]. On Lg as read in North American records. *Ann. geofis.* **10**, 1–21.

Love, A. E. H. [1911]. "Some Problems of Geodynamics," 180 pp. Cambridge Univ. Press, London and New York.

Lovering, J. F. [1958]. The nature of the Mohorovičić discontinuity. *Trans. Am. Geophys. Union* **39**, 947–955.

Macelwane, J. B. [1951]. Evidence on the interior of the earth derived from seismic sources. *In* "Internal Constitution of the Earth" (B. Gutenberg, ed.), 2nd ed., pp. 227–304. Dover, New York.

Marshall, P. [1912]. Oceania. "Handbuch der regionalen Geologie." Vol. 7, Pt. 2, 36 pp. Heidelberg.

Meinesz, F. A. V. [1931]. Une nouvelle méthode pour la réduction isostatique régionale de l'intensité de la pesanteur. *Bull. géodésique intern.* **29**, 33–51.

Meinesz, F. A. V. [1933]. Ergebnisse der Schwerkraftbeobachtungen auf dem Meere in den Jahren 1923–1932. *Ergeb. kosmischen Physik* **2**, 153–212.

Meinesz, F. A. V. [1934, 1948]. Gravity expeditions at sea. *Publ. Netherlands Geodetic Comm.* **2**, 1–139; **4**, 1–233.

Meissner, E. [1927]. Elastische Overflächen-Querwellen. *Proc. 2nd. Intern. Congr. Appl. Mech. Zürich 1926* (E. Meissner ed.) pp. 3–11.

Mohorovičić, A. [1910]. Das Beben vom 8. X. 1909. *Jahrb. Meteorol. Observatorium Zagreb* **9**, Pt. IV, Sect. 1, 63 pp.

Mohorovičić, S. [1927]. Ueber Nahbeben und die Konstitution des Erd- und Mondinnern. *Gerlands Beitr. Geophys.* **17**, 180–231.

Officer, C. B., Ewing, J. I., Edwards, R. S., and Johnson, H. R. [1957]. Geophysical investigations in the eastern Caribbean: Venezuelan Basin, Antilles Island arc, and Puerto Rico Trench. *Bull. Geol. Soc. Am.* **68**, 359–378.

Oliver, J., Ewing, M., and Press, F. [1955]. Crustal structure of the Arctic regions from the Lg phase. *Bull. Geol. Soc. Am.* **66**, 1063–1074.

Pratt, J. H. [1855]. On the attraction of the Himalayan mountains and of elevated regions beyond upon the plumb line in India. *Phil. Trans. Roy. Soc. London* **145**, 53–100.

Press, F. [1956a]. Velocity of Lg-waves in California. *Trans. Am. Geophys. Union* **37**, 615–618.

Press, F. [1956b]. Determination of crustal structure from phase velocity of Rayleigh waves, I. *Bull. Geol. Soc. Am.* **67**, 1647–1658.

Press, F. [1957]. Determination of crustal structure from phase velocity of Rayleigh waves, II: San Francisco Bay region. *Bull. Seismol. Soc. Am.* **47**, 87–88.

Press, F., and Ewing, M. [1952]. Two slow surface waves across North America. *Bull. Seismol. Soc. Am.* **42**, 219–228.

Press, F., and Ewing, M. [1955]. Earthquake surface waves and crustal structure. *Geol. Soc. Am. Spec. Papers* **62**, 51–60.

Press, F., and Gutenberg B. [1956]. Channel P waves Пg in the earth's crust. *Trans. Am. Geophys. Union* **37**, 754–756.

Press, F., Ewing, M., and Oliver, J. [1956]. Crustal structure and surface wave dispersion in Africa. *Bull. Seismol. Soc. Am.* **46**, 97–107.

Raitt, R. W. [1949]. Studies of ocean bottom structure off Southern California with explosive waves (abstr.). *Bull. Geol. Soc. Am.* **60**, 1915.

Raitt, R. W. [1956]. Seismic refraction studies of the Pacific Ocean Basin. 1, *Bull. Geol. Soc. Am.* **67**, 1623–1640.

Raitt, R. W. [1957]. Seismic refraction studies of Eniwetok atoll. *U.S. Geol. Survey Profess. Papers* **260-S**, 685–698.

Raitt, R. W., Fisher, R. L., and Mason, R. G. [1955]. Tonga Trench. *Geol. Soc. Am. Spec. Papers* **62**, 237–254.

Rayleigh, J. W. S. [1945]. "The Theory of Sound," Vol. 2, pp. 126–129. Dover, New York, (reprinted from 2nd ed., 1894).

Reich, H. [1953]. Ueber reflexionsseismische Beobachtungen der Prakla aus grossen Tiefen bei den grossen Steinbruchsprengungen in Blaubeuren am 4. März und am 10. Mai 1952. *Bull. inform. Union Géodésie Geophys. Intern.* **2**, 229–232.

Reich, H. [1957]. In Süddeutschland seismisch ermittelte tiefe Grenzflächen und ihre geologische Bedeutung. *Geol. Rundschau* **46**, 1–17.

Reich, H. [1958]. Seismische und geologische Ergebnisse der 2 to Sprengung im Tiefbohrloch Tölz I am 11. XII. 1954. *Geol. Jahrb.* **75**, 1–46.

Research Group for Explosion Seismology, Tokyo [1951, 1952, 1954]. Explosion—seismic observations. *Bull. Earthquake Research Inst. Tokyo Univ.* **29**, 97–105; **30**, 279–292; **32**, 79–86.

Richards, T. C. [1958]. Measurement of the thickness of the earth's crust in the Albertan plains area of western Canada. *J. Alberta Soc. Petrol. Geol.* **6**, 188–189.

Richter, C. F. [1958]. "Elementary Seismology," 768 pp. Freeman, San Francisco.

Riznichenko, Y. V. [1957]. On the study of the structure of the earth's crust during the third IGY. *Bull. Acad. U.S.S.R. Geophys. Ser.* **2**, 1–14.

Riznichenko, Y. V. [1958]. Seismische Tiefensondierungen zur Untersuchung der Erdkruste. *Studia Geophys. et Geodaet.* **2**, 133–140 (in Russian with German summary).

Rothé, J. P. [1958]. Quelques expériences sur la structure de la croûte terrestre en Europe Occidentale. *In* "Contributions in Geophysics" (H. Benioff, M. Ewing, and B. F. Howell, and F. Press, eds.), Vol. 1, pp. 135–151. Pergamon, New York.

Shor, G. G. [1955]. Deep reflections from Southern California blasts. *Trans. Am. Geophys. Union* **36**, 133–138.

Slichter, L. B. [1951]. Crustal Structure in the Wisconsin Area. Office of Naval Research, Rept. Oct. 31, 1951, 11 pp.

Stegena, L. [1958]. Seismische Untersuchungen der Tiefenstruktur der Erdkruste in Ungarn. *Studia Geophys. et Geodaet.* **2**, 177–180.

Stoneley, R. [1926]. The effect of the ocean on Rayleigh waves. *Monthly Notices Roy. Astron. Soc. Geophys. Suppl.* **1**, 349–355.

Stoneley, R. [1948]. The continental layers of Europe. *Bull. Seismol. Soc. Am.* **38**, 263–274.

Stoneley, R. [1953]. The transmission of Rayleigh waves across Eurasia. *Bull. Seismol. Soc. Am.* **43**, 127–135.

Stoneley, R. [1957]. The transmission of Rayleigh waves across an ocean floor with two surface layers. Pt. 1: Theoretical. *Bull. Seismol. Soc. Am.* **47**, 7–12.

Suess, E. [1892]. "Das Antlitz der Erde," 2nd ed., Vol. 1, pp. 6–7. Tempsky, Wien.

Tams, E. [1921]. Ueber Fortpflanzungsgeschwindigkeit der seismischen Oberflächenwellen längs kontinentaler und ozeanischer Wege. *Zentr. Mineral. Geol. Paläontol.* **1921**, 44–52, 75–83.

Tardi, P. [1957]. Expériences séismiques dans les Alpes occidentales en 1956; resultats obtenues par le "Groupe d'Etudes des explosions Alpines. *Compt. rend.* **244**, 1114–1117.

Tatel, H. E., and Tuve, M. A. [1958]. Carnegie Seismic Expedition to the Andes, 1957. (Abstr.). *Trans. Am. Geophys. Union* **39**, 533–534; see also IGY Bull., *ibid.* **39**, 580–582.

Tatel, H. E., Adams, L. H., and Tuve, M. A. [1953]. Studies of the earth's crust using waves from explosions. *Proc. Am. Phil. Soc.* **97**, 658–669.

Tsuboi, C. [1956]. Crustal structure in Northern and Middle California from gravity-pendulum data. *Bull. Geol. Soc. Am.* **67**, 1641–1646.

Tsuboi, C. [1957]. Crustal structure along a certain profile across the East Indies as deduced by a new calculation method. *Verhandel. Ned. Geol. Mijnbouwk. Genoot. Geol. Ser.* **18**, 287–294.

Turner, F. J., and Verhoogen, J. [1951]. "Igneous and Metamorphic Petrology," 602 pp. McGraw-Hill, New York.

Valle, P. E. [1956]. Sul gradiente di temperature necessario per la formazione di "low-velocity layers." *Ann. geofis.* **9**, 371–378.

Vanek, J. [1955]. Les études séismologiques en Tchechoslovaquie de 1951 à 1953. *Compt. rend. 10e assoc. intern. séismol. Rome 1954* **11**, 336–339.

Veytsman, P. S., Kosminskaya, I. P., and Riznichenko, Y. V. [1957]. New evidence for the structure of the earth's crust and mountain roots in Central Asia from data of seismic deep sounding. *Abstr. Repts. 9th Assembly I.G.G.U., Intern. Assoc. Seismol. Acad. U.S.S.R. Moscow*, pp. 34–36.

Washington, H. S. [1922]. Isostasy and rock density. *Bull. Geol. Soc. Am.* **23**, 372–410.

Wolff, F. v. [1943]. Stoff und Zustand im Innern der Erde. *Nova Acta Leopoldina Halle* [N.F.], **13**, 381.

Woolard, G. P. [1952]. The earth's gravitational field and its exploitation. *Advances in Geophys.* **1**, 281–313.

Worzel, J. L., and Shurbet, G. L. [1955]. Gravity anomalies at continental margins. *Proc. Natl. Acad. Sci. U.S.* **41**, 458–469.

4. The Mantle of the Earth

4.1 Subdivisions of the Mantle

The mantle includes three of the "regions" which have been defined by Bullen [1953, p. 209]: B, C, and D. Bullen [1956a,b] has subdivided D later into D′ and D″ (compare Fig. 2.2). A few geophysicists define the mantle to include the crust. Contrasting with many geophysicists (compare Section 4.2), the author believes that there is no definite indication of any discontinuity of first order in the mantle, and that the curves giving the velocities of elastic waves in the mantle as a function of depth are continuous (Fig. 2.1). However, between C and D′, at a depth of between 900 and 1000 km, the rate dV/dh of the increase in the wave velocity V with the depth h decreases either discontinuously or at least rapidly so that a "discontinuity of second order" may exist there. Possibly, there are additional minor discontinuities of second order in the region D′ (compare Fig. 2.1).

On the basis of the present data [Gutenberg, 1958], we take the boundary between B and C tentatively at a depth of 200 km, while Bullen had suggested a depth of 410 km. The details of this "boundary" are still controversial (see Section 4.2), and there is no definite decision, if it corresponds to a discontinuity, or if the transition from region B to region C is gradual, as the author believes. The boundary between the regions C and D′ is approximately at a depth of 950 km, and that between D′ and D″ tentatively at 2700 km depth. Neither of these boundaries seems to be sharp (Fig. 2.1), and the transition from one region to the other is probably gradual.

4.2 Region B from the Mohorovičić Discontinuity to about 200 km Depth. The "20°-Discontinuity"

Soon after isostasy (Section 3.7) had been established, it had been concluded that below the relatively strong "lithosphere" a layer with relatively small strength exists which permits gradual movements to approach a hydrostatic equilibrium. Barrell [1914, p. 659] has called it the "asthenosphere." It has been discussed in detail by Daly [1940]. It has usually been assumed that its depth is roughly 100 km. The establishing of the "asthenosphere low velocity layer" (see below and Section 6.9) has strengthened the concept of the asthenosphere.

Already during the earliest investigations of the velocity of longitudinal waves in the uppermost portion of the mantle, it had been realized that the travel time curve does not indicate a regular increase in velocity with depth. S. Mohorovičić [1915] had calculated discontinuities at depths of about

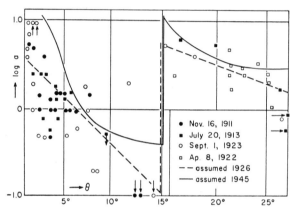

Fig. 4.1. Logarithm of amplitudes a of longitudinal waves (P) as function of distance Θ, observed in earthquakes of 1911 and 1913 (epicenter in South Germany), 1922 (South of Spitsbergen), and 1923 (Japan), reduced to the same magnitude, and assumed curve in arbitrary units [Gutenberg, 1926]. The curve assumed by Gutenberg [1945] gives the average $\log a/T$ (T = period) for the vertical component of P in shallow shocks of magnitude 7 in various regions. Note that the units for the two curves are different, so that their vertical displacement is not significant.

120 and 400 km. He had been the first to consider the effects of the crustal layers. Byerly [1926] had concluded that the slope of the travel time curve of a Montana earthquake changes abruptly at an epicentral distance of about 20° and that this corresponds to wave paths penetrating to a depth of about 400 km. Gutenberg [1926] had investigated if there are any indications for a decrease in wave velocity in the outer portion of the mantle as a consequence of the fact that the temperature there approaches the melting point of the material. The amplitudes of the longitudinal and transverse waves are very sensitive to such a suspected decrease of velocity with increasing depth as has been pointed out in Section 3.5. Actually,

Gutenberg [1926] had found (Fig. 4.1) that at angular distances Θ of between 1° and 15° the amplitudes of longitudinal waves decrease about exponentially with increasing distance and reach a minimum at $\Theta = 15°$ corresponding to a distance Δ along the surface of the earth of 1600 km (about 1000 miles). At this distance, they increase suddenly by a factor of more than ten. Beyond 15° they decrease relatively slowly. This has been found again for "average" conditions [Gutenberg, 1945], and similar results have been reported for earthquakes originating in specific regions, for example, for Czechoslovakia by Ruprechtová [1958], and for Japan by Kishimoto [1956]. In a discussion of recording of seismic waves from nuclear explosions [Anonymous, 1958] it was agreed that according to experiments, under certain conditions for the explosion, "the direction of the first motion of the longitudinal wave can be determined at a distance of approximately 1000 km, and also at distances of approximately 2000–3500 km." This shows that the "shadow zone" is also very clear in artificial explosions.

Contrasting with this relatively large effect of a small decrease in velocity with depth on the wave amplitudes as a function of distance, its effect on the travel times of the waves is relatively small, except for a "shadow zone." In drawing of travel time curves (transmission time as function of epicentral distance) shadow zones are frequently bridged by inclusion of small, relatively late waves which may have reached the point of observation by diffraction or scattering.

Gutenberg [1954a] believes that for shallow earthquakes and for artificial explosions the travel time curve of those longitudinal waves P, which have been refracted through the mantle, begins at a distance between about 100 to 200 km (depending on the structure of the crust) with an almost straight section which corresponds to an apparent velocity $d\Delta/dt$ of about 8.2 km/sec (Fig. 4.2; Table 3.4). At distances Δ beyond a few hundred kilometers, depending on the magnitude of the shock, the sensitivity of the instruments, the background noise, etc., the first waves visible on records are delayed ($d\Delta/dt = 7\frac{3}{4}$ km/sec) and very small (b in Figs. 4.2 and 4.3). This has been established especially well in shocks recorded in Southern California, where many stations are equipped with very sensitive instruments. The first waves b, arriving at distances between about 7° and 13° may be diffracted waves, channel waves, or waves resulting from scattered energy. The very small amplitudes in the critical range of distances are the source of the discrepancies in the interpretation and are the reason why the early results based on travel times could not give more than a rough approximation to the velocity–depth curve. Starting at an angular distance Θ of about 13°, the first longitudinal waves c, which are usually still small, arrive with a higher apparent velocity $d\Delta/dt$ of roughly 9 km/sec, and starting at a distance of about 15° (depending on the structure of the crust) the amplitudes of the first P-waves are relatively very large again (Figs. 4.1 and 4.3).

The transverse waves S through the upper portion of the mantle show similar behavior. Their travel time curve begins with an apparent velocity of about 4.7 km/sec, which has been established only in recent years,

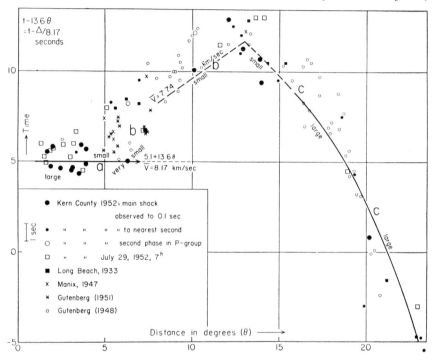

FIG. 4.2. Travel times t of longitudinal waves minus 13.6 Θ = $\Delta/8.17$ sec in Southern California earthquakes. $\Delta/8.17$ is subtracted from t to permit large time scale (Δ = distance in km). Based on Gutenberg [1954a].

mostly by use of artificial explosions. The older value of about 4.4 km/sec (compare Table 4.3) is characteristic for the apparent velocity of channel waves in the mantle (Table 4.1). The "shadow zone" of S-waves centers at about 10° distance and is even better developed than that for P [Gutenberg, 1948]. However, it cannot be studied as well as that for P, since S starts on seismograms in an already disturbed portion of the record.

Unfortunately, few investigators have paid sufficient attention to the amplitudes of P and S. However, their travel times t have been studied repeatedly as function of the epicentral distance. The fact that the travel time curve of P indicates a sudden increase in the apparent velocity $\bar{V} = d\Delta/dt$, corresponding to the beginning of the branch c in Fig. 4.2, has been pointed out first by Byerly [1926]. He had observed the change in direction of the curve at an angular distance Θ of about 20°. Subsequently the term

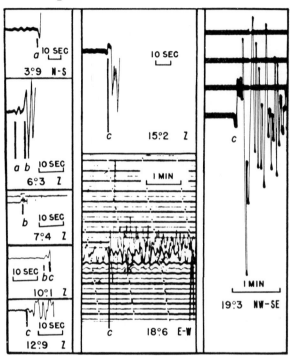

Fig. 4.3. Beginning of selected records of Kern County, California, earthquake of July 21, 1952. The letters a, b, c refer to the travel time curves in Fig. 4.2. Z = vertical, N–S = north–south, E–W = east–west component. Stations and instruments (lp = long-period, sp = short-period): 3.9° Berkeley, Galitzin, lp; 6.3°, Shasta, Benioff, sp; 7.4°, Tucson, Benioff, sp; 10.1°, Corvallis, Slichter; 12.9°, Seattle, Sprengnether, sp; 15.2°, Rapid City, Wood–Anderson, sp; 18.6°, Lincoln, McComb–Romberg; 19.3°, Saskatoon, Milne–Shaw, lp. Condensed from Gutenberg [1954a].

"20°-discontinuity" has been used, although with higher accuracy of the observations the beginning of the branch c of the travel time curve has been traced back to about 15° (Fig. 4.2) in agreement with the distance, where the amplitudes suddenly increase. Later, the term "20°-discontinuity" has been applied frequently not only to the discontinuity in the travel time curve, but also to the corresponding hypothetical discontinuity in the earth.

In calculations of the wave velocities V for longitudinal and v for transverse waves as a function of the depth, it usually has been *assumed* that the velocities do not decrease anywhere with depth in the upper mantle. However, on this assumption the calculated depths for the "20°-discontinuity" may be too great, possibly by a factor up to 2, if the velocity actually decreases with increasing depth somewhere in the upper portion of the mantle.

Jeffreys as well as Lehmann has repeatedly investigated the "20°-discontinuity." Jeffreys usually does not report depths, but distances from the earth's center in fractions of the radius R of the average bottom of the earth's crust (Mohorovičić discontinuity). Until about 1936, Jeffreys has assumed 42 km for the thickness of the crust [Jeffreys, 1936, p. 417] but afterwards 33 km. These values are to be added to his data for distances from the bottom of the crust. At first, Jeffreys [1936, p. 418] had calculated 481 ± 21 km for the depth where the "20°-discontinuity" of the travel time curve is caused. Later Jeffreys [1939, p. 513] has found $0.94R$ as its distance from the earth's center. This corresponds to a depth of $(6371 - 33) \times 0.06 + 33 = 413$ km, which is the figure quoted frequently in the literature, without mention of the fact that it had been given by Jeffreys only to the nearest $0.01R$, that is, to the nearest ±32 km. Still later, Jeffreys [1952, p. 97] stated: "If the 20° discontinuity is really sudden, its depth is about 500 km." In 1958 he confirmed the travel time curve for P at distances near 20° [Jeffreys, 1958a]. However, he has concluded [Jeffreys, 1958b] that in an Azores earthquake of 1931 the travel times of the longitudinal waves "imply that at the transition there must be a considerable discontinuity of velocity gradient, but only a small one of velocity" [Jeffreys, 1958b, p. 191]. "The depth of transition would be about 200 km" [Jeffreys, 1958b, p. 197]. This comes close to the velocity–depth curve of the author (Fig. 4.4), except that the author believes that the change in the velocity gradient near this depth is rapid, but gradual, not discontinuous.

There is general agreement that the relative amplitudes and the travel times near the "20° discontinuity" as well as the corresponding wave velocities in the uppermost 200 or 300 km of the earth differ locally. However, rather small local differences in this critical depth range may produce large differences in the corresponding seismograms, since the wave paths are very sensitive to small changes in the velocity, if dV/dr is near the critical value V/r (Eq. (3.15)), which is of the order of $+0.1$ km/sec per 100 km in the earth's uppermost portion.

In a detailed study, Lehmann [1934, p. 42] has concluded that "in view of all relevant results, our discontinuity surface seems likely to be at a depth of between 250 and 350 km." She found [Lehmann, 1955] that in northeastern America "the S curve was discontinuous with a break at about 14°" and that for shorter distances Δ(in km) the P- and S-curves could be taken as straight lines, the former with an apparent velocity $d\Delta/dt$ of 8.17 km/sec, the latter with 4.63 km/sec. Lehmann [1958] has interpreted travel time data as indicating a constant velocity V of 8.12 km/sec for P at depths

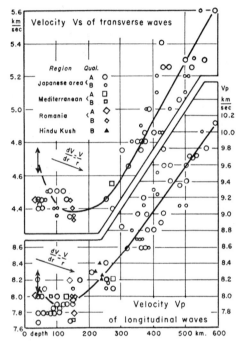

Fig. 4.4. Velocities V_P of longitudinal and V_S of transverse waves as function of depth, calculated from Eq. (4.3). Each point corresponds to many data for one earthquake. The arrows at $h = 40$ km correspond to the most frequent values for V and v respectively below M in Table 3.4; Based on Gutenberg [1953].

between the Mohorovičić discontinuity and about 220 km, where V jumps to about 8.40 km/sec. Below the depth of 220 km, she has found a gradual increase in the velocity approximately corresponding to the values given in Fig. 4.4.

Båth [1957] has made theoretical calculations for the extent of the shadow zones, for the travel times of the waves, and for their energies on the assumption of a low-velocity layer in the uppermost portion of the mantle ("asthenosphere," see Section 3.1). His results give good qualitative explanations for many essential points of the observations, but quantitative results require more data for the quantities involved in the theory.

Bullen [1953, p. 207] in discussing the depth of his boundary between his regions B and C refers to Jeffreys [1939], who, as mentioned above, has found "indications of a fairly sudden marked increase in the rate of increase of velocity with increase in depth at a distance of 0.94R from the earth's center, where R is the radius of the earth when stripped of its crustal layers." Bullen [1953, p. 208] points out that the depths of the boundaries between his regions A, B etc. "are given to the nearest kilometer in order to facilitate computation . . . , but in some cases are subject to appreciable uncertainty." Later, Bullen [1956a,b] has rounded off the original depth of the boundary between his layers B and C from 413 to 410 km. Both values have been quoted by various writers as "the depth of the 20°-discontinuity." Apparently, they have overlooked the fact that Bullen clearly has designated his data as those for "models," and that there are definite differences between his various models. Even in 1957 [Conference, 1958, p. 26], Bullen could not say which of his "Earth Models A and B is to be preferred."

Kishimoto [1956] has investigated earthquake records of nearby shocks in Japan. He has found there, too, the "abnormal diminution of amplitudes of direct seismic waves and, reversely, the large and clear appearance of a refracted seismic wave . . . for both P- and S-phases near the epicentral distance of 20°." He also has stressed the differences between various regions. Later Kishimoto [1958] reported travel time curves for Japanese earthquakes similar to that given in Fig. 4.2 for California; up to $\Theta = 4°$ he found an apparent velocity of 8.0 km/sec, from $4\frac{1}{2}°$ to $7\frac{1}{2}°$ of 7.7 km/sec. He concludes that the low-velocity layer seems to be possible in Japan, but that the minimum velocity is reached at a depth slightly smaller than 100 km.

There seems to be general agreement now that in all regions for which travel time curves could be constructed, the observed apparent velocities $\bar{V} = d\Delta/dt$ of longitudinal and transverse waves at least do not increase with distance Δ between about $\Delta = 100$ km and $\Delta = 1600$ km. In the range of distances between 100 and 200 km the P-waves which are refracted below the Mohorovičić discontinuity begin to arrive earlier than the direct waves through the crust. The exact distance where the waves which are refracted through the mantle begin to arrive earlier than the direct waves through the crust depends on the focal depth of the shock, on the local thickness of the crust, and on the wave velocities which are involved.

The fact that in the "shadow zone" for the waves through the uppermost portion of the mantle the apparent velocity does not increase, or even decreases, with depth shows that the velocity of the waves in the corresponding portion of the mantle decreases with depth by a rate of at least $dV/dr = V/r$ (Eq. (3.15)), or at least by 0.13 km/sec per 100 km for P and 0.07 km/sec for S.

In a homogeneous earth with the source at the surface, the travel time t at the distance Θ in degrees is given by

$$t = \frac{2r_0}{V}\left[\frac{\pi\theta}{360} - \frac{1}{12}\left(\frac{\pi\theta}{180}\right)^3\right] \tag{4.1}$$

neglecting terms of fifth and higher order; r is the earth's radius and V the velocity, assumed to be constant. If we consider longitudinal waves starting and ending at the Mohorovičić discontinuity, the deviation of observed travel times from the curve calculated on the assumption of the observed velocity of 8.1 to 8.2 km/sec at short distances (Table 3.4) is at least $+3$ sec at a distance near 15°. This is well above the probable errors (compare Fig. 4.2), and it follows again that the velocity must decrease slightly with depth in the upper mantle.

A different approach to find the velocity–depth curves has been made by Gutenberg [1953]. If the source of an earthquake is at the depth h, the wave equation (3.13) for a sphere in which the velocity V is a function of the depth $h = r_0 - r_h$, but does not change horizontally, gives

$$\frac{r_h \sin i_h}{V_h} = \frac{r_0 \sin i_0}{V_0} = \frac{r_0}{\bar{V}_0} \tag{4.2}$$

as $\sin i_0 = V_0/\bar{V}_0$; i is the angle of incidence, $\bar{V}_0 = (d\Delta/dt)_0$, the index h refers to the depth h and the index zero to the earth's surface. Equation (4.2) shows that for a shock occurring at a given depth h, the apparent velocity $\bar{V}_0$ at the surface reaches a minimum $\bar{V}_{\min}$ for $\sin i_h = 1$, that is, for the ray leaving the source horizontally. This corresponds to a point of inflection of the travel time curve. It follows from Eq. (4.2), considering that $r_h = r_0 - h$, that

$$V_h = (r_0 - h)\bar{V}_{\min}/r_0. \tag{4.3}$$

If there are sufficient observations available to determine the slope of the travel time curve at its point of inflection and thus $\bar{V}_{\min}$ for a given shock at a known depth h, Eq. (4.3) gives the velocity V_h at this depth h without further assumptions. Fig. 4.4 shows velocities for longitudinal and transverse waves which have been calculated from reported travel times of P and S as shocks originating at various depth h. Each point corresponds to data from one earthquake. In addition, the ranges of values for the velocities V of longitudinal waves and v of transverse waves just below the Mohorovičić discontinuity, which are listed in Table 3.4, are indicated in Fig. 4.4 by arrows near a depth of 40 km; values of v near 4.4 km/sec in Table 3.4 are omitted, since they probably correspond rather to Sa (Table 4.1) than to S.

There seems to be little doubt that the velocity of longitudinal waves reaches a minimum near a depth of about 100 km and that for transverse waves probably between depths of 100 and 200 km. The decrease in velocity with depth is greater for transverse than for longitudinal waves. This is confirmed by the fact, that for S-waves the "shadow zone" is better developed than for P-waves. For P, the maximum of $-dV/dh$ is apparently close to the critical value which is indicated in Fig. 4.4, while for S it seems to be noticeably greater than the corresponding critical value for S. This explains why in some regions no marked shadow zone for P-waves seems to exist at the surface, while for S such a shadow zone seems to have been reported for all regions where seismograms written in the range of distances between a few degrees and about 20° have been studied.

The boundary between the regions B and C is best taken at the depth where the velocity begins to increase with depth at a nearly constant rate, that is on the average at a depth of about 200 km. The "low-velocity channel" ends approximately at the depth where the maximum velocity existing at or near the top of the mantle is reached again, that is at a depth of about 250 km for P, 350 km for S. Both depths are not well defined and differ locally.

If the explanation of the "20° discontinuity" as the consequence of a low-velocity layer at the top of the mantle is correct, the range of distances with small or relatively late P-phases should decrease, if the depth of focus of earthquakes increases until it becomes greater than the depth of the low-velocity layer. Waves from earthquakes originating at greater depth should not exhibit a shadow zone. Gutenberg and Richter [1939] have found in an investigation of seismograms written at Huancayo, Peru, as a consequence of earthquakes originating at various depths down to 260 km, that this is indeed the case. Figure 4.5 shows ground amplitudes of P-waves recorded at various stations from sources at depths between about 20 and nearly 300 km; these amplitudes are reduced to amplitudes of P for waves having a period of 1 sec in a shock of magnitude 7. The decrease of the zone of relatively small amplitudes with increasing focal depth is evident. This

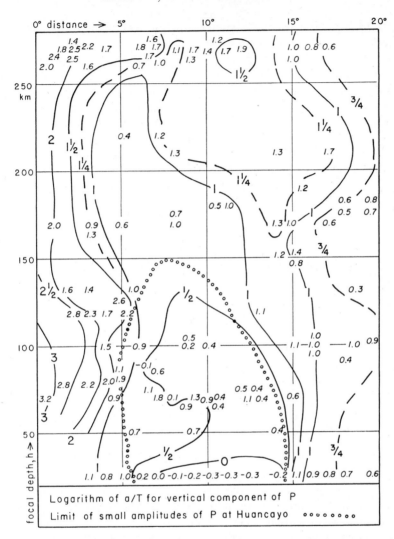

Fig. 4.5. Log a/T as function of epicentral distance for P-waves originating at focal depths up to 280 km (ordinates), reduced to values for a shock of magnitude 7; (a = ground amplitude in microns, T = period in sec.). Based on Gutenberg [1945].

confirms again the hypothesis of a low-velocity channel, extending downward in the mantle to a depth of 200 to 250 km.

Vesanen and associates [1959] have investigated the time interval (pP–P) as a function of focal depth and distance and have found that the trough of the asthenosphere channel is at an average depth of about 45 km in Alaska, 80 km in Japan, 95 km under the Tonga region, and 120 km under South America. The phase pP is a longitudinal wave which starts upward at the source and is once reflected at the earth's surface.

Such a low-velocity channel should act as a wave guide for P- and S-waves. Caloi [1953] was the first to find the corresponding guided longitudinal and transverse waves, which he called Pa and Sa respectively. They have been found independently by Press and Ewing [1955], and have been included in a general discussion of such waves in the atmosphere, the ocean, and the earth's body by Gutenberg [1954b]. Figure 4.6 shows examples of

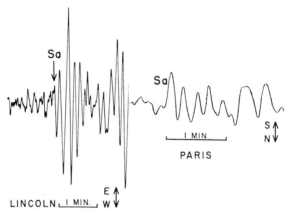

FIG. 4.6. Portions of records of main Kern County, California, earthquake of 1952 showing Sa-phase at Lincoln, Nebraska (Θ = 18.6°) and at Paris (Θ = 81.7°). Based on Gutenberg [1955].

records of Sa from an investigation of seismograms written after the Kern County, California, earthquake of 1952 [Gutenberg, 1955].

In a detailed study Caloi [1954] has pointed out that Pa- and Sa-waves are recorded most prominently if the source of the respective earthquake is in the mantle at depths of between 50 and 250 km. Pa and Sa have been reported by Caloi for epicentral distances almost to 180°; he has reproduced many records. There is no indication thus far that the velocities of these waves depend upon the epicentral distance or upon the path. Average values for their velocities are given in Table 4.1. It has been stated repeatedly that the Pa- and Sa-waves travel equally well under continents and under oceans. Their amplitudes are apparently not noticeably decreased if they pass from one to the other nor if they travel under mountain chains or other geologically disturbed zones. However, more data to confirm these findings are desirable. Nevertheless, these results show that the channel in which they travel exists regardless of variations in the thickness or structure of the earth's crust. Moreover, they indicate that the subcrustal material below oceans and continents probably differs little or not at all.

TABLE 4.1. OBSERVED VELOCITIES OF Pa- AND Sa-WAVES

Author	Velocity, km/sec		Distances θ used
	Pa	Sa	
Caloi [1954]	8.0	4.4	18° < θ < 175°
Gutenberg [1955]	8.06 ± 0.017	4.45 ± 0.008	7° < θ < 93°
Gutenberg [1955]	8.03 ± 0.034	4.44 ± 0.012	23° < θ < 93°
Press and Ewing [1955]	7.98 to 8.24	4.43 to 4.63	52° < θ < 125°

Press and Ewing [1955] have included in their list of shocks with recorded Pa- and Sa-waves earthquakes which had originated at depths between 20 and 200 km, but did not find "any obvious relation between focal depth and excitation." Gutenberg found well developed Pa- and Sa-waves on records of shocks which had originated at various depths between

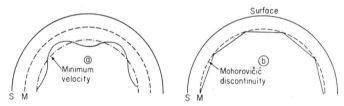

FIG. 4.7. Paths of Pa- and Sa-waves (schematic); (a) after Gutenberg [1954a] and after Caloi [1954], (b) after Press and Ewing [1955]. Vertical scale greatly exaggerated.

about 20 and almost 300 km. Neither Pa- nor Sa-waves seem to have been found thus far on records of shocks with a source at a depth of 300 km or more.

As mentioned above, low-velocity layers in the earth should act as a wave guide, especially for waves originating near the depth of minimum velocity (Fig. 4.7(a)). Caloi [1953, 1954, 1958] who has studied since 1935 the low-velocity channel corresponding to the decrease in amplitudes of body waves at distances between a few and about 15°, had expected this effect, and, as indicated above, has established the Pa- and Sa-waves. Gutenberg [1954a,b], too, came to the conclusion that Pa and Sa are waves guided by the low-velocity layer in the uppermost portion of the mantle. On the other hand, Press and Ewing [1955; Ewing and Press, 1956] have suggested as a possible alternate explanation (Fig. 4.7(b)) that Pa and Sa may be produced by a mechanism similar to the "whispering gallery" effect described by Rayleigh [1945]. However, the energy in longitudinal waves arriving from some depth below the Mohorovičić discontinuity should be split up at each reflection into four waves (one longitudinal and one transverse in each medium); and that in transverse waves (SH as well as SV), considering the large angles of incidence, into two, one refracted and one reflected transverse wave of the type of the incident wave. Thus, the amplitudes of the reflected waves should decrease fairly rapidly and become relatively small after three or four reflections.

Finally, independent investigations of the velocity of mantle Rayleigh waves by Takeuchi and associates [1959] and by Dorman et al. [1959] indicate that the observations are in better agreement with the calculated curves if a low velocity layer is assumed, corresponding to Fig. 4.4, than otherwise.

Similarly, Press [1959] has found that "G-wave velocities for continental and oceanic paths do not differ by more than about 2%. Since their velocity is controlled by the asthenosphere low-velocity zone, this must be present under continents and oceans."

The author believes that there is now a sufficient number of different methods which, without exception, support the hypothesis that under continents the velocities of longitudinal as well as of transverse waves decrease beginning at or slightly below the Mohorovičić discontinuity, reach a minimum at a depth of between 100 and 250 km which differs regionally, and otherwise are well represented by Fig. 4.4. Recent findings of Jeffreys [1958b] and of Lehmann [1958] for the change of velocity with depth are much closer to those given in Fig. 4.4 than their earlier results. All reported travel time data seem to give now a constant or decreasing velocity in the critical depth range, while the rapid decrease in amplitudes to distances up to 15° seems to require at least a slight decrease in velocity. Thus, we may conclude that under continents the actual velocity–depth curves are close to those given in Fig. 4.4, but show minor local variations.

Under oceans, the Mohorovičić discontinuity is closer to sea level than under continents, and the temperature at the ocean bottom is appreciably lower than that under the continents at the same depth. Consequently, in the uppermost portion of the mantle the effect of the temperature on the wave velocities can be expected to be smaller under ocean bottoms than under continents. Under ocean bottoms there may be just below the Mohorovičić discontinuity, more frequently than under continents, a relatively thin layer in which the velocity increases with depth, before the decrease of velocity with depth begins. This would explain the fact that waves refracted at the Mohorovičić discontinuity into the mantle are frequently better recorded from small explosions in the ocean than from those in continents. On the other hand, the Pa- and Sa-waves which have been observed to travel under ocean bottoms, indicate that there, too, a low-velocity layer exists at depths of 100 to 200 km which guides the Pa- and Sa-waves.

The cause of the velocity minimum in the uppermost portion of the mantle under continents and oceans is probably similar to that described in Section 3.2 for the cause of the crustal low-velocity channels. The velocity decreases with depth, where the increasing temperature lowers the velocity more than the increasing pressure increases it. Unfortunately, the conditions which control this change in velocity, are much less well known than in the crust. In the mantle, the increase in temperature with depth is uncertain, the material involved is in doubt, and no laboratory experiments have been extended to the temperatures and pressures involved. However, the last line of Table 3.2, on the basis of laboratory experiments, indicates that a decrease in velocity with depth below the Mohorovičić discontinuity is at least as likely as an increase.

The wavelengths of the Pa- and Sa-waves are of the order of the depth below which the channel begins. Consequently, it is not possible to calculate or even estimate the amplitudes to be expected in Pa- and Sa-waves at the surface, since no detailed theoretical discussion of the effect of a crustal layer having a thickness of the same order of magnitude as the wavelength is available for direct or diffracted waves. Since the details of the channel vary considerably with the local structure, relatively great differences in the recorded Pa- and Sa-waves are to be expected. Moreover, it is very probable that in a given earthquake the periods prevailing in the waves under consideration play a major role.

4.3 Region C between about 200 and 950 km Depth

Already in 1909, velocity–depth curves (Fig. 2.1) had indicated a fairly clear change in the slope of travel time curves at epicentral distances Θ near 45°. The earliest calculations had placed the corresponding deepest point of the rays emerging near $\Theta = 45°$ at a depth of about 1500 km, and Wiechert and others had believed that this depth marks the boundary of the core. Later calculations have shown that the depth of the "second order discontinuity" of dV/dr which corresponds to the sudden change in $d\Theta/dt$ near $\Theta = 45°$, is slightly below 1000 km, most probably near 950 km. This change in dV/dr has been found later in every investigation and was explained repeatedly as indication of a boundary between layers with different rate of change in composition. During the years 1925 to 1930, the expression *Zwischenschicht* (intermediate layer) was used occasionally for region C.

The first attempt to find how far down in the mantle the increase in wave velocities V (longitudinal) and v (transverse) with depth may be an effect of pressure in a homogeneous material was made by Williamson and Adams [1923] in an investigation of the density in the earth. In addition to homogeneity they assumed that the compression is adiabatic. Williamson and Adams used the following equations, in which m is the mass of a sphere with the radius r, ρ is the density, V the velocity of longitudinal waves, v that of transverse waves, k the bulk modulus, and g the gravity, all as function of r; G is the gravitational constant, for which they have used 6.66 $\times$ 10^{-8} cm^3/g sec^2, and ρ_0 is the density at the earth's surface

$$\frac{k}{\rho} = V^2 - \frac{4}{3} v^2 \qquad (4.4)$$

$$\frac{dp}{dr} = \frac{dp}{d\rho}\frac{d\rho}{dr} = -g\rho = -\frac{Gm\rho}{r^2}. \qquad (4.5)$$

On the assumption of a homogeneous and isotherm material, the bulk modulus k is by definition

$$k = \frac{1}{\rho}\frac{dp}{d\rho} \qquad (4.6)$$

so that

$$\frac{d \ln \rho}{dr} = \frac{Gm\rho}{r^2 k} \qquad \text{or} \qquad \ln \frac{\rho}{\rho_0} = -\int_{r_0}^{r} \frac{Gm\rho}{r^2 k} \, dr. \qquad (4.7)$$

On their theoretical assumptions and on the basis of observed velocities V and v which were still rather poorly known at the time of their investigation, Williamson and Adams [1923] concluded that the central core and the "peridotite shell immediately below the surface layer" (region C) are "sensibly constant in composition but not of constant density" while the crust and "the pallasite fringe surrounding the metallic core" (layer D) are of variable composition.

Birch [1951] raised the question, how far the mantle is homogeneous, and to what extent the change in temperature with depth departs from the adiabatic relation. Following Bullen [1949, p. 361] he introduces the quantity Φ which plays an important role in many investigations

$$\Phi = V^2 - \frac{4}{3} v^2 = \frac{k_S}{\rho} = \left(\frac{\partial p}{\partial \rho}\right)_S \qquad (4.8)$$

where S indicates the entropy. The coefficient of adiabatic incompressibility k_S, and that of isothermal incompressibility, k_T are given by

$$\frac{1}{k_S} = \frac{1}{\rho}\left(\frac{\partial \rho}{\partial p}\right)_S \qquad \frac{1}{k_T} = \frac{1}{\rho}\left(\frac{\partial \rho}{\partial p}\right)_T. \tag{4.9}$$

Following the main steps taken by Birch [1952] we introduce α, the coefficient of thermal expansion

$$\alpha = -\frac{1}{\rho}\left(\frac{\partial \rho}{\partial T}\right)_p \tag{4.10}$$

and find

$$\frac{d\rho}{dr} = \left(\frac{\partial \rho}{\partial p}\right)_T \frac{dp}{dr} + \left(\frac{\partial \rho}{\partial T}\right)_p \frac{dT}{dr} = \frac{g\rho^2}{k_T} - \rho\alpha\frac{dT}{dr}. \tag{4.11}$$

If c_p is the specific heat at constant pressure, τ the difference between the actual temperature gradient and the adiabatic gradient,

$$\frac{dT}{dr} = \frac{T\alpha}{\rho c_p}\frac{dp}{dr} - \tau = -\frac{T\alpha g}{c_p} - \tau. \tag{4.12}$$

From thermodynamic relations

$$\frac{k_T}{k_S} = 1 - \frac{T\alpha^2 k_T}{\rho c_p} \tag{4.13}$$

$$\frac{dk_S}{dp} = 1 - \frac{1}{g}\left(\frac{d\Phi}{dr}\right) - \frac{\alpha\Phi\tau}{g}. \tag{4.14}$$

On the other hand

$$\frac{dk_S}{dp} = \left(\frac{\partial k_S}{\partial p}\right)_S + \left(\frac{\partial k_S}{\partial T}\right)_p \frac{\tau}{\rho g}. \tag{4.15}$$

This leads finally [Birch, 1952, p. 237] to

$$\Gamma = 1 - \frac{1}{g}\left(\frac{d\Phi}{dr}\right) = \left(\frac{\partial k_S}{\partial p}\right)_S + \frac{\tau\alpha\Phi}{g}\left[1 + \frac{1}{\alpha k_S}\left(\frac{\partial k_S}{\partial T}\right)_p\right] \tag{4.16}$$

where Φ is given by Eq. (4.8). Birch now introduces "Grueneisen's ratio" γ [see Grueneisen, 1926, pp. 25–27]

$$-\gamma = \frac{d\log \nu}{d\log w} = \frac{w(\partial w/\partial t)_p}{c_p(\partial w/\partial p)_S} \tag{4.17}$$

where ν is the maximum frequency of vibrations in an isotropic solid; w is the volume. Birch [1952, p. 237] finds

$$\Gamma = 1 - \frac{1}{g}\left(\frac{d\Phi}{dr}\right) = \left(\frac{\partial k_T}{\partial p}\right)_T + T\alpha\gamma A + (T\alpha\gamma)^2 B + \frac{\alpha\Phi\tau}{g}C \tag{4.18}$$

where A, B, and C contain terms with $(\partial k_T/\partial p)_T$, $(\partial k_T/\partial t)_p$, $(\partial k_S/\partial t)_p$, $(\partial\alpha/\partial T)_p$ and $(\partial c_p/\partial t)_p$.

Birch discusses these terms and finds [Birch, 1952, p. 259] that, neglecting several minor terms, approximately

$$\Gamma = \left(\frac{\partial k_T}{\partial p}\right)_T - 5T\alpha\gamma - \frac{2\tau\alpha\Phi}{g}. \tag{4.19}$$

It should be noted that Grueneisen's ratio γ, Eq. (4.17), depends on the maximum frequency ν of the atomic vibration and thus on physical conditions at the depth h.

The left side of Eq. (4.19) can be found from observations; Φ is given by Eq. (4.8), and the gravity g does not change much with depth in the mantle (see Fig. 7.3). On the other hand, the values of the terms on the right hand side can be calculated, partly on a theoretical basis, assuming homogeneity. Figure 4.8 gives curves for Γ, (Eq. (4.16)), based on Jeffreys' [1939] and Gutenberg's [1958] data for $V(r)$ and $v(r)$, as well as a theoretical curve

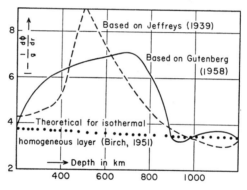

Fig. 4.8. $\Gamma = 1 - (d\Phi/dr)/g$ as function of depth, calculated from smoothed curves for observed velocities V of longitudinal and v of transverse waves as function of depth, which are based on Jeffreys [1939] and on Gutenberg [1958]. Theoretical curve after Birch [1951].

calculated by Birch [1951] for a homogeneous, isotropic mantle. For depths between 1000 and 2700 km, the three curves agree within the limits of error, but for depths between 200 and 900 km the curves based on observed velocities are appreciably higher than the theoretical curves. If the theory is correct, this indicates that region C is either not isothermal or not homogeneous or both.

Griggs [1954] has expressed some doubt if observed curves of the type shown in Fig. 4.8 are accurate enough to permit the conclusion that the outer portion of the mantle is inhomogeneous. The differences between the curves based on Jeffreys [1939] and on Gutenberg [1958] result partly from the fact that in the course of the calculations of $d\Phi/dr$ first the observed travel time curve $t(\Delta)$ is smoothed, then $dt/d\Delta$ has to be used to find the deepest point of a ray emerging at a given distance and the velocity there. This gives $V(r)$ and similarly $v(r)$. If at a given distance Δ the travel time t is taken slightly too great this may affect noticeably the derivative $dt/d\Delta$. If then $d\Phi/dr$ is calculated, Eq. (4.8), such small errors in V and v, which do not depend on each other, will be magnified in one depth range in finding the difference involving the squares of V and v, with a compensating error in the opposite direction in a neighboring depth range. Moreover, Jeffreys [1939] had interpreted the 20°-discontinuity as a consequence of a rapid increase in dV/dr at a depth between 400 and 500 km, while Gutenberg has supposed that the 20°-discontinuity is a result of a slight decrease in the velocities below the crust. The velocities which they find do not differ by more than about 0.2 km/sec (2%), and their original travel times by not over a few seconds. In any case it is unlikely that the differences in the calculated values of $d\Phi/dr$ affect the conclusion, that in region C the observed values in Fig. 4.8 are appreciably larger than those calculated theoretically by Birch. Bullen [1954], Miki [1955, 1956], Jacobs [1956], and others have discussed the problem on various assumptions and have reached the same main-result as Birch.

Birch [1954] concluded that *phase changes* may play an important role in region C. "With high-pressure phases required for the deeper part of the mantle, the region between about 300 and 800 km is most naturally interpreted as transitional between the region of familiar, low-pressure phases, just below the crust, and the deep region, where the transformation to high-pressure phases has become complete."

Birch has associated "deep-focus earthquakes" with the hypothetical phase changes in the mantle. However, various lines of evidence indicate that deep shocks are produced by similar stress systems and faulting processes as shallow shocks. Investigations of the direction of the first motion in the waves arriving at many stations after a given earthquake, indicate that the same type of mechanism of motion at the source prevails in shallow and deep earthquakes, possibly with one change at a specific depth, in extended regions where enough deep-focus shocks have occurred for detailed investigation (see Section 9.8). The decrease with depth in the number of shocks and in their average energy, which both are largest for shallow shocks, can be well explained on the assumption that differences in the constants which control flow processes at various depths, for example, differences in the yield strength or in the coefficient of pseudo-viscosity, play a major role (see Sections 9.3–9.5).

Among the phase changes which are possibly involved in the relatively rapid velocity increase in layer C, are, for example, those connected with jadeite [Yoder, 1950; Yoder and Weir, 1951]. Furthermore, Meinesz [1956] has pointed out that olivine may have an equilibrium-curve between two phases which follows closely the temperature–depth curve in the earth at depths between 200 and 900 km. He stresses the importance of such a gradual transition for the problem of subcrustal currents. Shimazu [1958] has suggested that physicochemical reactions may be the source of phase changes in the mantle.

Holser and Schneer [1957] have discussed in more detail effects of polymorphism in the earth's mantle. They conclude that "the wide variety of possible polymorphic transformations lessens the necessity of a correlation between variations in seismic velocities and changes of composition. We cannot correlate velocities with composition with the confidence previously assumed, at least unless many . . . possibilities are eliminated by quantitative calculation." The possible importance of phase changes in nepheline for the composition of the crust and mantle have been discussed by Boyd and England [1956], while Lovering [1958] has considered phase changes which may be responsible for the Mohorovičić discontinuity (Section 3.9).

Verhoogen [1953] has expressed doubts about theoretical assumptions of Birch and others. He has pointed out that the argument rests on the validity of the assumption that the free energy is proportional to the square of the strain. He believes "that the pressure coefficient of incompressibility dk/dp of a homogeneous phase may increase at low pressures and go through a maximum" and he tries to show that Birch's "suggestions of the occurrence of phase changes in the upper mantle are based on a pressure–density relation that is not likely to be applicable to silicate minerals."

Various other attempts have been made to explain the relatively rapid increase in the velocities as function of depth in the region C. Some, e.g., Haalck [1957], have taken up the old suggestion that it results from a change in composition with depth. MacDonald [1956] has discussed some fundamental problems involved, and has pointed out that k is a function of the coefficient of thermal expansion. Miki [1956] believes that "the C-layer does not satisfy the hydrostatic relation. The internal force in the C layer acts toward the earth's center. . . . It is of interest to consider this force with respect to the existence of deep focus earthquakes in the C layer."

4.4 The Mantle between a Depth of about 950 km and the Core Boundary (Region D)

In region D the observed and the calculated values of

$$\Gamma = 1 - \frac{1}{g}\frac{d\Phi}{dr}$$

(Eq. (4.16)) agree within the limits of error, according to various calculations; for depths near 1000 km, see Fig. 4.8. It is, therefore, not unreasonable to assume that the change of velocities with depth in region D is mainly an effect of the increase in pressure with depth.

There are, however, relatively small but clear indications that the change of velocities with depth in region D is not entirely regular, and,

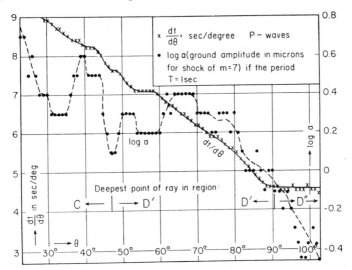

Fig. 4.9. Reciprocal $dt/d\Theta$ of apparent velocity, and log a/T (a = ground amplitude in microns; T = period) for longitudinal earthquake waves as function of epicentral distance Θ in degrees for an earthquake of magnitude 7. Based on Gutenberg [1958].

moreover, that there is a slight decrease in velocity (in region D″) if the core boundary is approached (Fig. 2.1). In Fig. 4.9, values of $dt/d\Theta$ are plotted for longitudinal waves arriving from a shallow source at distances between 23° and 103°. The figure shows, in addition, the logarithms of average maximum ground amplitudes a of the direct longitudinal waves in the same range of distances. The amplitudes are reduced to their values for a shock of magnitude $m = 7.0$ and to longitudinal waves having periods of 1 sec.

The curve for $dt/d\Theta$ should theoretically decrease sharply at distances where the deepest point of the arriving rays is in a layer in which the velocity increases rather rapidly with depth; it should be rather flat, if the deepest point of the arriving rays are in a layer with near-constant velocity. Exactly horizontal portions of $dt/d\Theta$, as approximately for distances greater than 90° in Fig. 4.9, indicate that at the deepest point of the ray arriving at such distances, the velocity decreases with depth at a rate near the critical rate, given by $dV/dr = V/r$. Near the boundary of the core this is about 0.4 km/sec per 100 km depth for longitudinal waves and roughly 0.2 km/sec per 100 km for transverse waves.

The ground amplitudes a should be relatively large at epicentral distances where waves arrive with their deepest point at depths where the velocity increases relatively rapidly with depth; a should decrease towards zero, if at the deepest point of the ray the velocity decreases with depth at approximately the critical rate.

The distances where the longitudinal waves emerge which have touched the boundaries between region C and D' and between D' and D'' are marked in Fig. 4.9. Rays arriving at a distance of 103° are believed to have touched the core. The corresponding distance for transverse waves is slightly different since Poisson's ratio changes with depth (Section 8.8). Neither for P nor for S can this distance be found accurately from observations, since the transition from the direct to the diffracted waves is gradual.

There are indications for additional irregularities within the upper portion of region D' (Fig. 4.9). This has been found repeatedly since 1911 [Zoeppritz et al., 1912]. However, the details are not certain. It is noteworthy that such irregularities have been found in the region D', where the increase in velocity with depth is frequently considered to be a consequence of the pressure increase only.

Observations of travel times as well as of amplitudes of P (Fig. 4.9) indicate that the increase in wave velocity slows down as the core is approached, and in region D'' finally seems to change gradually into a small decrease with depth (Fig. 2.1). Dahm [1936] and Macelwane [1951, p. 284] believed that there is a discontinuity at a depth of about 2800 km, and that the velocity decreases there *suddenly* from 13.24 to 12.57 km/sec, but this has not been confirmed.

Birch [1954, p. 85] raises the question, how region D', if it is uniform in composition and phase, as it seems to be, may have reached such a condition. He points out that "there are at least two possibilities: it might have been uniform initially . . . or it may be a uniform product of a process of differentiation which has affected the whole mantle." Birch inclines toward the second alternative.

The changes in region D'' are probably the effect of processes which are affected by differences between the solid mantle and the nonsolid outer core. No specific suggestions seem to have been made.

References

Anonymous [1958]. Report of the conference of experts to study the methods of detecting violations of a possible agreement on the suspension of nuclear tests. *Exp./Nuc.* **28,** 26 pp.

Barrell, J. [1914]. The strength of the earth's crust. *J. Geol.* **22.**

Båth, M. [1957]. Shadow zones, travel times, and energies of longitudinal seismic waves in the presence of an asthenosphere low-velocity layer. *Trans. Am. Geophys. Union* **38,** 529–538.

Birch, F. [1951]. Elasticity and constitution of the earth's interior. *Trans. N. Y. Acad. Sci.* [2] **14,** 72–76.

Birch, F. [1952]. Elasticity and constitution of the earth's interior. *J. Geophys. Research* **57,** 227–286.

Birch, F. [1954]. The earth's mantle. Elasticity and constitution. *Trans. Am. Geophys. Union* **35,** 79–85, 97.

Boyd, F. R., and England, J. L. [1956]. Phase equilibria at high pressure, *Carnegie Inst. Wash. Yearbook* **55,** 154–157.

Bullen, K. E. [1949]. Compressibility-pressure hypothesis and the earth's interior. *Monthly Notices Roy. Astron. Soc. Geophys. Suppl.* **5,** 355–368.

Bullen, K. E. [1953]. "An Introduction to the Theory of Seismology," 296 pp. Cambridge Univ. Press, London and New York.

Bullen, K. E. [1954]. On the homogeneity, or otherwise, of the earth's upper mantle. *Trans. Am. Geophys. Union* **35,** 838–841.

Bullen, K. E. [1956a]. Seismic wave transmission. *In* "Encyclopedia of Physics" (S. Flügge, ed.), Vol. 47, pp. 75–118. Springer, Berlin.

Bullen, K. E. [1956b]. Seismology and the earth's deep interior. *Australian J. Sci.* **19,** 99–100.

Byerly, P. [1926]. The Montana earthquake of June 28, 1925. *Bull. Seismol. Soc. Am.* **16,** 209–265.

Caloi, P. [1953]. Onde longitudinali e transversali guidate dall'astenosfera. *Atti accad. nazl. Lincei Rend. Classe sci. fis. mat. e nat.* [8] **15,** 352–357.

Caloi, P. [1954]. L'astenosfera come canale-guida dell'energia sismica. *Ann. geofis.* **7,** 491–501.

Caloi, P. [1958]. The crust of the earth, from the Apennines to the Atlantic, reconstructed in accordance with the data supplied by seismic surveys. *Z. Geophys.* **24,** 65–95.

Conference [1958]. *Compt. rend. assoc. intern. séismol. et phys. intérieur de la terre, Toronto, 1957* No. **12,** 301 pp. and appendixes.

Dahm, C. G. [1936]. Velocities of P and S waves calculated from the observed travel times of the Long Beach earthquake. *Bull. Seismol. Soc. Am.* **26,** 159–171.

Daly, R. A. [1940]. "Strength and Structure of the Earth," 434 pp. Prentice-Hall, New York.

Dorman, F., Ewing, M., and Oliver, J. [1959]. Study of shear velocity distribution in the upper mantle by surface wave analysis. Pt. I: Mantle Rayleigh waves. (Abstr.). Presented at meeting Seismol. Soc. Am., Tucson, April 1959. Program, p. 21.

Ewing, M., and Press, F. [1956]. Surface waves and guided waves. In "Encyclopedia of Physics" (S. Flügge, ed.), Vol. 47, pp. 119–139. Springer, Berlin.

Griggs, D. [1954]. Symposium on the interior of the earth. Discussion. Trans. Am. Geophys. Union 35, 93–96.

Grueneisen, E. [1926]. Zustand des festen Körpers. In "Handbuch der Physik" (H. Geiger and K. Scheel, eds.), Vol. 10, pp. 1–59. Springer, Berlin.

Gutenberg, B. [1926]. Untersuchungen zur Frage, bis zu welcher Tiefe die Erde kristallin ist. Z. Geophys. 2, 24–29.

Gutenberg, B. [1945]. Magnitude determination for deep-focus earthquakes. Bull. Seismol. Soc. Am. 35, 117–130.

Gutenberg, B. [1948]. On the layer of relatively low wave velocity at a depth of about 80 kilometers. Bull. Seismol. Soc. Am. 38, 121–148.

Gutenberg, B. [1953]. Wave velocities at depths between 50 and 600 kilometers. Bull. Seismol. Soc. Am. 43, 223–232.

Gutenberg, B. [1954a]. Low-velocity layers in the earth's mantle. Bull. Geol. Soc. Am. 65, 337–348.

Gutenberg, B. [1954b]. Effects of low-velocity layers. Geofis. pura e appl. 28, 1–10; Address presented at meeting Intern. Assoc. Seismol. and Phys. Earth's Interior, Rome, Sept. 1954.

Gutenberg, B. [1955]. Channel waves in the earth's crust. Geophysics 20, 283–294.

Gutenberg, B. [1958]. Velocity of seismic waves in the earth's mantle. Trans. Am. Geophys. Union 39, 486–489.

Gutenberg, B., and Richter, C. F. [1939]. New evidence for a change in physical conditions at depths near 100 kilometers. Bull. Seismol. Soc. Am. 29, 531–537.

Haalck, H. [1957]. Zur Frage der inneren Gliederung des Gesteinsmantels der Erde. Forsch. u. Fortschr. 31, 168–175.

Holser, W. T., and Schneer, C. J. [1957]. Polymorphism in the earth's mantle. Trans. Am. Geophys. Union 38, 569–577.

Jacobs, J. A. [1956]. The interior of the earth. Advances in Geophys. 3, 183–240.

Jeffreys, H. [1936, 1937]. The structure of the earth down to the 20° discontinuity. Monthly Notices Roy. Astron. Soc. Geophys. Suppl. 3, 401–422; 4, 13–39.

Jeffreys [1939]. The times of P, S and SKS and the velocities of P and S. Monthly Notices Roy. Astron. Soc. Geophys. Suppl. 4, 498–533.

Jeffreys, H. [1952]. "The Earth," 3rd ed., 392 pp. Cambridge Univ. Press, London and New York.

Jeffreys, H. [1958a]. The times of P up to 30° (second paper). Geophys. J. 1, 154–161.

Jeffreys, H. [1958b]. On the interpretation of Pd. Geophys. J. 1, 191–197.

Kishimoto, Y. [1956]. Seismometric investigation of the earth's interior. Mem. Coll. Sci. Univ. Kyoto A28, 117–142.

Kishimoto, Y. [1958]. Seismometric investigation of the earth's interior IV. On the structure of the earth's mantle (II). Mem. Coll. Sci. Univ. Kyoto A28, 391–399.

Lehmann, I. [1934]. Transmission times for seismic waves for epicentral distances around 20°. Geodaet. Inst. Medd. København 5, 45 pp.

Lehmann, I. [1955]. The times of P and S in northeastern America. *Ann. geofis.* **8,** 351–370.

Lehmann, I. [1958]. On the velocity distribution in the earth's upper mantle. (Abstr.). *Freiberger Forschungsh.* **B10,** 403.

Lovering, J. F. [1958]. The nature of the Mohorovičić discontinuity. *Trans. Am. Geophys. Union* **39,** 947–955.

MacDonald, G. J. F. [1956]. Equations of state of solids in the earth. *J. Geophys. Research* **61,** 387–391.

Macelwane, J. B. [1951]. Evidence on the interior of the earth from seismic sources. *In* "Internal Constitution of the Earth" (B. Gutenberg, ed.), 2nd ed., pp. 227–304. Dover, New York.

Meinesz, F. A. V. [1956]. A phase-transition layer between 200 and 900 km depth in the earth. *Koninkl. Ned. Akad. Wetenschap. Proc.* **B59,** 1–10.

Miki, H. [1955]. Is the layer C (413–1000 km) inhomogeneous? *J. Phys. Earth* **3,** 1–6.

Miki, H. [1956]. On the earth's mantle. *Mem. Coll. Sci. Univ. Kyoto* **A27,** 363–403.

Mohorovičić, S. [1915]. Die reduzierte Laufzeitkurve und die Abhängigkeit der Herdtiefe eines Bebens von der Entfernung des Inflexionspunktes der Laufzeitkurve. *Gerlands Beitr. Geophys.* **14,** 187–205.

Press, F. [1959]. Some implications on mantle and crustal structure from G waves and Love waves. *J. Geophys. Research* **64,** 565–568.

Press, F., and Ewing, M. [1955]. Waves with Pn and Sn velocity at great distances. *Proc. Natl. Acad. Sci. U. S.* **41,** 24–27; Presented meeting Seismol. Soc. Am. March 27, 1954.

Rayleigh, J. W. S. [1945]. "The Theory of Sound," Vol. 2, pp. 126–129. Dover, New York; (reprinted from 2nd ed. [1894], revised and enlarged).

Ruprechtová, L. [1958]. Dependence of amplitudes of seismic body waves on the distance. *Studia Geophys. et Geodet. (Ceskos. Akad.)* **4,** 397–399.

Shimazu, Y. [1958]. A chemical phase transition hypothesis of the origin of the C-layer within the mantle of the earth. *J. Earth Sci. Nagoya Univ.* **61,** 11–30.

Takeuchi, H., Press, F., and Kobayashi, N. [1959]. On mantle Rayleigh waves. (Abstr.). Presented at meeting Seismol. Soc. Am. Tucson, April 1959. Program p. 58.

Verhoogen, J. [1953]. Elasticity of olivine and constitution of the earth's mantle. *J. Geophys. Research* **58,** 337–346.

Vesanen, E., Nurmia, M., and Porkka, M. T. [1959]. New evidence for the existence of Gutenberg's asthenosphere channel. *Geophysica (Helsinki)* **7.** In press.

Williamson, E. D., and Adams, L. H. [1923]. Density distribution in the earth. *J. Wash. Acad. Sci.* **18,** 413–428.

Yoder, H. S. [1950]. The jadeite problem. *Am. J. Sci.* **248,** 225–248, 312–334.

Yoder, H. S., and Weir, C. E. [1951]. Change of free energy with pressure of the reaction nepheline + albite = 2 jadeite. *Am. J. Sci.* **249,** 683–694.

Zoeppritz, K., Geiger, L., and Gutenberg, B. [1912]. Ueber Erdbebenwellen V.*Nachr. Ges. Wiss. Göttingen Math.-physik. Kl.* **1912,** 121–106.

5. The Core

5.1 General Discussion of Travel Times through the Core, and of the Resulting Wave Velocities

As soon as Gutenberg [1914] had found a velocity–depth curve for longitudinal waves through the mantle and the core (Fig. 2.1) he calculated travel time curves for various longitudinal and transverse phases reflected at or refracted through the core boundary. For transverse waves he had assumed a Poisson's ratio of 0.277 in the core ($V/v = 1.8$). Those of these phases which are reflected at the core boundary in the mantle and those which travel inside the core as longitudinal waves have been observed with travel times close to those calculated. Some of their travel time curves have been verified already during World War I by Turner in England as travel time curves of "unknown" waves without knowledge of the times calculated by Gutenberg. However, no waves traveling as transverse waves through the core have been identified thus far.

The symbols for waves through the core have been changed repeatedly, and there is no complete international agreement yet about many of these symbols. At present, the following symbols are used, most of them internationally: P and S indicate respectively longitudinal and transverse waves through the mantle only. For waves which travel on a portion of their path through the core the following symbols are added: K, for longitudinal waves through the outer core (sometimes for longitudinal waves through the whole core); I for longitudinal and J for transverse waves (if they exist) through the inner core. The symbols are combined in the order in which the respective portions of the ray follow each other; e.g. PKIKP indicates a longitudinal wave through the whole earth; SKS travels as transverse wave both times in the mantle and as longitudinal wave in the outer core but does not enter the inner core; SKIKS passes, in addition, as longitudinal wave through the inner core. Sometimes PKP and PKIKP are denoted by P′, and occasionally PKIKP at distances of

less than 144° is indicated by P″. Reflection in the mantle at the core boundary is shown by "c" (e.g., PcP, ScP). Reflection inside the core at its boundary is not indicated by a special symbol, but is evident from the duplica-
tion of K (e.g., PKKP). Similarly, reflection at the surface of the earth is
shown by two consecutive symbols P and/or S (e.g., PP, SS, PS, PKPPKP).
In Fig. 5.1 paths of selected wave types are sketched.

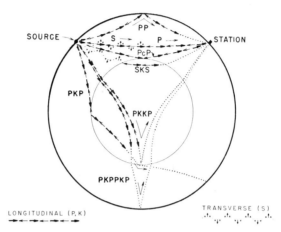

FIG. 5.1. Paths of selected wave types through the earth. The end of portions indicated by arrows correspond to a transmission time of 12 min. Designed by J. Nordquist.

As a consequence of the sudden decrease of the wave velocity at the
core boundary, even for waves arriving as transverse waves in the mantle
at the core boundary (Fig. 2.1), and of the rapid increase of velocity in the
transition zone from the outer to the inner core, the travel time curves of
waves through the core are complicated. Figs. 5.2(a) and 5.2(c) show
schematically travel time curves and wave paths if the velocity decreases
suddenly (or rapidly) with depth. Figs. 5.2(b) and (d) show the conditions
if the velocity increases suddenly so that waves arriving at the boundary
at an angle of incidence near 90° are totally reflected (or, respectively, are
strongly curved). The travel time curves of waves through the core are
combinations of the types sketched in Figs. 5.2(a) and (b).

There are three types of direct waves through the core: (a) PKP and
PKIKP, (b) SKP, PKS, SKIKP and PKIKS, and (c) SKS and SKIKS.
Figure 5.3 shows wave paths and wave fronts of longitudinal waves (P,
PKP, PKIKP) through the earth. The caustic at B in Fig. 5.3 corresponds
to the caustic at B in Fig. 5.2(a). Some details of Fig. 5.3 are uncertain;
the epicentral distances of the points A, C, and D, may be in error by as

much as 10°. The travel times of PKIKP near the point D (Fig. 5.3) are discussed in Section 5.3. Amplitudes and travel times of PKP have been studied in detail by Denson [1950], those of PKKP and PKPPKP by Gutenberg [1951], those of SKS and SKKS by Nelson [1952], and those of the SKP group by Forester [1956]. Tables of travel times for these waves are included in the tables of Jeffreys and Bullen [1940].

While some portions of the travel time curves for PKP and PKIKP are close together (compare Fig. 5.8 and the wave fronts in Fig. 5.3, especially near the caustic B), those of the SKP group and the SKIKP-group

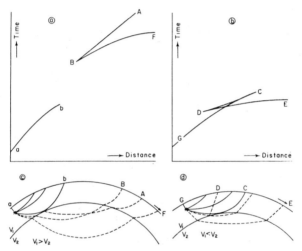

Fig. 5.2. Schematic travel time curves for waves passing through a two-layered sphere, (a) if the velocity increases, (b) if it decreases suddenly at a discontinuity; (c) and (d) show corresponding wave paths. V_1 is the velocity immediately above, V_2 that immediately below the discontinuity; the velocities are assumed to increase gradually with depth in each layer.

are well separated near their caustic B (compare Fig. 5.4), especially in deep-focus earthquakes. For a source in the surface, the travel times of SKP and PKS are the same, and similarly those for SKIKP and PKIKS. With increasing focal depth, the first portion of the wave through the mantle is shortened, and consequently the phases starting with S arrive earlier than those starting with P; the time differences increase to about 1 min for a focal depth of 700 km. Examples of records of the SKP-group are given in Fig. 5.5. Since these waves arrive relatively steeply at the surface, SKP is relatively large in the vertical component, PKS in the horizontal. For details, see Gutenberg [1958a].

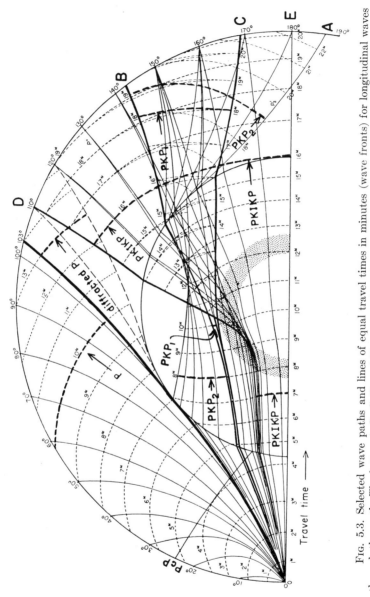

FIG. 5.3. Selected wave paths and lines of equal travel times in minutes (wave fronts) for longitudinal waves through the earth. The letters A, B, C, D, and E correspond to the letters in Fig. 5.2. Dotted: transition zone between outer and inner core.

The first determination of wave velocities in the core (dotted curve in Fig. 2.1) had been made by the method of trial and error. As no waves of any kind have their deepest point in the outermost portion of the core (compare Fig. 5.3 for PKP), no unique solution for the velocity as function of depth can be given. The largest uncertainty is immediately below the core boundary, but even there the error in the assumed velocity is probably less than $\pm\frac{1}{2}$ km/sec.

A great step forward was made by Wadati and Masuda [1934] when they described a method by which a travel time curve can be constructed

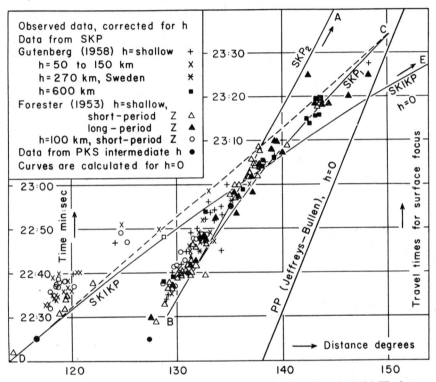

Fig. 5.4. Travel times for SKP and related phases after Gutenberg [1958b]. The letters A, B, C, E correspond to those in Fig. 5.2.

for waves starting and ending at the core boundary. Each ray which passes through the mantle and the core can be combined by use of one observable phase which has traveled only in the mantle and has been reflected at the core boundary, and one portion in the core only. For example, PKP = PcP + K (compare Figs. 5.1 and 5.3); SKS = ScS + K; PKKP = PcP + 2K; PKPPKP = 2PcP + 2K. The whole ray for such a phase (e.g., PKP) and its portion in the mantle (PcP) must have the same angle of incidence i_0 at the surface. Consequently, at the distances Δ_1 for the portion of the ray in the mantle and Δ of the whole ray, the travel time curves which correspond to each other (e.g., that for PcP and that for

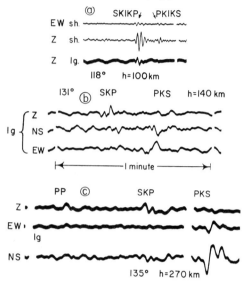

Fig. 5.5. Portions of seismograms showing SKP and related phases. EW, NS and Z refer to the east–west, north–south, and vertical components respectively; "sh" indicates instruments which have relatively high magnification for waves with short periods ($T \sim 1$ sec), "lg" instruments which record waves with periods of several seconds to $\frac{1}{2}$ min relatively well; h = depth of focus; epicentral distances in degrees. Epicenters and stations: (a) July 9, 1957 6° S 104° E, recorded at Pasadena; (b) April 10, 1956, 2° S 102° E recorded at Pasadena; (c) Aug. 9, 1956, 16° S, 175° W, recorded at Uppsala, waves arriving from north. Based on Gutenberg [1958a].

PKP) must have the same apparent velocity $\bar{V}_0 = (d\Delta/dt)_0$ at the surface. This follows from the fact that their angles of incidence i_0 at the surface are the same, and that

$$\bar{V}_0 = \frac{V_0}{\sin i_0} \tag{5.1}$$

where V_0 is the wave velocity at the earth's surface. Consequently, to find corresponding values for travel times t for the whole ray and for t_1, its portion in the mantle, as well as the corresponding distances Δ and Δ_1 (in km along the surface) one has to find the distance Δ_1, where the travel time curve of the respective phase through the mantle (e.g., PcP) has the same apparent velocity $\bar{V}_0$ (direction of the travel time curve) as the travel time curve for the whole ray (e.g., PKP) at the distance Δ. Then, corresponding distances Δ_K (measured along the earth's surface in km) or similarly, the angular distances Θ_K in degrees, in the core, as well as the corresponding travel times t_K in the core are found from

$$\Delta_K = \Delta - \Delta_1 \qquad \text{or} \qquad \Theta_K = \Theta - \Theta_1$$

and

$$t_K = t - t_1$$

(5.2)

Figure 5.6 shows a travel time curve for waves through the core which has been constructed in this way. Most points, found from various combinations, agree very well. The errors involved in the method are relatively

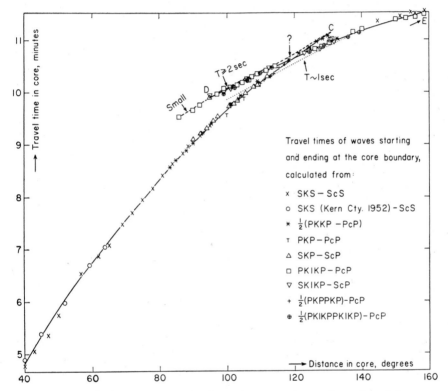

FIG. 5.6. Travel times of longitudinal waves between points at the surface of the core. The letters C, D, E correspond to those in Fig. 5.2.

small. If $d\Delta/dt$ or $d\Theta/dt$ for the whole ray are not determined correctly, both Θ_1 and t_1 will be found with an error in the same direction, and Θ_K and t_K will be either both too small or both too large; however, since the travel time curves of the phases involved in the calculation have the same slope at the corresponding distances Θ and Θ_1, the resulting point for the travel time curve through the core is close to the actual travel time curve at a slightly greater or slightly shorter distance than the correct point.

The Eq. (5.2) may be written

$$\Theta = \Theta_K + \Theta_1 \qquad t = t_K + t_1. \tag{5.3}$$

If, for a source in the earth's surface, the angle of incidence i_0 at the surface decreases, Θ_1 decreases to zero for $i_0 = 0$; at the same time Θ_K increases to 180°. A cusp of the type B in Fig. 5.3 for the travel time curve of a wave through the mantle and the core exists, if and where the absolute values of $d\Theta_1/di_0$ and $d\Theta_K/di_0$ are equal. Conditions for cusps have been discussed by Lehmann [1940]. The travel time curve for the core (Fig. 5.6) naturally does not show any irregularity corresponding to the cusps B for PKP, PKS, etc. (Figs. 5.3, 5.4), since these are a consequence of the "ray optics" for the complete rays through the earth. However, the travel time curve for waves through the core has a loop CD (Fig. 5.6) a portion of which has been found from various phases; this is of the type sketched in Fig. 5.2(b) and corresponds to the transition from the outer to the inner core. It is discussed in Section 5.3.

The travel time curve (Fig. 5.6) for waves starting and ending at the surface of the core can be used to calculate the wave velocities in the core. Assuming a radius of 3473 km for the core, the deepest point (distance r_s from the center of the earth) reached by a ray arriving at the core surface at the angular distance Θ_s degrees is given by

$$\log r_s = 3.5407 - 0.0024127 \int_0^{\Theta_s} q \, d\Theta \tag{5.4}$$

and the velocity V_s at the distance r_s from the center by

$$V_s = 0.017453 r_s \bar{V}_s \tag{5.5}$$

(compare Eqs. (2.1) and (2.2)) where $\cosh q$ is the ratio of the fixed apparent velocity at Θ_s to the apparent velocities at the distances from $\Theta = 0$ to $\Theta = \Theta_s$; $\bar{V}_s$ is the apparent velocity in degrees/sec at Θ_s. For reversed segments, the corresponding portion of the integral is negative [Slichter, 1932].

Results for V as function of r are shown in Fig. 2.1. They are not equally reliable for all depths. The beginning of the travel time curve for the core must be interpolated between the distances of zero degrees and the first calculated point of the travel time curve, corresponding to a distance of about 25°. This is the reason for the fact, mentioned above, that calculated curves for the velocities as a function of depth in the core are not based on unique solutions. However, the possible errors in the interpolation of the travel time curve for the core at distances between 0°, where the travel time is zero, and 25° are small if we can exclude a complicated structure of the outer portion of the core. There is no indication of any such complication so that we can assume that the missing portion of the travel time curve consists of a single curve, which must be convex upward throughout and pass smoothly into the observed portion of the travel time curve. Nevertheless, the velocity in the core close to its boundary remains uncertain within perhaps $\frac{1}{2}$ km/sec.

The velocities in the core are again somewhat uncertain in the transition zone between the outer and the inner core, since the reversed segment CD (Fig. 5.6) is too close to the segment DE to be observable, and the position of the points C and D is somewhat uncertain. Moreover, there seems to be dispersion for waves crossing the transition zone; this is discussed in Section 5.3. Finally, the velocity near the earth's center is not well established, since it affects relatively little the travel time of PKIKP near $\Theta = 180°$, which is the only phase available for the calculation of the wave velocity near $r = 0$.

5.2 The Outer Core (Region E)

At least until about 1930, investigations of waves through the core had been based mainly on records of instruments which gave much smaller magnification (usually less than 200) for waves having periods of the order of 1 sec, than the instruments available now (magnification frequently over 10,000; for details, see Benioff [1955]). Consequently, waves having periods of 1 to 2 sec, which includes most PKIKP-waves, had been observed only occasionally in records of large shocks. However, many waves through the outer core, which usually have relatively large amplitudes with periods of 5 to 15 sec, especially near the caustics (compare the record at Palisades, Fig. 5.7), had been studied. Originally, travel times for PKIKP-waves at distances over 140° had been combined with those for PKP_1 and for PKP_2 to one curve with two branches, joining each other in a cusp. The corresponding curve, [Gutenberg, 1914], for the wave velocities in the core is indicated in Fig. 2.1.

As has been mentioned in Section 5.1, the wave velocities in the portion of the outer core just below the mantle and those in the transition zone to the inner core are slightly uncertain. Otherwise, the presently assumed wave velocities in the outer core (Fig. 2.1) can be considered to be as accurate as those in the mantle.

No transverse waves through the core have been established thus far in spite of very careful search. In a few instances waves have been reported with travel times which are in the range of those to be expected for S-waves

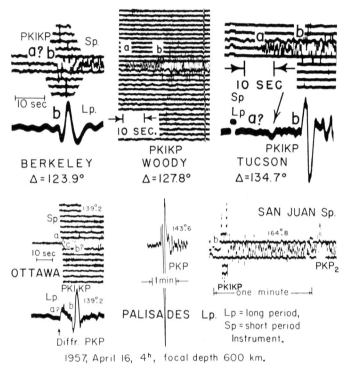

FIG. 5.7. Portions of records of an earthquake with a focal depth of 600 km in the East Indies. Compiled from Gutenberg [1957, 1958a,b]. "Sp" recorded by short-period. "Lp" by long-period instruments.

through the core, but most of them could be identified as those of other phases which should have arrived at the observed times. Moreover, the search for a caustic of transverse waves through the core corresponding to that of PKP (e.g., Palisades, Fig. 5.7) has been absolutely unsuccessful thus far.

5.3 The Transition Zone in the Core (Region F)

The history of the interpretation of waves through the core has been summarized in Section 2.1. While there is no disagreement any more about the fact that the core consists of two parts with a transition zone between them, there are still two different interpretations (Fig. 2.1) of the observed travel times (Fig. 5.6). Jeffreys [1952] assumes that the wave velocity decreases with depth just above the inner core, and increases suddenly at the boundary of the inner core, while Gutenberg and others believe that there is a gradual increase in velocity in a transition zone without a preceding decrease.

The problem is further complicated by the fact that at epicentral distances between about 125° and 140° waves with periods of $\frac{1}{2}$ to 1 sec arrive about 10 to 20 sec earlier than the definite PKIKP impulse with periods

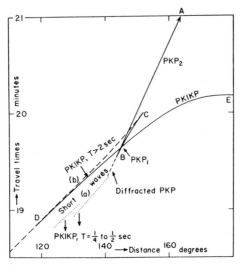

FIG. 5.8. Travel times of longitudinal waves which start at the earth's surface and pass through the core. After Gutenberg [1957, 1958a,b]. The letters A, B, C, E, correspond to those in Fig. 5.2.

of about 2 or more sec. The early short-period phases have been observed by various seismologists for about 20 years. Gutenberg [1957, 1958a,b] believes that they are most likely the effect of dispersion in the transition zone, where short-period waves seem to travel faster than long-period waves. Fig. 5.7 gives examples of longitudinal waves through the core recorded at various stations from a 600 km deep earthquake in the East Indies; the dispersion is observed similarly in shallow shocks. Fig. 5.8 shows travel time curves for the PKP-group; the travel times of all observations on which it is based have been reduced to zero focal depth.

The amplitudes of the first short-period PKIKP-waves (*a* in Figs. 5.7 and 5.8) which are recorded at epicentral distances of between about 130°

and 140° are rather small. Consequently, the first waves may be missed sometimes in reading the records. Their identification depends for example on the magnitude of the shock, the magnification and characteristics of the instrument, the background (microseisms), and on properties of the ground at the station. Moreover, in most seismograms only waves with a few distinct periods are well developed, and seismogram "spectra" show several sharp peaks for longitudinal, and others for transverse waves. These peaks differ from shock to shock. Under these circumstances, it is difficult to draw travel time curves of PKIKP-waves having a specific period. In addition, the maximum speed of 1 mm/sec of routine recording drums does not permit accurate reading of periods of a small fraction of one second. Consequently, the velocity–depth curves for waves having periods of $\frac{1}{2}$ and 1 sec in the transition zone between the outer and inner core in Fig. 2.1 are tentative only.

The fact that the short-period PKIKP-waves (a) could not be traced definitely to distances greater than those of the beginning of the diffracted PKP-waves near the distance of 140° (Fig. 5.8) is somewhat disturbing. However, it is unlikely for several reasons [Gutenberg, 1958b] that they are short-period PKP-waves which are diffracted to shorter distances than 140°, far beyond the caustic B of PKP and beyond the minimum distances, at which the long-period diffracted PKP-waves are observed. The apparently common end of the travel time curves of the long-period diffracted PKP-waves and of the short-period PKIKP-waves (a) is probably a coincidence. Moreover, the various branches of PKIKP, similar to (a) and (b) in Fig. 5.8, fulfil all requirements to be expected, if dispersion in a transition zone between the outer, liquid, and an inner, solid core is the source of the observed branches of the travel time curve for PKIKP.

The problem of effects of the transition from the solid to the liquid state in a material on the corresponding wave velocities has been investigated theoretically as well as by laboratory experiments by Kuhn and Vielhauer [1953]. From findings in experiments with a resin (Fig. 5.9) they have concluded that in a liquid glass not only the modulus of rigidity is much smaller than in the corresponding solid glass, but that the bulk modulus, too, is reduced. In applying these results to the observations for waves which have crossed the transition zone between outer and inner core, one has to consider the great differences in temperature and pressure and also differences between a resin and the material in the core. Nevertheless, we may conclude that dispersion of the longitudinal waves in the transition zone could well be a consequence of a transition from the liquid state of the material in the outer core to the solid state in the inner core. In this case it can be expected that the intersection of the curve for the temperature of the melting point of the material with the curve for the actual temperature in the core is very flat (compare Fig. 6.1) and that consequently the transition zone is rather thick. Short waves having periods of 0.1 to 1 sec (lengths of the order of 1 to 10 km) can be expected to have a higher velocity in such a

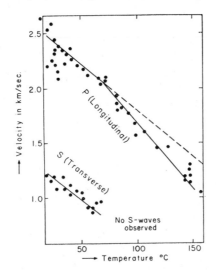

FIG. 5.9. Velocities observed in an organic glass by Kuhn and Vielhauer [1953]. The logarithm of the viscosity coefficient was 5.8 at 60° C, 3.5 at 90° C.

transition zone than long waves (lengths up to over 100 km). Neither the experiments of Kuhn and Vielhauer (Fig. 5.9) nor similar experiments by Knopoff [1959, p. 360] show a decrease in wave velocity just before the transition from the liquid to the solid state is reached. All these velocity curves are very similar to those found by Gutenberg (Fig. 2.1) for the transition zone from the outer to the inner core.

The rather indefinite beginning and ending of the transition zone F makes it difficult to define the "boundaries" between the transition zone F and the outer and the inner core, zones E and G respectively. Tentatively, radii of 1700 km and of 1200 km for the boundaries of the transition zone F may be taken.

5.4 The Inner Core (Region G)

Within the limits of error (Section 5.1), the velocity of longitudinal waves in the inner core is 11.2 km/sec regardless of the depth. On the basis of their assumed travel time curves for PKIKP at great epicentral distances (approaching 180°), some authors have found a slight increase, others a slight decrease in velocity with depth in the inner core, usually not exceeding 0.2 km/sec for the whole inner core. For examples Jeffreys [1952] finds an increase from 11.16 km/sec at $r = 1250$ km to 11.31 km/sec at the center, Gutenberg [1958a] a (doubtful) decrease from 11.25 to 11.15 km/sec.

There are no observations of phases which are known to have crossed the inner core as transverse waves J. However, this does not permit the conclusion that transverse waves cannot be transmitted through the inner core. If the transition from the outer to the inner core is gradual, practically no energy could be transformed from the longitudinal waves K in the outer core to transverse waves J in the inner core. If there is a discontinuity, the ratio of the energy of transverse waves which are refracted into the inner core, to the energy of the longitudinal waves arriving at the boundary from the outer core, should be rather small. Consequently, waves of the types PKJKP, SKJKS, or SKJKP could probably not be found without exact knowledge where to look for them.

Bullen [1950a,b] has discussed the possibility of estimating the velocity of transverse waves through the inner core on the assumption of his hypothesis that under high pressure the bulk modulus (or the compressibility) depends on the pressure only [Bullen, 1949]. Bullen assumes, probably with sufficient approximation, that in the inner core $\Phi = V^2 - \frac{4}{3}v^2$ is proportional to V^2. He introduces

$$n = 1 - \frac{4v^2}{3V^2} = \frac{\Phi}{V^2}. \tag{5.6}$$

For n_0 at the earth's center Bullen [1950a, p. 51] writes

$$n_0 = 0.75(1 - \epsilon) \tag{5.7}$$

where ϵ depends on the jump of the density at the boundary of the inner core. If the density does not change from the outer to the inner core, ϵ is zero; for the largest value of ϵ corresponding to the greatest jump in density (to about 20) to be expected, Bullen finds $\epsilon = 0.17$. If we assume with Bullen that at great depths the bulk modulus depends only on the pressure and combine Eqs. (5.6) and (5.7) we find

$$v = 0.433V(1 + 1.5\epsilon). \tag{5.8}$$

For $V = 11.2$ km/sec and $\epsilon = 0$, this gives $v = 4.8$ km/sec, and for $\epsilon = 0.17$ we find $v = 6.1$ km/sec.

Finally, Knopoff and MacDonald [1958] have pointed out that the rapid increase in the velocity of longitudinal waves in the transition zone between the outer and the inner core may be the effect of a magnetic field.

5.5 State and Composition of the Core

When it was found (details in Section 8.3) that the body tides of the earth are larger than it is expected for a completely solid earth, it was concluded that the core is not solid. This hypothesis is supported by data furnished by investigation of the Chandler movements of the earth's poles (Section 8.2). The lack of observed transverse waves through the outer core gives it further weight. It is widely believed that the earth has either started as a hot body or that it was molten at least once during its history, and that at least the outer core has not yet cooled below the melting point of its material. On the other hand, the earth's deep portions may be getting hotter (Section 6.7). The indication of dispersion of longitudinal waves in the transition zone and the increase in their velocity there would be well explained on the assumption that the outer core is liquid, the inner core solid. Apparently, no evidence contradicts this hypothesis. Bullen [1958] has given a summary of reasons, why he believes that the inner core is probably solid.

Birch [1952, p. 267] has applied the equations, which he has developed for the investigation of possible changes of phase or composition in the mantle (Eqs. (4.8) to (4.18)) to the outer core. If we assume that the velocity of transverse waves is so small compared with that of longitudinal waves that v^2 can be neglected in comparison with V^2, $\Phi = V^2$, and $\Gamma = 1 - (d\Phi/dr)/g$ is found from Gutenberg's curve in Fig. 2.1 to be about 3.5 in the outer core down to about $r = 2000$ km, and to decrease to about $2\frac{1}{4}$ as the transition zone is approached. On the other hand, Birch finds that on the basis of Jeffreys' velocity–depth curve (Fig. 2.1) Γ would increase from about 3.5 to 4. Theoretically, Birch has calculated values for Γ decreasing from about 3.2 at the core boundary to about 3.0 at the transition zone, if region E is homogeneous and isothermal, and has concluded that the outer core may be nearly isothermal and homogeneous. No similar calculations can be made for the inner core, where the velocity of transverse waves is not known but is probably not negligible compared with that of longitudinal waves.

The problem of the composition of the core is still far from being settled. Most investigators by far believe that the whole core consists mainly of an iron–nickel alloy which in the outer core has a temperature above its melting point, in the inner core probably below it. A few others prefer the assumption that the outer core consists of rock of the same composition as that in the mantle, but in a different phase or state, and still others think that hydrogen plays a role in the composition of the core. The prevailing belief that iron is the main element in the core is frequently based partly on its frequency in meteors. However, in this connection we have to avoid a vicious circle: (a) meteorites, which are portions of an original planet, contain frequently iron and therefore iron can be expected to form a major portion of the earth; (b) since the composition of all known meteorites combined corresponds roughly to that of the earth (including the *iron* core) they can be considered to be portions of a former planet.

Among other hypotheses on the composition of the core are those of Bullen [1955]. He points out, for example, that the assumption of a common composition of the terrestrial planets would require a core containing mainly iron. Birch [1952] finds that the density of the core is slightly smaller than it would be expected for pure iron at the conditions in the core; similar conclusions have been drawn by Elsasser [1951] and by Knopoff and Uffen [1954] in a detailed investigation of the densities involved, by Jacobs [1956] and by others (compare Section 7.6.2). MacDonald and Knopoff [1958] conclude that the outer core consists most likely of $(Fe, Ni)_{1.6}Si$.

Among those who believe that the material of the outer core or of the whole core are one or two different phases of the material in the mantle is Ramsey [1949, 1950]. He concludes that the core contains metallic phases of the material in the mantle, and that at least twelve major phase transitions are possible, before the atoms of the main elements, oxygen, silicon, magnesium, and iron, have been broken down completely.

Egyed [1957] has suggested an hypothesis differing from that of Ramsey, but he also assumes that, with the exception of the uppermost parts of the mantle, the earth "is made up of three phases of the same homogeneous ultrabasic silicate mass." In the inner core, the material "shows a lattice-like structure which is not influenced by the pressures within the earth." This would explain the constant velocity of longitudinal waves in the inner core. "The state of the mass forming the outer core corresponds to the next ultra high-pressure phase" and the rigidity is negligible compared with the other elastic moduli so that only longitudinal waves are observed. Layer C of the mantle "represents the transition from the high-pressure modification of layer D to the familiar silicate minerals of the more differentiated layer B."

A different hypothesis has been introduced by Lynch [1937], and one similar to Lynch's has been discussed in detail by Kuhn and Rittmann

[1941]. They have suggested that the core contains appreciable amounts of hydrogen, which has remained from the original matter forming the earth.

Objections have been raised to all hypotheses about the composition of the core. At present, hypotheses are preferred in which iron is considered to be the main element in the whole core and in which it is assumed that the outer core is liquid, the inner core solid. However, future observations or theoretical findings about the matter in the core under pressures of $1\frac{1}{2}$ to $3\frac{1}{2}$ million atmospheres and temperatures of several thousand degrees centigrade may result in changes of the prevailing views.

5.6 The Earth's Magnetic Field and the Core

Already over 100 years ago, Gauss had confirmed earlier suggestions that the main source of the earth's magnetic field is in the earth's interior. After the existence of the core had been established, it was believed that permanent magnetism of the earth's "iron core" accounts for most of the earth's magnetic field. When, however, it was pointed out that the Curie point for iron is reached in the earth's lower crust or upper mantle, a different hypothesis was needed.

Elsasser [1939] first considered thermoelectric currents in the core as source of the magnetic field. Later he suggested that slow motions in the earth's core could provide currents by dynamo-like actions and thus could be the source of the magnetic field. He developed these ideas to a more definite hypothesis in many publications [Elsasser, 1946, 1947, 1950, 1951, 1955, 1956a,b]. Other major improvements of this hypothesis have been added by Bullard in several papers (starting with Bullard [1948]; summaries in Bullard [1954, 1955a,b]) and by Runcorn [1954]. Runcorn has considered the effect of electromotive forces which are produced on the surface of the core by motions inside the core, and has suggested experiments for the study of possible currents in the core. Other contributions to the problem of the earth's magnetism have been made, e.g., by Takeuchi [1956] and by Vestine [1954] who considers effects of a different speed of rotation of mantle and core, and by Knopoff and MacDonald [1958].

Critical summaries of hypotheses to explain the earth's magnetism have been given for example by Elsasser [1958], Hales [1956], Hide [1956], and Runcorn [1956]. Publications concerning the theory of the earth's magnetic field are so extensive that they would require a whole volume for a detailed discussion. "The basic theory, magneto-hydrodynamics, is of considerable complexity and the working out of specific models is a formidable task."

"A subject with considerable ramifications has started to develop. Semi-quantitative treatments of certain parts of it have been based on more or less plausible assumptions." [Bullard, 1955b].

According to Elsasser [1958], the strongest argument for the dynamo theory of the earth's magnetism is the irregularly changing magnetic field of the earth. It has been pointed out repeatedly, especially by Vestine ([1954] and elsewhere) that not only the field observed at the earth's surface changes, but that, in addition, neither the rate of change, nor the strength of the field are constant. Moreover, the magnetic poles are moving relative to the poles of rotation.

The average order of magnitude of the velocity of the motion in the core required by the preceding hypotheses has been estimated to be roughly 10 km/year. There is no definite answer yet to the question of the source of the energy which maintains the motion in the core [Elsasser, 1950; Runcorn, 1954; Urey, 1952, p. 179]. Thermal convection currents in the core have been suggested, small differences in the chemical constitution of portions of the core, or incomplete equilibrium in the core. The combined theoretical results still show that the dynamo theory offers a possible explanation of the earth's magnetic field and its changes, but there is no proof for this theory. Elsasser [1958] concludes "The earth's core seems to be a quite tolerable model for the magnetohydrodynamic processes that fill the universe on the vastest possible scale."

References

Benioff, H. [1955]. Earthquake seismographs and associated instruments. *Advances in Geophys.* **2**, 219–275.

Birch, F. [1952]. Elasticity and constitution of the earth's interior. *J. Geophys. Research* **57**, 227–286.

Bullard, E. C. [1948]. The secular change in the earth's magnetic field. *Monthly Notices Roy. Astron. Soc. Geophys. Suppl.* **5**, 248–257.

Bullard, E. C. [1954]. The interior of the earth. *In* "The Earth as a Planet" (G. P. Kuiper, ed.), pp. 57–137. Univ. Chicago Press, Chicago, Illinois.

Bullard, E. C. [1955a]. Introduction, discussion meeting. *Proc. Roy. Soc. (London),* **A233**, 289–296.

Bullard, E. C. [1955b]. Introduction to a discussion on "movements in the earth's core and electric conductivity." *Ann. géophys.* **11**, 49–108.

Bullen, K. E. [1949]. Compressibility-pressure hypothesis and the earth's interior. *Monthly Notices Roy. Astron. Soc. Geophys. Suppl.* **5**, 335–368.

Bullen, K. E. [1950a]. An earth model based on a compressibility-pressure hypothesis. *Monthly Notices Roy. Astron. Soc. Geophys. Suppl.* **6**, 50–59.

Bullen, K. E. [1950b]. Theoretical travel-times of S waves in the earth's inner core. *Monthly Notices Roy. Astron. Soc. Geophys. Suppl.* **6**, 125–128.

Bullen, K. E. [1955]. Physical Properties of the earth's core. *Ann. geophys.* **11**, 53–64.

Bullen, K. E. [1958]. Solidity of the inner core. *In* "Contributions in Geophysics" (H. Benioff, M. Ewing, B. F. Howell and F. Press, eds.), Vol. 1, pp. 113–120. Pergamon, New York.

Denson, M. E. [1950]. Longitudinal waves through the earth's core. Ph.D. thesis, Calif. Inst. Technol.; Condensed in [1952] *Bull. Seismol. Soc. Am.* **42**,119–134.

Egyed, L. [1957]. A new conception of the internal constitution of the earth. *Geol. Rundschau* **46**, 101–121.

Elsasser, W. M. [1939]. On the origin of the earth's magnetic field. *Phys. Rev.* **55**, 489–498.

Elsasser, W. M. [1946, 1947]. Induction effects in terrestrial magnetism. *Phys. Rev.* **69**, 106–116, **70**, 202–212, **72**, 821–823.

Elsasser, W. M. [1950]. Causes of motions in the earth's core. Report, ONR project N-6-ori-139, Inst. Advanced Study, Princeton, 25 pp.

Elsasser, W. M. [1951]. Quantum theoretical densities of solids at extreme compression. *Science* **113**, 105–107.

Elsasser, W. M. [1955]. Hydromagnetism. *Am. J. Phys.* **23**, 590–609.

Elsasser, W. M. [1956a]. Hydromagnetism. *Am. J. Phys.* **24**, 85–110.

Elsasser, W. M. [1956b]. Background of the geomagnetic dynamo theory. *J. Geophys. Research* **61**, 340–347.

Elsasser, W. M. [1958]. The earth as a dynamo. *Sci. American* May 1958, 44–48.

Forester, R. D. [1956]. Studies of the travel times, periods and energy of seismic waves SKP and related phases. Ph.D. thesis, Calif. Inst. of Technol.; Condensed in *Bull. Seismol. Soc. Am.* **46**, 185–201.

Gutenberg, B. [1914]. Ueber Erdbebenwellen. VIIA. *Nachr. Ges. Wiss. Göttingen Math. physik. Kl.* **1914**, 166–218.

Gutenberg, B. [1951]. PKKP, P'P', and the earth's core. *Trans. Am. Geophys. Union* **32**, 373–390.

Gutenberg, B. [1957]. The "boundary" of the earth's inner core. *Trans. Am. Geophys. Union* **38**, 750–753.

Gutenberg, B. [1958a]. Wave velocities in the earth's core. *Bull. Seismol. Soc. Am.* **48**, 301–314.

Gutenberg, B. [1958b]. Caustics produced by waves through the earth's core. *Geophys. J.* **1**, 238–248.

Hales, A. L. [1956]. The interior of the earth. *Trans. S. African Inst. Elec. Engrs.* **47**, 248–257.

Hide, R. [1956]. The hydrodynamics of the earth's core. *In* "Physics and Chemistry of the Earth" (L. H. Ahrens, K. Rankama, and S. K. Runcorn, eds.), Vol. 1, pp. 94–137, McGraw-Hill, New York.

Jacobs, J. A. [1956]. The interior of the earth. *Advances in Geophys.* **3**, 183–240.

Jeffreys, H. [1952]. "The Earth," 3rd ed., 392 pp. Cambridge Univ. Press, London and New York.

Jeffreys, H., and Bullen, K. E. [1940]. "Seismological Tables," 48 pp. Brit. Assoc. Advance. Sci., London.

Knopoff, L. [1959]. Velocity of sound in two-component systems. *J. Geophys. Research* **64**, 359–361.

Knopoff, L., and MacDonald, G. J. F. [1958]. The magnetic field and the central core of the earth. *Geophys. J.* **1**, 216–223.

Knopoff, L., and Uffen, R. J. [1954]. The densities of compounds at high pressures and the state of the earth's interior. *J. Geophys. Research* **59**, 471–484.

Kuhn, W., and Rittmann, A. [1941]. Über den Zustand des Erdinnern und seine Entstehung aus einem homogenen Urzustand. *Geol. Rundschau* **32**, 215–256.

Kuhn, W., and Vielhauer, S. [1953]. Beziehungen zwischen der Ausbreitung von Longitudinal- und Transversalwellen in relaxierenden Medien. *Z. physik. Chem. (Leipzig)* **202**, 124–190.

Lehmann, I. [1940]. On SKS. *Geodaet. Inst. Medd. København* **15**, 13 pp.

Lynch, J. [1937]. A new theory of the earth's core. *Trans. Am. Geophys. Union* **18**, 123–124.

MacDonald, G. J. F., and Knopoff, L. [1958]. On the chemical composition of the outer core. *Geophys. J.* **1**, 284–297.

Nelson, R. L. [1952]. A study of the seismic waves SKS and SKKS. Ph.D. thesis. Calif. Inst. Technol.; Condensed in [1954]. *Bull. Seismol. Soc. Am.* **44**, 39–55.

Ramsey, W. H. [1949]. On the nature of the earth's core. *Monthly Notices Roy. Astron. Soc. Geophys. Suppl.* **5**, 409–426.

Ramsey, W. H. [1950]. On the compressibility of the earth. *Monthly Notices. Roy. Astron. Soc. Geophys. Suppl.* **6**, 42–49.

Runcorn, S. K. [1954]. The earth's core. *Trans. Am. Geophys. Union* **35**, 49–62 (followed by discussion on pp. 63–78.)

Runcorn, S. K. [1956]. The magnetism of the earth's body. *In* "Encyclopedia of Physics" (S. Flügge, ed.), Vol. 47, pp. 498–533. Springer, Berlin.

Slichter, L. B. [1932]. The theory of the interpretation of seismic travel-time curves in horizontal structures. *Physics* **3**, 273–294.

Takeuchi, H. [1956]. The dynamo theory of the earth's main magnetic field. *J. Phys. Earth* **4**, 11–20.

Urey, H. C. [1952]. "The Planets." Yale Univ. Press, New Haven, Connecticut.

Vestine, E. H. [1954]. The earth's core. *Trans. Am. Geophys. Union* **35**, 63–72.

Wadati, K., and Masuda, K. [1934]. On the travel time of earthquake waves, pt. 6. *Geophys. Mag. (Tokyo)* **8**, 187–194.

6. Temperature and Thermal Processes in the Earth

6.1 Temperatures and Temperature Gradients at the Earth's Surface

6.1.1 Temperatures at the Surface

The average temperature at the earth's surface varies between roughly 0°C and −40°C in the region of the North Pole, roughly −10° and −50° in the region of the South Pole, and is about 26° throughout the year in the equatorial belt. The mean temperature at the earth's surface is about 15° with average variations of about 2° during the year.

The temperature at a given point at the earth's surface depends mainly on the radiation from the sun which reaches it and the angle with the surface at which the radiation arrives. Other quantities involved include the radiation back towards the sky and the heat exchange by air currents. The average solar heat flow reaching the ground in the continents is of the order of magnitude of 10^{-2} cal/cm² sec. Consequently, the heat flow from the earth's interior of the order of 10^{-6} cal/cm² sec (Section 6.3) is negligible in comparison. The temperature of ocean bottoms is controlled by the local temperature of the water, which in deep oceans is near 0°C.

6.1.2 Periodic Variations of the Temperature in the Uppermost Portion of the Crust

In the layers close to the surface in continents, all periodic changes of the temperature decrease about exponentially with depth. The amplitude a of the range of the temperature T at the depth z, and the delay of its extreme values can be estimated [Ingersoll *et al.*, 1948, p. 47] from

$$a = a_0 e^F \sin\left(\frac{2\pi T}{t} + F\right) \qquad (6.1)$$

where

$$F = - z \sqrt{\frac{\pi}{\kappa t}}$$

a_0 is the amplitude (range of temperatures) at the surface, t is the period under consideration (e.g., 1 year = 3.558×10^7 sec; 1 day = 86,400 sec), κ is the thermal diffusivity of the soil:

$$\kappa = k/\sigma\rho \tag{6.2}$$

where k is the heat conductivity, σ the heat capacity per unit mass, ρ the density. The range a^* of the temperature at the depth z is given by

$$a^* = a_0 e^{-z\sqrt{\pi/\kappa t}} \tag{6.3}$$

and the delay (lag) t_d of the extreme values of the temperature by

$$t_d = \tfrac{1}{2}z \sqrt{\frac{t}{\pi\kappa}}. \tag{6.4}$$

Table 6.1 shows that observations of the yearly changes in temperature at a given depth are fairly well represented by these equations. Selected values of κ and of F are given in Tables 6.2 and 6.3 respectively.

TABLE 6.1. ANNUAL RANGE OF TEMPERATURES AND TIME LAG OF EXTREME VALUES, CALCULATED FROM EQS. (6.3) AND (6.4), ASSUMING $\kappa = 0.0027$ CM²/SEC AND $a_0 = 28.2°C$, AND CORRESPONDING VALUES OBSERVED IN JAPAN. AFTER INGERSOLL et al. [1948], P. 52.

Depth m	Annual range, °C		Lag, days	
	Calculated	Observed	Calculated	Observed
0.0	—	28.2	0	0
0.6	19.2	18.7	21.6	9.0
3.0	4.6	5.2	106.0	93.5
7.0	0.4	0.4	247.0	267

TABLE 6.2. THERMAL DIFFUSIVITY κ IN CM²/SEC AFTER INGERSOLL et al. [1948, APPENDIX A].

Material	κ	Material	κ
Granite	0.013	Dry soil	0.003 ±
Limestone	0.008	Wet soil	≤0.01
Sandstone	0.011	Rock	0.01 ±

The daily temperature changes below the surface become negligible at a depth of the order of 1 m. Supposing $\kappa = 0.0049$, a range of 20°C at the surface is reduced to 1.4° at a depth of 30 cm, and to less than 0.004° at a

TABLE 6.3. FACTOR F IN EQ. (6.1) FOR $t = 1$ YEAR, AFTER ORSTRAND [1951].

Depth, m	κ, cm²/sec		
	0.0031 (dry soil)	0.0064 (crustal rocks)	0.0133 (sandstone)
1.52	0.422	0.548	0.659
4.57	0.075	0.165	0.286
10.67	0.0024	0.015	0.054

depth of 1 m. [Ingersoll et al., 1948, p. 50]. At a depth of 30 cm the calculated time lag is about 10 hours. All such calculated values agree substantially with observations.

6.1.3 Thermal Gradients in Continents

In continents, thermal gradients have been determined by measuring the temperature at various depths in many bore holes. Usually, maximum thermometers are used, frequently in water, but often in stable air, if possible several at the same time during several hours; means obtained during several periods of measurements are averaged. The gradients differ widely from region to region as well as with depth, depending mainly on the thermal conductivity. Occasionally, heat sources play a role, for example volcanic heat [Lovering, 1955] or material with relatively high radioactivity. Other disturbing factors include variations in temperature during former glacial periods [Birch, 1954b].

Orstrand [1951] has collected many results of temperature gradient measurements. If the temperature T is measured in degrees centigrade, as usually in this chapter, the gradients show values of dT/dz between more than 0.1 deg/m to less than 0.01 deg/m. This corresponds to a range for the reciprocal dz/dT between less than 10 to over 100 m/deg. Frequently, 30 m/deg is taken as a representative value. Most of the determinations have been made in areas of commercial interest (drilling of oil wells), which means that many results have been obtained in geologically disturbed areas, but relatively few in regions of geophysical interest. For the problem of the loss of heat into the interstellar space the heat flow through the surface (Section 6.3) is of much greater importance than the thermal gradient.

6.1.4 Thermal Gradients in Ocean Bottoms

A method of measuring the thermal gradient in the ocean bottom has apparently first been tried out by Petterson [1949]. During the following years the method has been used by Bullard and associates [1956] in the Pacific and Atlantic Oceans. This method is based on the measurement of the temperature difference in the ocean bottom along a vertical probe which, in the experiments described, was about $\frac{1}{2}$ m long and about 3 cm in diameter. The temperature difference "is measured by a thermistor bridge and amplifier or by thermo-junctions connected to a galvanometer." In the experiments, the probe was first left about 100 m above the ocean bottom for about 15 min, then pushed into the bottom at a speed of 2–3 m/sec and left in the bottom for 30–40 min. The behavior of the probe was studied in detail experimentally and theoretically [Bullard, 1954b]. Bullard et al., [1956, p. 159] estimate that under favorable circumstances the errors in the resulting temperature gradient do not exceed 3%.

Maxwell and Revelle [1956, p. 396] have reported 15 gradients measured in the bottom of the Pacific Ocean. They are between about 0.021 and 0.215 deg/cm, with an average of 0.08; the reciprocal is 13 m/deg. Bullard [1954b] has reported five gradients observed in the North Atlantic Ocean; they are between 0.024 and 0.055 deg/cm with an average of 0.04; the reciprocal is 26 m/deg. Herzen [1959] has reported that the range of heat flow through the ocean bottoms (0.14×10^{-6} to 8.09×10^{-6} cal/cm^2 sec) seems to be greater than that through the surface in the continents (See p. 130).

6.2 Thermal Conductivity in the Earth

6.2.1 Thermal Conductivity in the Crust

Methods of measuring the thermal conductivity k of rocks in the laboratory have been described for example by Birch and Clark [1940], by Bullard and Niblett [1951], and by Beck and Beck [1958]. The thermal conductivity of a given sample decreases for most rocks with increasing temperature. For samples from ocean bottoms the water content is important, so that such samples must be protected against changes in water content. Bullard [1954b, p. 425] refers to a red clay from the bottom of the Pacific Ocean, in which k decreased from 0.0027 to 0.0020 cal/cm deg sec as the water content increased from 32 to 50% of the wet weight.

From data published mainly by Birch and Clark [1940] and by Birch

[1942] it follows that k is about 0.005 cal/cm deg sec for many rocks in the crust, but near 0.01 for ultrabasic rocks. Birch and Clark [1940, p. 228] have found about 0.012 for olivine and pyroxene at 0° and 0.008 cal/cm deg sec at 200°. For the top of the sediments in the bottom of the Atlantic Ocean, Bullard [1954b, p. 421] has observed values between 0.0023 and 0.0027 cal/cm deg sec, while Maxwell and Revelle [1956, p. 396] have reported values between 0.0016 and 0.0025 for the top layer of the sediments in the Pacific Ocean.

6.2.2 "Thermal Conductivity" in the Mantle

The transmission of heat inside the earth involves three major processes: conduction (coefficient k_1), radiation (coefficient k_2), and subcrustal flow of material. While under the conditions in the earth's crust the heat transfer by radiation is negligible, it becomes increasingly important with increasing depth as T^3, the third power of the absolute temperature, enters the equations. Frequently, the coefficient k_2 indicating the amount of radiation in this connection, is called "coefficient of radiative conductivity." We write

$$k = k_1 + k_2. \tag{6.5}$$

Both, k_1 and k_2, must be calculated theoretically for the earth's interior. The resulting values for both depend not only on assumptions made as basis for the theory, but also on assumed numerical values of physical constants in the earth's interior. Consequently, at best the order of magnitude of the resulting value of k can be given. This is one of the reasons for the relatively great uncertainty in our knowledge of the temperature in the deep portions of the mantle and, consequently, in the core.

Apparently, Birch and Clark [1940, p. 541] were the first to point out the possible importance of radiative heat in the earth's mantle. Recently, effects of radiative heat on temperature changes in the earth have been studied, e.g., by Preston [1956], Clark [1957], Lubimova [1958], and by Lawson and Jamieson [1958]. On the basis of theoretical discussions of radiative transfer of heat by Van der Held [1952] and others, Clark [1957, p. 936] arrived at the following approximate equation

$$k_2 = \frac{16n^2 K T^3}{3\omega} \tag{6.6}$$

where n is the refractive index, K is the Stefan–Boltzmann constant, T is the absolute temperature, and ω is the opacity which indicates the absorption. For calculations, Clark has used $n = 1.7$, he has assumed that the increase in ω with the absolute temperature T from its value ω_0 at low temperatures depends on the electric conductivity σ and that approximately

$$\omega = \omega_0 + \frac{120\pi\sigma_0\epsilon^{-E/2KT}}{n}. \tag{6.7}$$

In addition, Clark has assumed that the electric conductivity σ does not depend on ω and, consequently, that σ is equal to its value σ_0 at low temperatures. For σ_0 he has taken about 10 ohm^{-1} cm^{-1}. E is the width of the energy gap of the crystal, about 3 ev, ϵ is the electronic charge, K is Boltzmann's constant. Clark finally has used the following equation to calculate k_2 (Table 6.4)

$$k_2 = \frac{22 \times 10^{-12}T^3}{\omega_0 + 2200\epsilon^{-3/2KT}} \tag{6.8}$$

TABLE 6.4. COEFFICIENT k_2 OF RADIATIVE CONDUCTIVITY IN CAL/CM SEC DEG CALCULATED FOR DIFFERENT TEMPERATURES T (IN DEGREES ABSOLUTE) BY CLARK [1957], FROM EQ. (6.8); ω_0 IS THE OPACITY PER CM AT LOW TEMPERATURES.

T	k_2		
	$\omega_0 = 5$	$\omega_0 = 10$	$\omega_0 = 30$
500°	0.001	0.000	0.000
1000	0.004	0.002	0.001
2000	0.032	0.017	0.006
2500	0.048	0.028	0.011

Clark [1957, p. 936] concludes that for $\sigma = 1$ ohm^{-1} cm^{-1}, a temperature of a greater order than 3000° abs is required to make the radiative conductivity greater than the ordinary conductivity is at room temperature. However Clark [1957, p. 937] points out that he has discussed the contribution of radiation to the heat transfer in the earth "in perhaps more detail than available data warrant. . . . The question is the importance of the effect rather than its existence."

The importance of radiative conduction in the earth has also been studied by Lawson and Jamieson [1958]. They have made assumptions similar to those of Clark, but they do not suppose that $\sigma(\omega)$ is constant and approximately equal to σ_0, nor do they believe that it is justifiable to neglect the effect of pressure on the refraction index n. They assume that n is given by $c\rho + 1$, where such a value for the constant c is to be chosen that at a depth of 33 km $n = 1.7$; they also try to introduce other corrections. For the opacity ω they have calculated values ranging from 0.1/cm at a depth of 400 km to 3.8/cm at 2900 km, if the absolute temperature T is 1000°, and from 0.26/cm at 400 km to 17/cm at a depth of 2900 km if it is 5000°. The corresponding values of k_2 range from about $\frac{1}{4}$ cal/deg cm sec at depths of between about 400 and 1000 km and $T = 1000°$ abs to about 10 at $T = 5000°$ abs; from 0.1 to $1\frac{1}{2}$ at a depth of 1800 km and temperatures of 1000° and 5000° respectively; and from 0.01 to about $\frac{1}{4}$ cal/deg cm sec if the same temperatures exist at the boundary of the core. Lawson and Jamieson conclude that "the effective conductivity of the earth's mantle can be of the order of magnitude of 0.5 to 2.0 cal/deg cm sec from about 400 km to the base, i.e., of the same order of magnitude as in the liquid core. . . . The desirability of more accurate data is immediately apparent."

Lubimova [1958] has used for k_2 the same equation (6.6) as Clark and has assumed that

$$k_1 \sim KNuA \left(\frac{Mu^2}{T}\right)^{3/4}$$ (6.9)

where N is the number of elementary cells in 1 cm^3, M is the mass of a cell, and A a lattice constant; u is given by

$$\frac{1}{u^3} = \frac{1}{3}\left(\frac{1}{V^3} + \frac{2}{v^3}\right)$$ (6.10)

where V and v are the velocities of longitudinal and transverse waves respectively. Lubimova finds

$$k = k_1 + k_2 = B\rho^{2/3} \frac{u^{1/2}}{T^{5/4}} + \frac{16n^2KT^3}{3\omega}$$ (6.11)

where B is a constant to be determined from the surface conditions and ρ is the density. Contrasting with Clark, she finds that, except for the uppermost portion of the mantle, the temperature in the interior of the earth has increased with time, and that, consequently, the thermal conductivity has also increased.

Characteristic values for the total conductivity which she has calculated are given in Table 6.5. Lubimova has found that k has a minimum near the earth's surface, which has increased from about 0.003 cal/deg cm sec, roughly 3×10^9 years ago, to about 0.005 cal/deg cm sec at present, and that this minimum has been approaching the earth's surface, where k is 0.006 cal/deg cm sec. This minimum of k near the earth's surface is very important, since its magnitude and extension controls the cooling or heating up of the earth's mantle (Sections 6.8 and 6.9). Lubimova [1958, p. 131] points out "that thermal conductivity of the first hundred kilometers is determined by its molecular component, which decreases as the temperature rises and thereby prevents considerable heat losses in spite of high conductivity of the earth's interior."

All those who have tried to calculate the heat conductivity k in the earth agree that the theory itself as well as the numerical constants involved may contain appreciable errors. Verhoogen [1956, pp. 23, 24] points out that "unfortunately the prediction of the thermal conductivity of a dielectric substance and its variations with pressure and temperature constitutes one of the most difficult problems in solid state physics." "If, as appears

TABLE 6.5. THERMAL CONDUCTIVITY $k = k_1 + k_2$ IN CAL/DEG CM SEC AFTER LUBIMOVA [1958, FIG. 7] ASSUMING $k = 0.006$ AT THE SURFACE AND EQ. (6.11) INSIDE THE EARTH'S MANTLE AT DIFFERENT TIMES AFTER SOLIDIFICATION; FOR THE ASSUMED TEMPERATURE INSIDE THE EARTH, SEE FIG. 6.1.

Depth km	Time, 10^9 years			
	0.4	1.2	1.6	4.5
40	0.004	0.003	0.004	0.007
200	0.0065	0.007	0.009	0.014
1000	0.016	0.020	0.028	0.035
1500	0.018	0.024	0.034	0.041
2000	0.020	0.028	0.040	0.047

possible, the thermal conductivity at great depths is ten or twenty times larger than the accepted values, all numerical calculations regarding the thermal history of the earth may need to be revised." Lubimova [1958, p. 127] believes that "the most uncertain value is the coefficient of absorption ω, which is very sensitive to the increase of T and the radiation frequency." Unfortunately, the temperature T, which enters with the third power Eqfs. (6.8) and (6.11)) and its changes during the earth's history (Section (6.7) are very uncertain.

There is general agreement, that we can expect noticeably greater thermal conductivity at a depth of 1000 km than in the crust. While Lubimova arrives at factors of 10 or more, Clark points out that the amount of the increase is still uncertain. Uffen [1952] has combined a simplified Debye theory of the thermal conductivity of solids with seismic data and with recent estimates of the temperature variations to compute the ratio of "the lattice conductivity at any depth to that at 100 km depth. . . . It is found that the lattice conductivity and diffusivity increase between the surface and the bottom of the mantle by factors of approximately eight and four respectively" [Uffen, 1954].

Many of the preceding data have been given here in detail to show the relatively great uncertainty of the results about heat conductivity in the mantle. This is one of the main reasons for the relatively large differences between the curves for the temperature as function of depth which have been found by various authors for the deep interior of the earth.

6.2.3 Thermal Conductivity in the Core

It is usually assumed that the core consists mainly of metals, in which, according to the Wiedemann–Franz law,

$$k_1 = 3 \left(\frac{K}{\epsilon}\right)^2 T\lambda \tag{6.12}$$

where K is the Boltzmann constant, ϵ the electron charge, λ the electronic conductivity, and T the absolute temperature. Lubimova [1958, p. 126] points out that in metals λ changes proportional to T^{-1}, so that k_1 should be approximately constant in the core if it consists of metals. On the other hand, k_2 should be relatively small, since the absorption of radiative energy in metals is large; ω reaches 10^5/cm. Lubimova [1958, p. 126] has taken 0.5 cal/deg cm sec for the heat conductivity k in the core.

6.3 Heat Flow through the Earth's Surface

If k is the thermal conductivity in cal/deg cm sec, T the temperature, and z the depth in cm, the heat flux Q through the earth's surface is given in cal/cm² sec by

$$Q = -k \frac{dT}{dz}. \tag{6.13}$$

The minus sign indicates upward flow and is usually disregarded. In Table 6.6 absolute values for Q are listed. In addition to observational errors in the determination of k and dT/dz, errors may result from the fact that repeatedly k has not been determined exactly at the same place as dT/dz, or that an average of k for an extended region has been used.

If irregularities in relatively small areas or belts are disregarded, it follows as main result of the determinations of Q which are now available, that within the present limits of error the average heat flow is the same through the surface of continents as that through ocean bottoms. This is contrary to the theoretical expectations in the past which had been based on the radioactive heat developed in rock samples during laboratory experiments. Since these had shown that in granites much more heat is developed from the decay of radioactive elements than in basalts, and more in basalts than in ultrabasic rocks, it had been expected that the heat flow through the ocean bottom, where granitic rocks are missing, should be

TABLE 6.6. OBSERVED HEAT FLOW Q THROUGH THE EARTH'S SURFACE IN
CONTINENTS AND THROUGH OCEAN BOTTOMS IN 10^{-6} CAL/CM^2 SEC.
n = NUMBER OF OBSERVATIONS

Region	Q		n	Author (A) or Reference (R)
	Range	Average		
Continents				
California		1.3	1	A: Benfield [1947]
California		0.73 ± 0.01	15	A: Clark [1957]
Colorado	1.0–1.7	1.3	3	A: Birch [1947, 1954a]
Texas		2.0	1	A: Birch and Clark [1940]
Canada	0.7–1.3	0.95	11	R: Bullard [1954a]
Great Britain	1.2–1.9	1.5	4	A: Benfield [1939]
Great Britain	1.1–2.1	1.50 ± 0.08	8	R: Jeffreys [1952, p. 282]
Great Britain		1.57	17	A: Chadwick [1956]
Great Britain	1.5–2.9	2.2	6	A: Bullard and Niblett [1951]
Great Britain		1.2	2	A: Bullard and Niblett [1951]
Swiss Alps	1.6–2.2	1.9	3	A: Clark and Niblett [1956]
South Africa	0.8–1.5	1.52	7	R: Bullard [1954a]
Japan		2.05	1	A: Uyeda et al. [1958]
Iran	0.5–1.2	0.9	18	R: Bullard [1954a]
Tasmania	2.0–2.5	2.2	5	R: Jacobs [1956a]
Ocean bottoms				
Atlantic Ocean	0.6–1.4	1.0	5	A: Bullard [1954b]
Atlantic Ocean	0.6–1.4	0.9	8	A: Bullard et al. [1956]
Pacific Ocean	0.7–5.3	1.5	25	A: Bullard et al. [1956]
Eniwetok		1.0 ± 0.2	1	A: Birch [1956]

appreciably smaller than the heat flow through the continental surfaces (Section 6.5). Actually, according to Bullard et al., [1956], 16 out of 25 determinations of heat flow through the bottom of the Pacific Ocean are within 50% of the value 1.2×10^{-6} cal/cm^2 sec, which is considered to be the average for the continents. Bullard, Maxwell, and Revelle list three unusually high values (2.7, 3.6, and 5.3, all times 10^{-6} cal/cm^2 sec) in the general region of the Albatross Plateau in the eastern Pacific Ocean, while relatively small values (0.25, 0.5, 0.7, and 0.8, all times 10^{-6} cal/cm² sec) have been observed over in the Acapulco Trench.

If we assume a heat flow of 1.2×10^{-6} cal/cm² sec for the whole earth, the total heat flow through the earth's surface (including ocean bottoms) is about 6×10^{12} cal/sec, or 2×10^{20} cal/year.

6.4 Heat Emitted by Volcanoes and Heat Generated by Earthquake Waves

Heat losses of the earth consist almost completely of the approximately 6×10^{12} cal/sec conducted through the crust. Lotze [1927] has considered a loss of heat from volcanic eruptions of the order of 2×10^{10} cal/sec for the earth, while Verhoogen [1946] has estimated that the average heat which has escaped during volcanic activity since pre-Cambrian is of the order of 3×10^9 cal/sec.

The energy transmitted by earthquake waves seems to be of the order of 10^{25} ergs/year [Gutenberg, 1956]. This corresponds to the energy of a heat flow of the order of 10^{10} cal/sec. However, the resulting effect is probably mainly to transfer energy from one relatively small area to other portions of the crust or deeper into the earth, where it is converted again to heat by frictional processes during the propagation of the earthquake waves.

6.5 Generation of Heat in the Earth

The temperature which is calculated for the interior of the earth depends mainly, (a) on the temperature distribution with depth which is assumed for an arbitrary starting point, for example, for the time when the distribution of material inside the earth had approached such an approximation to equilibrium that no processes of redistribution of material on a large scale existed any longer; (b) on the assumed generation of heat inside the earth; (c) on the assumed transfer of heat by conduction and radiation inside the earth; and (d) on the assumed heat transfer by subcrustal currents. We are going to consider now problems related to (b), the generation of heat inside the earth. The main source by far is the development of heat during the decay of radioactive material which decreases with time, depending on the life of the various radioactive elements involved. This is one of the fundamental problems in the investigation of the earth's history, and it is intended for detailed presentation in another volume of the present series.

The main difficulty in estimating the heat developed from radioactive sources in the earth as a function of depth and time lies in the fact that we have only samples of rocks from the uppermost portion of the earth's crust, so that we cannot expect accurate results for the heat produced in this way in the earth's interior. Geochemical research has given strong indications that during the early history of the earth the main radioactive elements had accumulated in the uppermost portion of the earth, and some other evidence, for example, the very small content of radioactive material in iron meteorites, points in the same direction.

The amount of heat which is produced by a given element in a given layer of the earth in a unit of time depends on the amount of this element in gram per gram of each of the various rock types in the layer, the heat production per second in one gram of the element during its decay, and the relative amount of each rock type in the layer. The density of the rock types must be introduced to convert mass into volume.

Characteristic results are listed in Tables 6.7 to 6.9. Table 6.10 gives

TABLE 6.7. HEAT PRODUCTION IN CAL/G SEC IN VARIOUS ELEMENTS.
AFTER BULLARD [1954a, P. 109] AND JACOBS [1956a, P. 215].

Bullard		Jacobs	
Element	Heat production	Element	Heat production
Uranium	2.34×10^{-8}	U^{238}	2.33×10^{-8}
		U^{235}	14.9×10^{-8}
Thorium	0.63×10^{-8}	Th^{232}	0.67×10^{-8}
Potassium	8.5×10^{-13}	K^{40}	0.67×10^{-8}
		K	8.2×10^{-13}

examples of the relatively large differences which are found in a given rock type, while Table 6.11 shows heat produced in 1 cm³ as a function of depth assuming a specific structure of the earth with continental crust. Finally Table 6.12 gives an indication of the order of magnitude of the change in heat production during the earth's history.

Since all the calculations are based on an accumulation of various assumptions, the final results differ greatly. Lubimova [1958, p. 120] has given a series of curves showing the decrease of heat generation during the earth's history on the basis of various assumptions. They range from a maximum of about 30×10^{-16} to a minimum [according to Urey 1955] of

TABLE 6.8. CONCENTRATION OF RADIOACTIVE ELEMENTS IN DIFFERENT ROCK TYPES AND IN METEORITES IN G/G. AFTER BULLARD [1954a, p. 108] AND JACOBS [1956b, p. 396].

Material	Bullard			Jacobs				
	U	Th	K	U^{238}	U^{235}	Th^{232}	K^{40}	K
Granitic	4×10^{-6}	13×10^{-6}	0.035	2.9×10^{-6}	2.1×10^{-8}	10^{-7}	3.1×10^{-6}	0.026
Intermediate				1.4×10^{-6}	1.0×10^{-8}	4.3×10^{-6}	1.3×10^{-6}	0.011
Basaltic	1×10^{-6}	3×10^{-6}	0.013	0.9×10^{-6}	0.65×10^{-8}	3.2×10^{-6}	1.1×10^{-6}	0.009
Ultrabasic	2×10^{-8}	(6×10^{-8})	3×10^{-4}					
Dunite				1.3×10^{-8}	0.96×10^{-10}	4.6×10^{-8}	1.2×10^{-9}	10^{-5}
Stony meteorites	3×10^{-8}	10×10^{-8}	2×10^{-3}					
Iron meteorites	$\frac{1}{2} \times 10^{-8}$	4×10^{-8}	0					

TABLE 6.9. HEAT PRODUCED IN DIFFERENT ROCK TYPES AND IN METEORITES; (a) IN 10^{-14} CAL/G SEC, (b) IN 10^{-14} CAL/CM³ SEC.

Material	After Bullard [1945a]					After Birch [1951, p. 119]			
	(a)				(b)	(a)			
	U	Th	K	total	total	U	Th	K	total
Granitic	9.2	8.2	3.0	20	53	9.2	8.2	3.5	20.9
Basaltic	2.3	1.9	1.1	5.3	15	2.2	1.9	0.95	5.1
Ultrabasic	0.05	(0.04)	0.03	0.12	0.4				
Dunite						0.03	(0.07)	0.03	0.1
Stony meteorites	0.07	(0.06)	0.2	0.3	1.0				
Iron meteorites	0.012	0.025	0.0	0.04	0.3				

TABLE 6.10. HEAT PRODUCED (IN 10^{-14} CAL/CM^3 SEC) IN ROCK SAMPLES, AFTER JEFFREYS [1952, P. 280].

Rock type	Region	Heat
Granitic	Greenland, Iceland, Scotland, Ireland, Japan	51 ± 3
Granitic	Finland	145 ± 8
Granitic	Alps	149 ± 14
Basaltic	Greenland, Iceland, Scotland, Ireland	39 ± 2
Basaltic	England, Germany, France, Hungary	45 ± 3
Plateau basalts		26 ± 1
Island basalts		29 ± 6
Dunites		17 ± 2

TABLE 6.11. HEAT IN 10^{-6} CAL/CM^3 YEAR, PRODUCED IN ASSUMED LAYERS IN THE EARTH BELOW CONTINENTS AFTER JACOBS [1956a].

Depth, km	Assumed material	K	U^{238}	U^{235}	Th
0–15	Granitic	15	11	14	7.1
15–30	Acidic	6.9	5.4	7.1	3.1
30–45	to	6.1	3.7	4.8	2.3
45–60	basic	3.0	2.6	3.2	1.6
60–1600	Dunite	0.0085	0.069	0.091	0.046
1600–3000	Pallasite	0.013	0.059	0.076	0.039
3000–6371	Iron (Meteorite)	0.007	0.043	0.055	0.028

TABLE 6.12. HEAT EVOLVED IN THE EARTH, IN 10^{16} CAL/HR, ACCORDING TO TOMKEIEFF [1956, P. 239], CALCULATED BY VOITKEVICH [1950].

Element	Years before present time			
	0	2×10^9	3×10^9	4×10^9
Uranium	21.3	29.4	34.1	39.0
Actinouranium	0.9	6.3	17.3	43.4
Thorium	20.3	22.8	24.1	25.3
Potassium	4.7	19.5	39.5	80.4
Total	47.1	77.7	115.1	188.1

about 5×10^{-16} cal/cm^3 sec during the early history of the earth, about (4 to 5) $\times 10^9$ years ago, and between roughly 7×10^{-16} and $\frac{1}{4} \times 10^{-16}$ cal/cm^3 sec today. Thus, these estimates differ by factors of the order of magnitude of 10.

On the basis of the difference in structure between the continental and the oceanic crust, especially the lack of granitic material under ocean bottoms and the much thinner layer of basaltic material under the oceans than under the continents, it had been generally concluded from the available basic data on heat generation (e.g., Tables 6.8 to 6.10) that appreciably more heat should be produced in the uppermost $50\pm$ km of the earth below continents than under ocean bottoms. Consequently, it came as a great surprise when it was found (compare Section 6.3 and Table 6.6) that the heat flow through the ocean bottom is the same within the limits of error as that through the continental surface. At first, it was believed widely that the method of measuring the thermal gradient in the ocean bottom (Section 6.1.4) had a systematic error. This is being denied by the specialists, though it seems to have been impossible to apply the method which is used to measure the thermal gradient in the ocean bottom to measurements on land, for example, in deep lakes.

The possibility that the gradients in the ocean bottoms are affected by recent temperature changes in the water, has been considered by Bullard et al., [1956, p. 170]. They point out that the existing data on temperatures in the deep water near the ocean bottom "although scarce, suggest that the temperature changes in the past have never been sufficiently large to account for any significant proportion of the observed gradient." "The amount of heat generated in the sediments by radioactive decay is found to be of the order of 0.004 microcal/cm² sec." [Bullard et al., 1956, p. 171]. After discussing other processes, Bullard, Maxwell, and Revelle conclude that "the total heat liberated within the oceanic sediments will not exceed one per cent of the observed values."

After detailed discussion of various possibilities to account for the heat flow through the ocean bottom, Bullard et al., [1956, p. 178] suggest "that the radioactivity originally in the upper part of the mantle has been concentrated in the crust, allowing the continental heat to escape by conduction, while beneath the oceans the same amount of radioactivity is still distributed through the mantle and the heat is brought to the surface by convection or by unexpectedly high thermal conductivity."

Verhoogen [1956, p. 26] believes "that the radioactivity of continental masses has been largely overestimated. Granites may on the average be less radioactive than surface sampling suggests." This inference of Verhoogen is possibly supported by the result, mentioned above, that on the assumption of the usually adopted layering in the continents and of the heat developed in granites and basalts from radioactive decay, it is found that the heat generated in the crust of the continents would account approximately for the total heat flow through the surface of the continents. This has always been a disquieting conclusion. However, neither this suggestion nor that of Bullard, Maxwell, and Revelle can be considered a definite solution of the problem.

If we combine all results discussed in the present section, we must concede that at present we can find at best the order of magnitude of the heat generated at various depths in the earth by radioactive decay. The resulting numerical values cannot be expected to furnish reliable quantitative data for use in theoretical investigations of processes which involve decisively the amount of heat generated at various depths in the earth.

6.6 The Melting Points of Materials in the Earth

Volcanoes offer an opportunity to find the melting points of lavas at the earth's surface. In Table 6.13 characteristic values are listed. For

TABLE 6.13. TEMPERATURE T IN °C OF LAVAS, AFTER ORSTRAND [1951], BASED MAINLY ON WASHINGTON [1939].

Locality	T	Authorities
Kilauea	1200	Day and Shepherd; Jaggar
Vesuvius	1100–1200	Brun; Perret
Stromboli	1150	Brun
Etna	1060; 1300	Bartoli and Philipp, resp.
Sakura-jima	1050	Kato
Oshima	1200–1300	Tsuboi

greater depths, the increase of the melting point T^* with pressure p for a given phase of the material is given by the Clapeyron equation

$$dT^*/dp = \Delta W/\Delta S \qquad (6.14)$$

where $\Delta W/\Delta S$ is the ratio of the volume change to the entropy change at the melting point. Verhoogen [1956, p. 26] gives the following values for the initial slope of the curve for dT^*/dp in deg/1000 bars: Fosterite 4.7; diopside 13; albite 26; olivine not over 3.5.

The change dT^*/dp of the melting point T^* with increasing pressure p, corresponding to the increasing depth in the earth, has been discussed on various assumptions. Uffen [1952, p. 894] uses Lindemann's [1910] theory which relates the melting temperature T^* to a critical frequency of lattice oscillations which he calculates by use of Debye's theory of solids. Uffen obtains the following equation for the ratio of the melting point T_d^* at a depth d in the mantle to the melting point T_{100}^* at a depth of 100 km on the assumption that the material is uniform in the mantle between the depths of 100 and d km:

$$T_d^*/T_{100}^* = \Phi_d/\Phi_{100} \tag{6.15}$$

where Φ is given by Eq. (4.8). He also finds on other assumptions

$$\frac{T_d^*}{T_{100}^*} = \left[\frac{(v^3 + 2V^3)_{100}}{(v^3 + 2V^3)_d}\right]^{2/3} \left[\frac{(Vv)_d}{(Vv)_{100}}\right]^2 \tag{6.16}$$

where V and v are respectively the velocities of longitudinal and transverse waves. Application of Eqs. (6.15) and (6.16) requires that there is no change in material with depth in the mantle. This condition may not be fulfilled, as we have seen in Sections 4.3 and 4.4.

Simon [1953] has started from his detailed experimental research on the melting point of helium. He has based his calculations of the melting point in the earth's interior, especially in the core, on a semiempirical equation which he had developed earlier for the ratio T^* of the melting temperature at the pressure p to the melting temperature T_0^* at the normal pressure

$$p/a = (T^*/T_0^*)^c - 1. \tag{6.17}$$

Here a is a constant related to the internal pressure, and c a constant, for which Simon quotes values of 1.5 to 2 for substances held together by van der Waal's forces, but values of about 4 to 5 for alkali metals. Simon assumes $c = 4.5$ for iron. Simon finds that on the other hand

$$ac = L/\Delta W \tag{6.18}$$

where L is the heat of fusion, ΔW the change in volume during melting. On the basis of experimentally determined numerical values for the quantities involved, Simon finally uses for iron $ac = 600,000$ atm, (about 6×10^{11} dynes/cm^2) and $a = 150,000$ atm, $c = 4$. Clark [1958] has started to determine the constants a and c in Eq. (6.17) experimentally.

Bullard [1954a, p. 114] assumes that in the mantle $ac = 1.5 \times 10^{11}$ dynes/cm^2, and he believes that $c = 2$ is most likely. In a comparison between results from Uffen's and Simon's equations for the melting point in the portions of the mantle near the core boundary, Bullard refers to Uffen's calculations which give $T^* = 5000°$. On the other hand, Bullard calculates on the basis of Simon's equation (6.17) that $T^* = 6700°$, if he uses his own values for a and c. Bullard concludes that this difference of 1700° between the corresponding results "is an indication of the great uncertainty of calculations involving so large an extrapolation."

On the basis of a solution by Lindemann [1910], Gilvarry [1957, p. 86] gives the following equation for the ratio of the melting point T^* of a given material in the earth to its melting point T_0^* at the surface

$$\frac{T^*}{T_0^*} = \left(\frac{s^*}{s_0^*}\right)^2 \frac{k^*}{k_0^*} \frac{\rho_0^*}{\rho^*}. \tag{6.19}$$

The asterisks * refer to properties of the solid at melting. Especially, k^* is the bulk modulus, ρ^* the corresponding density; the subscript zero refers to the origin of the fusion curve, and s^* is a function of Poisson's ratio σ^*:

$$s^* = \left[\frac{3}{2(1+\sigma^*)}\right]^{\frac{1}{2}} \left[\frac{9/4\pi}{[2(1-\sigma^*)]^{-\frac{3}{2}} + 2[1-2\sigma^*]^{-\frac{3}{2}}}\right]^{\frac{1}{3}} \tag{6.20}$$

Finally, Jeffreys [1952, p. 272] has used the equation

$$\frac{dT^*}{dp} = \frac{T^*}{L}\left(\frac{1}{\rho_1} - \frac{1}{\rho_2}\right) \tag{6.21}$$

where ρ_1 and ρ_2 are the densities in the liquid and solid respectively and L is the latent heat of fusion.

Gilvarry [1957, p. 87] has calculated curves for the melting point in the mantle on various assumptions. For T^* he assumes about 1400°C at the top of the mantle and he finds on most assumptions values of about 5000° near the boundary of the core, with extremes of between 4000° and 9000°. However, these calculations assume homogeneity for the mantle.

Equation (6.18) cannot be applied directly to the core. Gilvarry [1957, p. 90] discusses various assumptions; for pure iron he finds fusion temperatures between about 3000° and 5000°C at the outer core boundary, increasing to values of between about 3500° and over 8000° in the earth's center. Simon [1953], who has tested his original equation (6.17) with laboratory experiments on helium, has concluded that at the pressure to be expected at the boundary between mantle and core the melting point of pure iron would be about 2800°C; his results give a melting temperature of about 3600° at the depth of the transition from the outer to the inner core and of about 3800° at the earth's center. Simon begins his conclusions by stating that "the limitations of our extrapolation need scarcely be emphasized."

After the preceding calculations had been made, Strong [1959] extended experimental determination of the melting point of iron to much greater pressures than had been used before. He found that the melting point of iron at a pressure of 96,000 atm is at 1740 ± 15°C, and that the curve for the observed melting points as a function of pressure up to 96,000 atm is well represented by Simon's equation (6.17) if $a = 75{,}000$ atm and $c = 8$.

By extrapolating to a pressure of 1.4×10^6 atm, Strong found that the melting point of iron near the core boundary is between 2300° and 2400°C. Since an increase in the value of c in equation (6.17) results in a smaller increase in the melting temperature T^* with increasing pressure p according to Eq. (6.17), it would follow that the melting point of iron at the transition from the outer to the inner core is several hundred degrees lower than that estimated by Simon (Fig. 6.1). If the inner core is solid iron, its temperature would be roughly 2500°C.

6.7 Calculated Temperature Changes in the Earth during its History

If we try to calculate the changes in temperature in the earth during its history, we have to introduce several poorly known quantities in addition to those which we have used in the preceding section. The first assumption which we have to make concerns the temperature in the earth as a function of depth for the time which we have selected as starting point. Here we have to make a decision concerning the problem whether the earth had originated as a cold or as a hot body. The next unknown quantity is the amount of heating during the earth's history from motion of heavy material towards the center [Urey, 1952, p. 163]. Moreover, we must consider the effects of other types of subcrustal currents during the earth's history.

Since the thermal conductivity in the earth during its history depends on the temperature as a function of depth, an assumption has to be made about the result of the investigation itself. Here we do not even know whether nearly the whole earth has been getting warmer during most of its history [Lubimova, 1958, p. 128], or only its deep interior, as it has been suggested by others, or if it is cooling nearly throughout. The answer to this question depends greatly on the assumptions which are made about the heat which is developed in the radioactive materials in the earth as a function of depth and time. The combined effects of errors in all assumptions involved in the answers to these and other fundamental questions cast considerable doubt on the accuracy of final results. The following are outlines of some basic investigations.

Slichter [1941, p. 574] gives the following equation for the transport of heat in a sphere of uniform heat conductivity, in which *convection* is occurring only in meridional planes

$$\rho c \frac{\partial T}{\partial t} = k \left(\frac{\partial^2 T}{\partial r^2} + \frac{2}{r} \frac{\partial T}{\partial r} \right) - \rho c \left(v_r \frac{\partial T}{\partial r} + \frac{v_\theta}{r} \frac{\partial T}{\partial \theta} \right) \tag{6.22}$$

where ρ is the density, c the specific heat, k the heat conductivity, v_r and v_Θ are the velocity components of the convection current. In general, the radial temperature gradient $\partial T/\partial r$ exceeds the transverse gradient $\partial T/r\,\partial\Theta$, and the convective term $\rho c v_r(\partial T/\partial r)$ represents the greater part of the convective transport of heat; the term $2k(\partial T/\partial r)/r$ gives the order of magnitude of the conductive transport. Slichter concludes that "convective cooling might easily predominate." However, too little is known about the hypothetical convection currents to estimate even the order of magnitude of their velocities.

Jeffreys [1952, p. 286] is mainly interested in the change in temperature in the uppermost 200 km of the earth, where the effect of convection currents on the temperature may be relatively small. Starting at a time when the cooling in the crust and upper mantle has become considerable, the problem may be taken as one of flow of heat in one dimension. The equation of heat conduction may then be written

$$\rho c \frac{\partial T}{\partial t} = \frac{\partial}{\partial z}\left(k\frac{\partial T}{\partial z}\right) + P_z \tag{6.23}$$

where P_z is the rate of generation of heat per unit volume as a function of the depth z. Jeffreys has assumed for some of his calculations that

$$P_z = Ae^{-z/H} \tag{6.24}$$

where A is the constant heat production in a surface layer of the thickness H. It appears that in this case roughly three quarters of the heat flow through the surface results from radioactive decay, and one quarter from the original heat.

In considering the effect of heat generation $P(r)$ by radioactive materials, Slichter [1941, p. 576] uses the radius $r = r_0 - z$ and finds

$$\rho k \frac{\partial T}{\partial t} = \frac{1}{r^2}\frac{\partial}{\partial r}\left(kr^2\frac{\partial T}{\partial r}\right) + P(r). \tag{6.25}$$

He introduces various assumptions about $P(r)$ and finds [Slichter, 1941, p. 594] that the heat flow due to the original temperature of the earth is of the order of 0.3×10^{-6} cal/cm² sec, or about one quarter of the total heat flow. Thus his results agree with those of Jeffreys within the limits which are introduced by the approximations used in the methods.

Lubimova [1958, p. 125] has solved Eq. (6.25) by use of an integrator. She has included her results on thermal conductivity (Section 6.2) and has assumed an originally "cold" earth (temperature in the core about 1000°C). Some of her results are included in Table 6.14 (b).

Jacobs [1956b, p. 391] writes

$$T(r,t) = T'(r,t) + T''(r,t) \qquad (6.26)$$

where T' satisfies the equation

$$\rho k \frac{\partial T'}{\partial t} = \frac{\partial k}{\partial r} \frac{\partial T'}{\partial r} + k \left(\frac{2}{r} \frac{\partial T'}{\partial r} + \frac{\partial^2 T'}{\partial r^2} \right). \qquad (6.27)$$

At the surface, $T' = 0$, and at the time $t = 0$, T' is the original distribution of temperature in the earth, given by $f(r)$. $T''(r,t)$ must satisfy an equation similar to (6.27) with an additional term $\sum_i h_i(r) e^{-\lambda_i t}$, where λ_i is the decay constant of the ith radioactive substance and $h_i(r)$ the corresponding initial heat production per unit volume. The boundary conditions are $T'' = 0$ for the surface at the time t, and $T'' = 0$ for $t = 0$. Jacobs has discussed possible solutions by summation of solutions for separate layers; for a solution on specific assumptions, see Table 6.14(a).

TABLE 6.14. CHANGE IN TEMPERATURE (IN °C) IN THE EARTH DURING INTERVALS OF 10^9 YEARS, (a) AFTER JACOBS AND ALLAN [1954] AND JACOBS [1956b, P. 398], SUPPOSING THE MODEL OF TABLE 6.11; (b) AFTER LUBIMOVA [1958, FIG. 6]. T_0 IS THE ASSUMED ORIGINAL TEMPERATURE (IN °C), t IS THE TIME SINCE THAT OF THE ASSUMED ORIGINAL TEMPERATURE DISTRIBUTION, IN 10^9 YEARS. ALL DATA GIVE ONLY THE ORDER OF MAGNITUDE.

t	Depth in km (a)				Depth in km (b)			
	50	500	1000	2900	500	1000	2900	5000
0–1	+600	+60	+100	+90	+1200	+1200	+1200	+1200
1–2	−300	+10	+60	+60	+ 500	+ 500	+ 900	+ 900
2–3	−150	−30	+40	+50	+ 100	+ 100	+ 500	+ 500
3–4	−110	−50	+30	+40	+ 200	+ 200	+ 500	+ 500
T_0	670	2310	2860	3960	400	550	800	1100

Until about 1950, it had been taken as granted by nearly all earth-scientists, that the earth is cooling throughout. After it had been pointed out, that the earth may have developed from a "cold" origin, the possibility of heating of the interior has been discussed, usually guardedly [Gutenberg, 1951, p. 162]. Recent calculations indicate that the upper portion of the mantle seems to be cooling at present (Table 6.14), but that its deeper portion as well as the core are probably getting hotter. Lubimova [1958, p. 131] considers it "significant that the outer layers [300 ± km] were not heated but rather cooled down during the last $(1 - 2) \times 10^9$ years." However, she believes that the heat loss in the outer lyers is not as great as has been suggested by many, since the "thermal conductivity of the upper first hundred kilometers is determined by its molecular component, which decreases as the temperature rises and thereby prevents considerable heat losses in spite of high conductivity in the earth's interior." Lubimova [1958, p. 116] finds that on the assumption of an originally molten earth any heat generation in the deep interior of the earth would be excluded.

Jacobs [1956a, p. 213] gives curves for the temperature changes with time for various depths on different assumptions for the layering and heat generation in the earth. Practically all show an increase in temperature in the crust and in the upper mantle during the first few hundred years, followed by cooling, while the deeper layers of the mantle and the core have been continuously getting hotter.

Verhoogen [1956, p. 38] points out that a temperature of the order of 3000° "at the core boundary is not consistent with an initially hot earth in conductive equilibrium." He finds that the temperature at the core boundary is of the order of 3000° to 4000°, if the core consists of iron. However, we should not be surprised if new results, for example on convection currents or on heat conductivity in the earth, will lead again to the hypothesis that a much greater portion of the earth is cooling than is found on the basis of the present data. One of the main obstacles to the conclusion that an appreciable portion of the earth's interior is cooling, is the relatively low thermal conductivity which has been calculated recently for the layers near the surface of the earth. If these layers of low conductivity exist, they must reduce greatly the outflow of heat from greater depths.

6.8 Estimated Temperatures in the Earth

The preceding discussions leave no doubt that all estimates of the temperature in the mantle and in the core are based on a number of equations and of numerical constants for most of which our information is based on far extrapolations. All calculations of the present temperatures in the earth in which temperature changes during the earth's thermal history are used, depend on the "original" temperature in the earth. While such assumptions do not affect appreciably the calculated temperature in the crust, they are a serious source of errors for the calculations of the temperatures in the mantle and core; these errors increase with the increase in depth in the earth for which the temperature is estimated.

Curves for the temperature as a function of depth in the earth which are based on the temperature calculated for fixed points in the earth, are affected by other sources of errors. For example, if the temperature at the hypothetical transition from solid to liquid iron at the boundary between outer and inner core is used to estimate the temperature there, the errors enter which are involved in the assumed melting point of iron as a function of depth in the core. Moreover, we have to consider that it is by no means certain that the transition from the outer to the inner core corresponds to the transition from liquid to solid material, and that there is doubt about the material in the core, which certainly is not pure iron.

The assumptions about the amount of heat generation from radioactive materials in the crust and in the uppermost portion of the mantle are another serious source of errors. One indication for this is the difficulty which has been encountered in the attempts to reconcile the observed nearly equal heat flow through continents and ocean bottoms with the calculated noticeably different heat flow through these two units on the basis of the heat development in rock samples (Section 6.5), so that hypotheses had to be developed with the specific purpose of removing these contradictions. Moreover, we have to consider that the heat transfer in large portions of the mantle is quite uncertain on account of the doubts about the magnitude of the radiative heat conduction, and that the unknown amount of heat transfer by convection had to be disregarded entirely.

A few curves for the temperatures (in °C) in the earth, which are based on recent estimates, are reproduced in Fig. 6.1 together with some curves for the fusion temperature as function of the depth in the earth. Most authors of the data on which the curves in Fig. 6.1 are based, have given several, sometimes appreciably different, sets of data or curves, of which those are entered in the figure which seem to have been preferred by their respective author. Verhoogen [1956, p. 39] has summarized estimates for the temperature published between 1915 and 1956 by 16 authors. For the core boundary, these temperatures vary from 1500° to 10,000°C. It is Verhoogen's opinion that no inconsistencies arise "from the assumption that the average gradient in the mantle is about 0.6°/km, the temperature at the core boundary being around 3000°C."

Miki [1954] has "derived several features of the temperature distribution within the earth's interior . . . from the modern theory of solids." On various assumptions he has found values of between 5000° and nearly 10,000° at the core boundary. Shima [1956] has calculated temperatures between about 3000° and nearly 7000° for this boundary on similar reasoning. Hughes [1955] has discussed the electric conductivity in the earth's mantle, and has concluded on this basis that the temperature at a depth of 1000 km is of the order of 3000°, and of the order of 10,000° at the core boundary, though "the extrapolation from the measured values is very great."

In 1911, Wiechert had pointed out in lectures, that the temperature in the earth's center must be less than 8000°, as otherwise the density in the core would be too small. Today, our results concerning the temperature in the deep portions of the earth are about as uncertain as the scientific

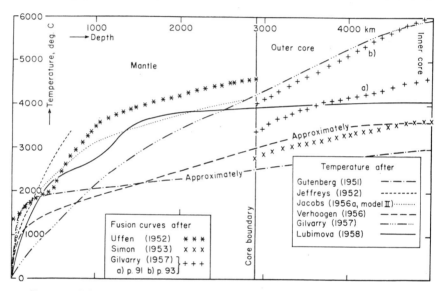

FIG. 6.1. Calculated fusion temperatures and estimated temperatures in the earth. Some curves are based on graphs preferred by the respective author, others are averages of several graphs or tables. All contain uncertain assumptions.

guesses in 1911. However, we see now more clearly the many sources of errors, among them the doubtful assumptions on which the fundamental calculations of the thermal conductivity in the earth's interior are based and the insufficient knowledge of the material in the earth and of its melting point as a function of depth. Even where the equations which are used are good approximations, frequently several numerical constants are uncertain. With this in mind, we may come to the following tentative conclusions: It seems that only the crust and perhaps portions of the outer mantle are cooling, while the whole deeper portions of the earth seem to be getting hotter. Considering that at least the outer core is molten, it does not seem likely that the temperature at the core boundary is less than about 2500°.

If the inner core is solid, the temperature there is probably not appreciably over 3500°C. On the other hand, Knopoff and MacDonald [1958, p. 221] find that the hypothesis of a strong magnetic field in the inner core leads to a temperature in excess of 4000° abs near the center of the earth.

It does not seem probable that the temperature increases much inside the core. On the basis of our present information, the author believes at the time of writing that the temperatures in the earth are probably somewhere between the curve of Gutenberg [1951] in Fig. 6.1 and that of Lubimova [1958].

6.9 Possibility of Molten Portions in the Upper Mantle; Roots of Volcanoes

The question has been raised frequently, if the volcanoes are outlets from an extended deep-seated molten portion in the earth's upper layers, or if they communicate with relatively small pockets of magma, and what role is played by the lowering of pressure in the volcano, if it erupts. The strong correlation of belts of earthquake foci at depths between about 60 and 200 km and belts of active volcanoes (Figs. 3.12, 3.13), the minimum (or lack of increase) in the velocity of elastic waves in the same depth range, and the proximity of the temperature and fusion curves (Fig. 6.1) in the upper portion of the mantle give support to the hypothesis that, at least in some regions, the rocks in this critical depth range may locally be molten.

Rittmann [1958] and Gorshkov [1958] have discussed the problem of the "roots of volcanoes" in more detail. Gorshkov [1958; see also summary, Gorshkov, 1958, pp. 26–28] finds that transverse waves arriving from Japanese earthquakes at seismological stations in Kamchatka (distance about 26°) are screened out somewhere along their path, if they pass under active volcanoes, but that they arrive properly at nearby stations if they miss the volcanic area on their path. Under the volcano, "The depth of the magmatic focus appears to be 50–60 km. . . . The solution of the problem on the depth of the magmatic focus and elastic constants of its substance, one of the cornerstones of volcanology, is considered to be preliminary." Thus far, there is no indication that similarly close approach of the temperature to the melting point occurs in the mantle at depths appreciably greater than roughly 200 km.

The results discussed in this section and the increasing evidence for the low-velocity layer centered at a depth of about 100 km (Section 4.2) strengthen the over half a century old concept of the asthenosphere (Section 3.1). Moreover, they support the hypothesis, pointed out by the author for about thirty years, that the viscosity and the resistance to plastic flow have a minimum in the upper portion of the earth's mantle, and that consequently the asthenosphere is the main locus of processes which produce movements of extended portions of the earth's crust relative to the mantle. This includes horizontal movements of blocks of the earth's crust relative to each other (Section 9.8) as well as the prevailingly vertical movements in the crust which maintain isostasy (Sections 3.7 and 3.8.5).

References

Beck, A. E., and Beck, J. M. [1958]. On the measurement of the thermal conductivities of rocks by observations on a divided bar apparatus. *Trans. Am. Geophys. Union* **39**, 1111–1123.

Benfield, A. E. [1939]. Terrestrial heat flow in Great Britain. *Proc. Roy. Soc.* **A173**, 428–450.

Benfield, A. E. [1947]. A heat flow value for a well in California. *Am. J. Sci.* **245**, 1–18.

Birch, F. [1942]. Thermal conductivity of rocks. *In* "Handbook of Physical Constants" (F. Birch, J. F. Schairer, and H. C. Spicer, eds.). *Geol. Soc. Am. Spec. Papers* **36**, 251–258.

Birch, F. [1947]. Temperature and heat flow in a well near Colorado Springs. *Am. J. Sci.* **245**, 733–753.

Birch, F. [1951]. Recent work on the radioactivity of potassium and some related geophysical problems. *J. Geophys. Research* **56**, 107–126.

Birch, F. [1954a]. The present state of geothermal investigations. *Geophysics* **19**, 645–659.

Birch, F. [1954b]. Thermal conductivity, climatic variation and heat flow near Calumet, Michigan. *Am. J. Sci.* **252**, 1–25.

Birch, F. [1956]. Heat flow at Eniwetok Atoll. *Bull. Geol. Soc. Am.* **67**, 941–942.

Birch, F., and Clark, H. [1940]. The thermal conductivity of rocks and its dependence upon temperature and composition. *Am. J. Sci.* **238**, 529–558, 613–635.

Bullard, E. C. [1954a]. The interior of the earth. *In* "The Earth as a Planet" (G. P. Kuiper, ed.), pp. 57–137. Univ. Chicago Press, Chicago, Illinois.

Bullard, E. C. [1954b]. The flow of heat through the floor of the Atlantic Ocean. *Proc. Roy. Soc.* **A222**, 408–429.

Bullard, E. C., and Niblett, E. R. [1951]. Terrestrial heat flow in England. *Monthly Notices Roy. Astron. Soc. Geophys. Suppl.* **6**, 222–238.

Bullard, E. C., Maxwell, A. E., and Revelle, R. [1956]. Heat flow through the deep sea floor. *Advances in Geophys.* **3**, 153–182.

Chadwick, P. [1956]. Heat-flow from the earth at Cambridge. *Nature* **178**, 105–106.

Clark, S. P. [1957]. Radiative transfer in the earth's mantle. *Trans. Am. Geophys. Union.* **38**, 931–938.

Clark, S. P. [1958]. Melting points of alkali halides at high pressure. *Carnegie Inst. Wash. Yearbook* **57**, 174–176.

Clark, S. P., and Niblett, E. R. [1956]. Terrestrial heat flow in the Swiss Alps. *Monthly Notices Roy. Astron. Soc. Geophys. Suppl.* **7**, 176–195.

Gilvarry, J. J. [1957]. Temperature in the earth's interior. *J. Atmospheric Terrest. Phys.* **10**, 84–95.

Gorshkov, G. S. [1958]. On some theoretical problems of volcanology. *Bull. volcanol.* [II] **19**, 103–113.

Gutenberg, B. [1951]. The cooling of the earth and the temperature in its interior. *In* "Internal Constitution of the Earth" (B. Gutenberg, ed.), 2nd ed., pp. 150–166. Dover, New York.

Gutenberg, B. [1956]. The energy of earthquakes. *Quart. J. Geol. Soc. London* **112**, 1–14.

Herzen, R. V. [1959]. Heat-flow values from the southeastern Pacific. *Nature* **183**, 882–883.

Hughes, H. [1955]. The pressure effect on the electrical conductivity of peridot. *J. Geophys. Research* **60**, 187–191.

Ingersoll, L. R., Zobel, O. J., and Ingersoll, A. C. [1948]. "Heat Conduction," 278 pp. McGraw-Hill, New York.

Jacobs, J. A. [1956a]. The interior of the earth. *Advances in Geophys.* **3**, 183–240.

Jacobs, J. A. [1956b]. The earth's interior. *In* "Encyclopedia of Physics (S. Flügge, ed.), Vol. 47, pp. 364–406. Springer, Berlin.

Jacobs, J. A., and Allan, D. W. [1954]. Temperature and heat flow within the earth. *Trans. Roy. Soc. Can. III* **48**, 33–39.

Jeffreys, H. [1952]. "The Earth," 3rd ed., p. 289. Cambridge Univ. Press, London and New York.

Knopoff, L., and MacDonald, G. J. F. [1958]. The magnetic field and the central core of the earth. *Geophys. J.* **1**, 216–223.

Lawson, A. W., and Jamieson, J. C. [1958]. Energy transfer in the earth's mantle. *J. Geol.* **66**, 540–551.

Lindemann, F. A. [1910]. The calculation of molecular vibration frequencies. *Physik. Z.* **11**, 609.

Lotze, F. [1927]. Die Joly'sche Radioaktivitätshypothese zur Erklärung der Gebirgsbildungen. *Nachr. Ges. Wiss. Göttingen Math. physik. Kl.* **1927**, 75–114.

Lovering, T. S. [1955]. Temperatures in and near intrusions. *Econ. Geol.* **50**, 249–281.

Lubimova, H. A. [1958]. Thermal history of the earth with consideration of the variable thermal conductivity of its mantle. *Geophys. J.* **1**, 115–134.

Maxwell, A. E., and Revelle, R. [1956]. Heat flow through the Pacific Ocean basin. *Publs. Bur. Central Seismol. Intern. Trav. Sci. (A)* **19**, 395–405.

Miki, H. [1954]. Temperature distributions within the earth. *J. Phys. Earth* **2**, 1–4.

Orstrand, C. E. van [1951]. Observed temperatures in the earth's crust. *In* "Internal Constitution of the Earth" (B. Gutenberg, ed.), 2nd ed., pp. 107–149. Dover, New York.

Petterson, H. [1949]. Exploring the bed of the ocean. *Nature* **164**, 468–470.

Preston, F. W. [1956]. Thermal conductivity in the depths of the earth. *Am. J. Sci.* **254**, 754–757.

Rittmann, A. [1958]. Physico-chemical interpretation of the terms magma, migma, crust and substratum. *Bull. volcanol.* [II] **19**, 85–102.

Shima, M. [1956]. Temperature distribution within the mantle. *J. Phys. Earth* **4**, 49–51.

Simon, F. E. [1953]. The melting of iron at high pressures. *Nature* **172**, 746.

Slichter, L. B. [1941]. Cooling of the earth. *Bull. Geol. Soc. Am.* **52**, 561–600.

Strong, H. M. [1959]. Fusion curve of iron to 96,000 atmospheres: Temperature of the earth's core. *Nature* **183**, 1381–1382. See also [1959]. The experimental fusion curve of iron to 96,000 atmospheres. *J. Geophys. Research* **64**, 653–659.

Tomkeieff, S. I. [1956]. Geochemistry in the U.S.S.R. (1948–1953). *In* "Physics and Chemistry of the Earth" (L. H. Ahrens, K. Rankama, and S. K. Runcorn, eds.), Vol. 1, pp. 235–284. McGraw-Hill, New York.

Uffen, R. J. [1952, 1954]. A method of estimating the melting point gradient in the earth's mantle. *Trans. Am. Geophys. Union* **33**, 893–896; *ibid.* **35**, 380–381.

Urey, H. C. [1952]. "The Planets," 245 pp. Yale Univ. Press, New Haven, Connecticut.

Urey, H. C. [1955]. The cosmic abundances of potassium, uranium and thorium and the heat balances of the Earth, the Moon and Mars. *Proc. Natl. Acad. Sci. U. S.* **41**, 127–144.

Uyeda, S., Ukutake, T., and Tanaoka, I. [1958]. Studies of the thermal state of the earth. I: Preliminary report of terrestrial heat flow in Japan. *Bull. Earthquake Research Inst. Tokyo Univ.* **36**, 251–272.

Van der Held, E. F. M. [1952]. The contribution of radiation to the conduction of heat. *Appi. Sci. Research* **A3**, 237–249.

Verhoogen, J. [1946]. Volcanic heat. *Am. J. Sci.* **244**, 745–771.

Verhoogen, J. [1956]. Temperatures within the earth. *In* "Physics and Chemistry of the Earth" (L. H. Ahrens, K. Rankama, S. K. Runcorn, eds.), Vol. 1, pp. 17–43. McGraw-Hill, New York.

Voitkevich, G. V. [1950]. Radioactivity of potassium and the thermal regime of the earth (in Russian). *Doklady Akad. Nauk. S.S.S.R.* **74**, 771–773.

Washington, H. S. [1939]. Temperature of lavas. *In* "Internal Constitution of the Earth" (B. Gutenberg, ed.), 1st ed., pp. 99–100. McGraw-Hill, New York.

7. Density, Pressure, Gravity, and Flattening in the Earth

7.1 The Mean Density of the Earth

Equations for the mean density ρ_m of the earth have been given already in the 19th century [e.g., Helmert, 1884, p. 83], most of them with a higher approximation than corresponds to the accuracy of the present data for the numerical constants involved. Lambert [1951, p. 341] uses one of Helmert's equations in the form

$$\rho_m = \frac{3g_e}{4\pi aG}\left(1 + \frac{3}{2}f + \frac{3}{7}f\alpha\right) \tag{7.1}$$

where

$$f = \omega^2 a/g_e$$

g_e is the gravity at the equator, a the equatorial radius of the earth, G the gravitational constant, α the flattening of the earth, and ω the angular velocity of the earth's rotation in radians/sec. If the internationally accepted ellipsoid is used for the earth, $f = 0.003468$. As g_e and a are known within better than 1 in 10,000, and α enters only in a term forming a small correction, the determination of the earth's mean density depends mainly on the determination of G.

Determinations of G (or ρ_m or of the mass of the earth) have already been attempted, nearly 200 years ago, by use of observations of deviations of the plumb line near mountains of known form and mass. Later, the difference in gravity over a lake, in one observation filled with water and in another empty, has been used to find G, or the change in gravity with depth in a mine. More accurate values have been obtained by the determination of the attraction which a given mass (up to over 5000 kg) exerts upon a balance or a torsion balance; for details, see, e.g., Hopfner [1936,pp. 283–286] or Jones [1954, p. 19]. On the basis of recent laboratory experiments G has been found to be $(6.670 \pm 0.005) \times 10^{-8}$ dynes cm^2/g^2 [Lindsay, 1957].

The value for ρ_m, the mean density of the earth, which had been proposed internationally in 1924 but had not been adopted, is 5.526 g/cm³. The value which has been used for about 30 years [Hopfner, 1936, p. 286] and still is considered best by many [e.g., Jones, 1954, p. 20] is 5.52 g/cm³. According to Lambert [1951, p. 341], ρ_m is 5.51 to 5.52. Heiskanen [1957, section 2, p. 101] gives 5.517 g/cm³.

7.2 Equations Used in the Determination of the Density in the Earth as a Function of Depth

Unfortunately, the density ρ in the earth (supposed to be spherical) cannot be found uniquely as a function of the radius r from observations at the surface. However, there are several conditions which must be fulfilled by any function $\rho(r)$. (1) It must give the correct density for the uppermost layers which is usually assumed to be about 2.8 in the crust and 3.3 at the top of the mantle (see Section 3.7). (2) It must give the correct mean density ρ_m for the earth

$$\rho_m = \frac{3}{r_0^3} \int_0^{r_0} \rho r^2 \, dr = 5.52 \tag{7.2}$$

where r_0 is the radius of the earth. (3) It must fulfill Clairaut's differential equation; this equation holds for any equipotential ellipsoidal surface inside the earth which is supposed to consist of an infinite number of ellipsoidal layers of constant density. Clairaut's equation may be written [e.g., Hopfner, 1936, p. 290]

$$\frac{\partial^2 \alpha}{\partial c^2} + \frac{2\rho c^2}{\int_0^c \rho c^2 \, dc} \frac{\partial \alpha}{\partial c} + \left(\frac{2\rho c}{\int_0^c \rho c^2 \, dc} - \frac{6}{c^2} \right) \alpha = 0 \tag{7.3}$$

where c is the polar axis of the ellipsoid in question (e.g., the surface of the earth) and α the corresponding flattening. (4) It must lead to the observed nutation and the observed effect of the earth on the moon's motion; however, the requirements (4) are practically fulfilled, if Eq. (7.3) is fulfilled. (5) The density can be assumed to increase with depth [e.g., Jardetzky, 1958, p. 9].

Another possibility is to assume that the earth consists of homogeneous and isotherm layers. In each of these the following equation [Birch, 1952, p. 236] can be used as a good approximation

$$\frac{d\rho}{dr} = -\frac{g\rho}{\Phi}(1 - \beta\Phi\tau/g) \tag{7.4}$$

where, as in Eq. (4.8)

$$\Phi = V^2 - \frac{4}{3}v^2 = \frac{k_s}{\rho} \tag{7.5}$$

β is the volume thermal expansion, τ is the difference between the actual gradient of temperature and the adiabatic gradient, and k_s is the adiabatic bulk modulus (incompressibility). Bullen [1956a, p. 112] uses this equation in the form

$$\frac{d\rho}{dr} = -\frac{Gm\rho(1 - \delta)}{\Phi r^2} \tag{7.6}$$

where

$$\delta = \frac{\beta_p k\tau}{g\rho} = \frac{\beta_p\Phi\tau}{g} \tag{7.7}$$

$$m = \frac{r^2 g}{G} \tag{7.8}$$

$$dm/dr = 4\pi r^2\rho \tag{7.9}$$

m is the mass inside a sphere with the radius r, G the gravitational constant, and β_p the coefficient of expansion at constant pressure. Birch believes that δ is of the order of 0.1τ. Bullen points out that for depths greater than about 1000 km, δ can probably be taken as zero. In this case

$$\frac{d\rho}{dr} = -\frac{Gm\rho}{\Phi r^2}. \tag{7.10}$$

This equation corresponds to Eq. (7.14), to be discussed later, which had been developed by Williamson and Adams [1923]. It has been used by Bullen [1936, p. 396] and by Bullard [1957, p. 23; note misprint]. Bullard has considered, in addition [Bullard, 1957, p. 36] the term containing δ in Eq. (7.6).

7.3 Assumed Continuous Density–Depth Curves

The first attempts to determine the density in the earth as a function of the depth have been based on the assumption that the density ρ increases continuously with depth and is a simple function of r. Such assumptions are still of interest in research in which no great accuracy is needed and where the general behavior of a quantity (e.g., rigidity) is to be studied which contains $\rho(r)$. Among the functions $\rho(r)$ which have been in use for over 100 years are those of Legendre and of Roche. Legendre has assumed that

$$\rho = \rho_c \frac{\sin nr}{nr} \tag{7.11}$$

where approximately $\rho_c = 11$ and $nr_0 = 2.5$ (compare Fig. 7.1). Roche has supposed that ρ can be represented by

$$\rho = \rho_c \left[1 - M \left(\frac{r}{r_0} \right)^2 \right] \tag{7.12}$$

where approximately $M = 0.76$ and $\rho_c = 10.1$. For a discussion of these and other simple equations for the density in the earth as a function of the radius r, see e.g., Haalck [1925], Hopfner [1936, pp. 297 ff.], or Ansel [1936, pp. 628 ff.].

Bolt [1957a] has discussed eight models for the density in the earth on the assumption of continuous density–depth curves; some of these consist of two curves joining each other at the core boundary where they have a discontinuous derivative $d\rho/dr$. Bolt introduces a parameter

$$\Theta = \Phi \frac{d\rho}{dp} \tag{7.13}$$

to take care of deviations from homogeneity; in homogeneous material $\Theta = 1$. Bolt concludes that most assumed equations for $\rho(r)$ require too small a density at the earth's center unless there is a sudden increase of the density at the core boundary.

7.4 Density–Depth Curves Assuming Straight Lines Separated by Discontinuities

Wiechert [1897] was the first to assume that the earth consists of a mantle and a core, in each of which the density can be assumed to be constant for first order approximations in calculations (Section 2.1). Klussmann [1915, p. 1] extended Wiechert's equations to fit a three-layered earth with constant density in each portion. For the average density in the outer portion of the mantle, Klussmann selected four different values, 3.0, 3.2,

3.4, and 3.6 g/cm³. He took as variables the densities in the lower portion of the mantle and in the core. He found (loc. cit. p. 29) for the lower mantle mean densities between 7.2 (corresponding to 3.0 in the upper mantle) and 5.4 (corresponding to 3.6) and between 8.3 and 9.6 respectively for the core.

The next step was taken by Haalck [1925] who assumed that the density increases in the outer mantle at a constant rate to a second order discontinuity, which he assumed to be at a depth of 1200 km. This corresponds to the second order discontinuity which we have found now to be at a depth of about 950 km (Fig. 2.1). For the inner portion of the mantle, Haalck assumed a different constant rate of density increase down to the core boundary where he assumed a sudden increase in density. He supposed that the density in the core is constant. Results on one of his various numerical assumptions have been entered in Fig. 7.1.

7.5 Density–Depth Curves on the Assumption that the Earth Consists of Homogeneous Shells

Williamson and Adams [1923] were the first to calculate the density in the mantle of the earth on the assumption that the mantle is homogeneous and isotherm, and that the density increase with depth corresponds to the increase in pressure. Furthermore, they supposed, as is done usually, that the pressure is hydrostatic. Williamson and Adams used for these calculations Eq. (7.10) in the form which they had originally developed

$$\frac{d \ln \rho}{dr} = - \frac{Gm}{\Phi r^2} \tag{7.14}$$

where Φ is given by Eq. (7.5), m by Eq. (7.8). They calculated $\rho(r)$ assuming two values for ρ_0, 3.0 and 3.5 g/cm³. The values which they found for the density in the mantle corresponding to $\rho_0 = 3.5$ are indicated in Fig. 7.1. Finally, they estimated the density in the core on the assumption that the core consists of metal.

In his first calculation of the density of the earth, Bullen [1936] had supposed that the various units of the earth are homogeneous. For the mantle, he had used Eq. (7.10) which is equivalent to (7.14), and a density of 3.32 at a depth of 35 km. In order to reduce on his assumptions the moment of inertia of the core to the required value, and on the basis of the seismological data, available in 1936, he had assumed that at a depth of 400 km the density jumps to 4.1. For the density in the core, he finally had adopted an equation of the form (7.12) and had found [Bullen, 1936, p. 399] as an approximation for the density in the core

$$\rho = 12.26 - 0.173(r/10^8)^2 - 0.0060(r/10^8)^3. \qquad (7.15)$$

The density–depth curve of Bullen [1936] is included in Fig. 7.1. Apparently, it is almost as close an approximation as we can find at present. How-

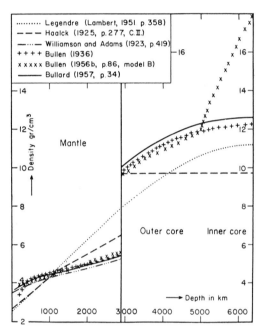

Fig. 7.1. Density ρ as function of depth in the earth, calculated by various authors. Legendre has supposed a continuous function of the form $\rho = \rho_c \,[\sin(nr)]/nr$ throughout the earth, Haalck a function $\rho = a + br$ for the mantle to a depth of 1200 km, then without jump a similar function with a different value of b, to the core boundary, and in the core a greater constant value of ρ.

ever, Birch [1953] has pointed out that this curve leads to an improbably high moment of inertia for the core. In the interim, Bullen [1940, 1942, 1949, 1952, 1954, 1956b,c] has tried to improve the density–depth curve. Figure 7.1 and Table 7.1 contain the values which he found in 1956 on the assumption that the bulk modulus depends on the pressure only, if the pressure exceeds 0.4×10^{12} dynes/cm²; this corresponds to depths in the earth in excess of about 1000 km.

Bullard [1954] has published results of his research. Later Bullard [1957] has used improved curves for the velocity of seismic waves in the earth, and has calculated density–depth curves by integrating Eq. (7.10), considering Eq. (7.9). Bullard has used six assumptions for Φ, in some of which

TABLE 7.1. DENSITY ρ IN G/CM^3, GRAVITY g IN CM/SEC^2 AND PRESSURE p IN 10^{12} DYNE/CM^2 (A) CORRESPONDING TO BULLEN'S [1952, P. 389] MODEL X, AND (B) TO THE SOLUTION I OF BULLARD [1957, PP. 34, 39] AS A FUNCTION OF THE DEPTH h IN KM IN THE EARTH.

(A)				(B)			
h	ρ	g	p	h	ρ	g	p
33	3.32	985	0.009	32	3.67	985	0.009
100	3.39	987	0.031	160	3.79	985	0.047
200	3.48	990	0.065	286	3.91	984	0.095
300	3.57	992	0.100	—	—	—	—
413	3.67	995	0.141	413	4.02	984	0.144
500	3.92	997	0.175	539	4.11	983	0.194
600	4.15	997	0.214	666	4.19	982	0.246
800	4.52	995	0.300	855	4.35	980	0.352
1000	4.72	991	0.392	983	4.38	980	0.380
1200	4.85	986	0.49	1172	4.49	980	0.447
1600	5.11	976	0.68	1616	4.56	984	0.662
2000	5.35	972	0.89	1933	4.89	992	0.813
2400	5.59	975	1.10	2250	5.04	1008	0.970
2600	5.70	981	1.21	2570	5.19	1036	1.14
2900	5.87	1000	1.38	2900	5.62	1082	1.32
2900	6.50	1000	1.38	2900	10.06	1082	1.32
3000	6.98	1000	1.45	3247	10.26	1000	1.69
3400	8.80	988	1.76	2594	11.06	910	2.05
3800	10.53	945	2.14	3941	11.46	812	2.39
4200	12.20	872	2.55	4288	11.79	707	2.70
4600	13.81	770	2.98	4635	12.06	597	2.97
4980	15.29	640	3.37	4982	12.28	482	3.20
5500	17.1	540	3.8	5676	12.54	244	3.51
6000	18.8	200	4.1	6023	12.61	122	3.59
6371	20.0	0	4.2	6370	12.63	0	3.47

he has supposed that there is a first order discontinuity at a depth of 984 km. His results calculated on his assumption 1, which include a continuous change in wave velocities in the mantle, are reproduced in Fig. 7.1 and in Table 7.1. His values for the density as a function of depth which are based on other assumptions show differences in the density which rarely exceed 0.6 g/cm^3 at any depth.

Bolt [1957b] has investigated 24 models of the earth. He has assumed in all that the core is chemically homogeneous, and has found that at a given depth in the upper portion of the mantle the possible range of densities is relatively small (see also Fig. 7.1) and that the heterogeneity towards the base of the mantle increases as the jump in density at the core boundary decreases.

7.6 General Results Related to the Problem of the Density in the Earth

7.6.1 The Change in Density at the Core Boundary

If elastic waves arrive at a discontinuity, their energy is divided among up to four waves: one reflected and one refracted longitudinal wave and one reflected and one refracted transverse wave. The ratios of the energy going into each of these waves to that of the incident wave depend on the ratios of the velocities and densities at the two sides of the discontinuity. Consequently, the observed amplitudes of the waves involved as well as the direction of the first motion in longitudinal waves (change or no change from compression to dilatation and vice versa) can sometimes be used to find limits for the ratio of the densities at the two sides of the discontinuity.

Gutenberg [1951] has studied directions and amplitudes of longitudinal waves PKKP (reflected inside the core; compare Fig. 5.1) and has found that the data do not fit the assumption that there is no change in density at the core boundary. The scattering of the results does not permit drawing of accurate conclusions; the assumption of an increase in the density by a factor of roughly 1.8 at the core boundary seems to fit the observations best. Båth [1954] has studied similarly the waves PcP reflected in the mantle at the core boundary and he, too, has concluded that the density increases discontinuously from the mantle to the core.

7.6.2 Densities of Materials under High Pressure

Among others, Elsasser [1951], Bullen [1952], and Knopoff and Uffen [1954] have tried to determine the densities of elements at pressures exceeding 10^5 atm, corresponding to depths in the earth exceeding about 300 km (the pressure at the core boundary is about 1.4×10^6 atm). Quantum calculations begin to hold at pressures of the order of 10^8 atm, which is far in excess of the $3\frac{1}{2} \times 10^6$ atm in the earth's center. The problem is to find a method to bridge the gap between results obtained from quantum calculations and those found from laboratory experiments [Bridgmann, 1949].

Knopoff and Uffen [1954] have based their calculations of the densities of compounds in the earth on results obtained by Feynman *et al.*, [1949] and by others for the pressure–density relationship at absolute zero for pure solid elements on the assumption of a Fermi–Thomas model for the electrons surrounding the nuclei. In addition, Knopoff and Uffen have

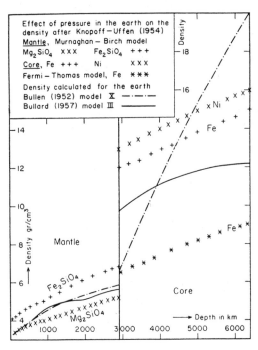

Fig. 7.2. Density in the earth for two models, calculated changes in density for two minerals as function of depth in the mantle, and for iron and nickel in the core.

used results of Birch's [1952] application of Murnaghan's theory for finite strain to geophysical problems. The density–pressure curves of Knopoff and Uffen (Fig. 7.2) have been calculated on the assumptions that for a given substance no phase transition exists in the earth and that the temperature is absolute zero. However, Knopoff and Uffen find that the effect of temperatures at the core boundary up to 10,000° on the calculated densities should be less than 8%. Knopoff and Uffen finally conclude that the density in the core corresponds approximately to the density distribution found by Bullen [1952] on the assumption of his model X (Table 7.1), if the core has an iron content of about 90%, with fayalite and fosterite furnishing the rest of the material. Bullen's model X has a density jump from 5.9 to 6.5 g/cm³ at the core boundary, a density of about 14.6 at the depth of 4800 km, and of 20 g/cm³ in the earth's center. However, Knopoff and Uffen [1954, p. 480] conclude that "a density of 18 at the center of the earth is . . . the upper limit of density allowable for any material consistent with either a silicate or iron-nickel structure."

7.7 Estimated Densities in the Earth

Figures 7.1 and 7.2 illustrate the general result which has been found repeatedly, that the density in the mantle is fairly well known and that it corresponds approximately to the densities calculated for silicates. There is less and less agreement between various calculations of the density in the core as the earth's center is approached.

Various results indicate that the assumption of a core consisting of pure iron would either give a slightly too small mean density for the core or would require an increase in the density with depth in the inner core which is faster than the increase which can be expected from the effect of pressure increase in an iron core (see, for example, Bullen, 1952, model X; compare also Fig. 7.2 and Table 7.1). However, the possibility of a gradual increase of heavier material with depth in the inner core is not excluded.

While the results for the density in the core leave appreciable doubt about the actual values (Fig. 7.1; Table 7.1), those for the mantle agree fairly well among themselves and are probably a good approximation.

7.8 Gravity in the Earth

The gravity g at a distance r from the earth's center is given with sufficient approximation by

$$g = Gm/r^2 \qquad \text{where} \qquad m = 4\pi \int_0^r r^2\rho \, dr \qquad (7.16)$$

so that

$$g = \frac{4\pi G}{r^2} \int_0^r \rho r^2 \, dr = \frac{3g_0}{\rho_m r_0} \frac{1}{r^2} \int_0^r \rho r^2 \, dr \qquad (7.17)$$

if we introduce for the gravitational constant

$$G = \frac{3g_0}{4\pi \rho_m r_0} \qquad (7.18)$$

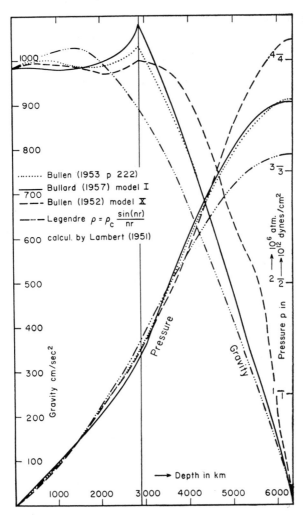

Fig. 7.3. Pressure and gravity in the earth, calculated for several models. The model of Legendre assumes a continuous change in density with depth from the surface to the center.

from Eq. (7.1), neglecting terms containing f; m and ρ_m are respectively the mass of the sphere with the radius r and its mean density; ρ is the density as function of r; the index zero refers to the earth's surface. Considering that

$$m = \tfrac{4}{3}\pi r^3 \rho_m \quad \text{and} \quad \int_0^r \rho \, d(r^3) = r^3 \rho_m \qquad (7.19)$$

we find from Eq. (7.17)

$$\frac{dg}{dr} = 4\pi G(\rho - \tfrac{2}{3}\rho_m).\tag{7.20}$$

It follows from Eq. (7.20) (see, e.g., Hopfner [1936], p. 307, based on Helmert [1884], p. 492, "Theorem of Saigey") that at the distance r from the earth's center, gravity does not change with depth, if the density ρ at r equals $\tfrac{2}{3}$ of the mean density of the sphere with the radius r. Since near the earth's surface ρ is smaller than $\tfrac{2}{3}\rho_m$, which is about 3.7, gravity increases slightly with depth in the crust and in the upper mantle; it has to be considered that the mean density ρ_m of a sphere with the radius r increases with depth.

Calculations (Fig. 7.3; Table 7.1) indicate that gravity has a small maximum at the core boundary (the curve corresponding to Legendre's equation can be disregarded here) and then decreases rapidly towards the center of the earth. In many calculations it may be assumed that to a first approximation g is constant (1000 cm/sec²) throughout the crust and the mantle of the earth.

7.9 The Pressure in the Earth

The pressure p in the earth is given by

$$dp/dr = -g\rho = -Gm\rho/r^2\tag{7.21}$$

where m is the mass of the sphere with the radius r.

If we assume constant density in each of i layers in the crust with the thicknesses h_i and the corresponding densities ρ_i, Eq. (7.21) may be written for crustal layers with sufficient approximation for most purposes

$$p = g_0 \sum_i \rho_i h_i.\tag{7.22}$$

Below the continents, p increases by an amount of the order of 270 atm/km; in oceans under H km of water the pressure is about $100H$ atm/km. This is about $170H$ atm smaller than at the same depth under continents with their surface near sea level, and an additional $270h$ atm smaller than under mountain areas of the elevation h km.

The pressure in the mantle and in the core can be found by integration of Eq. (7.21), after g has been calculated on the basis of an assumed density–depth function. Figure 7.3 and Table 7.1 show characteristic values for the pressure as a function of the depth. The pressure at the core boundary is about 1.3 to 1.4 million atmospheres, that in the earth's center about $3\frac{1}{2} \pm \frac{1}{2}$ million atmospheres.

7.10 Flattening of Near-Equipotential Ellipsoidic Surfaces in the Earth

The theory which permits the calculation of the flattening $\alpha = (a - c)/a$ of a near-equipotential ellipsoidic surface inside the earth, for which a and c are respectively the equatorial and polar axes, is considered to be a problem of geodesy and has been discussed extensively by geodesists. Lambert [1951, p. 347] uses the following transformation of Clairaut's differential equation (7.3)

$$\left(r^2 \frac{d^2\alpha}{dr^2} + 6r \frac{d\alpha}{dr}\right)\rho_m + 2\left(r^2 \frac{d\alpha}{dr} + \alpha r\right)\frac{d\rho_m}{dr} = 0 \qquad (7.23)$$

where r is the mean radius of the sphere, corresponding to the ellipsoid, and ρ_m the mean density within r.

Radau [1885] introduced a new variable

$$\eta = \frac{r}{\alpha}\frac{d\alpha}{dr} = \frac{d(\log \alpha)}{d(\log r)} \qquad (7.24)$$

so that Eq. (7.23) may be written

$$\left(r\frac{d\eta}{dr} + \eta^2 + 5\eta\right)\rho_m + 2r(1+\eta)\frac{d\rho_m}{dr} = 0. \qquad (7.25)$$

Radau has transformed this equation into

$$\frac{d}{dr}(\rho_m \sqrt{1+\eta}) + \rho_m \frac{5\eta + \eta^2}{2r\sqrt{1+\eta}} = 0. \qquad (7.26)$$

If we form $d(\rho_m r^5 \sqrt{1+\eta})/dr$, and consider Eq. (7.26), we find

$$\frac{d}{dr}(\rho_m r^5 \sqrt{1+\eta}) = 5\rho_m r^4 f(\eta) \qquad (7.27)$$

where

$$f(\eta) = \frac{1 + \frac{1}{2}\eta - \frac{1}{10}\eta^2}{\sqrt{1+\eta}}. \qquad (7.28)$$

The advantage of introducing η is that the function $f(\eta)$ is close enough to 1 to be taken as unity with a good approximation. This has been verified. Jeffreys [see, e.g., 1952, p. 142] has calculated that $f(\eta)$ has a maximum of 1.00074 for $\eta = \frac{1}{3}$. Since $f(\eta) = 1$ for $\eta = 0$, and $f(\eta) = 0.99928$ for $\eta = 0.57$, Jeffreys concludes that $f(\eta) = 1.00000 \pm 0.00074$ between $\eta = 0$ and $\eta = 0.60$. On the other hand, Bullen [1936, p. 401] has calculated the following approximate values of η inside the earth

Depth in km	0	100	1000	2000	2500	2900	6370
η		0.56	0.53	0.51	0.46	0.31	0.04	0.00

Since η is between 0 and 0.60, Jeffreys' condition is fulfilled, and Bullen concludes that in the earth $f(\eta) = 1.000 \pm 0.0008$ for all values of r. Thus, if one assumes that $f(\eta) = 1$, one does not introduce noticeable errors, unless the calculated values for η in the tabulation above are appreciably wrong.

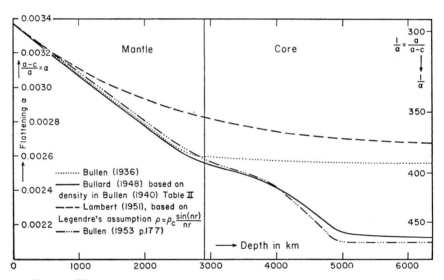

FIG. 7.4. Flattening of equipotential surfaces in the earth on various assumptions. The Legendre model assumes a continuous change of density with depth throughout the earth.

On the assumption that everywhere in the earth $f(\eta) = 1$ it follows from Eq. (7.27) after several transformations [Lambert, 1951, p. 349] that for a sphere with the radius r^*

$$\tfrac{2}{5}\sqrt{1 + \eta} = 1 - \tfrac{3}{2}\beta \qquad (7.29)$$

where

$$\beta = \frac{I}{mr^{*2}} \qquad (7.30)$$

I is the moment of inertia of the sphere with the radius r^* and is given by

$$I = \tfrac{8}{3} \int_0^{r^*} \rho r^4 \, dr \qquad (7.31)$$

and m is given by Eq. (7.16). Thus, β can be found, if the density as a function of r is known, and then Eq. (7.29) gives η. The flattening α as a function of depth may then be found by numerical integration of Eq. (7.24).

Values of the flattening thus obtained by Bullen [1936] have been entered in Fig. 7.4, together with later determinations. It should be noted that the uppermost curve in Fig. 7.4 is based on the (incorrect) assumption of a continuous gradual change of the density with depth through the whole earth, following Eq. (7.11) of Legendre. All curves show a decrease of the flattening with depth. More complicated figures of equilibrium have been discussed, e.g., by Jardetzky [1958].

References

Ansel, E. A. [1936]. Zur Theorie des irdischen Schwerefeldes. *In* "Handbuch der Geophysik" (B. Gutenberg, ed.), Vol. 1, pp. 536–730. Borntraeger, Berlin.

Båth, M. [1954]. The density ratio at the boundary of the Earth's core. *Tellus.* **6**, 408–413

Birch, F. [1952]. Elasticity and constitution of the earth's interior. *J. Geophys. Research* **57**, 227–286.

Birch, F. [1953]. Uniformity of the earth's mantle. *Bull. Geol. Soc. Am.* **64**, 601–602.

Bolt, B. A. [1957a]. Earth models with continuous density distribution. *Monthly Notices Roy. Astron. Soc. Geophys. Suppl.* **7**, 360–368.

Bolt, B. A. [1957b]. Earth models with chemically homogeneous cores. *Monthly Notices Roy. Astron. Soc. Geophys. Suppl.* **7**, 372–378.

Bridgmann, P. W. [1949]. Linear compression to 30000 kg/cm², including relatively incompressible substances. *Proc. Am. Acad. Arts Sci.* **77**, 187–234.

Bullard, E. C. [1954]. The interior of the earth. *In* "The Earth as a Planet" (G. P. Kuiper, ed.), pp. 57–137. Univ. Chicago Press, Chicago, Illinois.

Bullard, E. C. [1957]. The density within the earth. *Verhandel. Ned. Geol. Mijnbouwk. Genoot. Geol. Ser.* **18**, 23–41.

Bullen, K. E. [1936]. The variation of density and the ellipticities of strata of equal density within the earth. *Monthly Notices Roy. Astron. Soc. Geophys. Suppl.* **3**, 395–401.

Bullen, K. E. [1940]. The problem of the earth's density variation. *Bull. Seismol. Soc. Am.* **30**, 235–250.

Bullen, K. E. [1942]. The density variation of the earth's central core. *Bull. Seismol. Soc. Am.* **32**, 19–30.

Bullen, K. E. [1949]. Compressibility—pressure hypothesis and the earth's interior. *Monthly Notices Roy. Astron. Soc. Geophys. Suppl.* **5**, 355–368.

Bullen, K. E. [1952]. On density and compressibility at pressures up to thirty million atmospheres. *Monthly Notices Roy. Astron. Soc. Geophys. Suppl.* **6**, 383.

Bullen, K. E. [1953]. "An Introduction to the Theory of Seismology," 296 pp. Cambridge Univ. Press, London and New York.

Bullen, K. E. [1954]. On the homogeneity, or otherwise, of the earth's upper mantle. *Trans. Am. Geophys. Union* **35**, 838–841.

Bullen, K. E. [1956a]. Seismic wave transmission. *In* "Encyclopedia of Physics" (S. Flügge, ed.), Vol. 47, pp. 112–117. Springer, Berlin.

Bullen, K. E. [1956b]. Seismology and the broad structure of the earth's interior. *In* "Physics and Chemistry of the Earth" (L. H. Ahrens, K. Rankama, and S. K. Runcorn, eds.), Vol. 1, pp. 68–93. McGraw-Hill, New York.

Bullen, K. E. [1956c]. The influence of temperature gradient and variation of composition in the mantle on the computation of density values in earth model A. *Monthly Notices Roy. Astron. Soc. Geophys. Suppl.* **7**, 214–217.

Elsasser, W. M. [1951]. Quantum theoretical densities of solids at extreme compression. *Science* **113**, 105–107.

Feynman, R. P., Metropolis, N., and Teller, E. [1949]. Equations of state of elements based on the generalized Fermi-Thomas theory. *Phys. Rev.* **75**, 1561–1572.

Gutenberg, B. [1951]. PKKP, P'P', and the earth's core. *Trans. Am. Geophys. Union* **32**, 373–390.

Haalck, H. [1925]. Ueber die Lagerung der Massen in Innern der Erde und deren Elastizitätskonstanten auf Grund der neuesten Ergebnisse. *Z. angew. Geophys.* **1**, 257–280.

Heiskanen, W. A. [1957]. Geodetic data. *In* "American Institute of Physics Handbook" (D. E. Gray, ed.), pp. 2–92 to 2–101. McGraw-Hill, New York.

Helmert, F. R. [1884]. "Die mathematischen und physikalischen Theorien der höheren Geodäsie," Vol. 2. Teubner, Leipzig.

Hopfner, F. [1936]. Figur der Erde, Dichte und Druck im Erdinnern. *In* "Handbuch der Geophysik" (B. Gutenberg, ed.), Vol. 1, pp. 139–308. Borntraeger, Berlin.

Jardetzky, W. S. [1958]. "Theories of Figures of Celestial Bodies," 186 pp. Interscience, New York.

Jeffreys, H. [1952]. "The Earth," 3rd ed., 392 pp. Cambridge Univ. Press, London and New York.

Jones, H. S. [1954]. The mass of the earth. *In* "The Earth as a Planet" (G. P. Kuiper, ed.), pp. 18–20. Univ. Chicago Press, Chicago, Illinois.

Klussmann, W. [1915]. Ueber das Innere der Erde. *Gerlands Beitr. Geophys.* **14**, 1–38.

Knopoff, L., and Uffen, R. J. [1954]. The densities of compounds at high pressures and the state of the earth's interior. *J. Geophys. Research* **59**, 471–484.

Lambert, W. D. [1951]. Density, gravity, pressure and ellipticity in the interior of the earth. *In* "Internal Constitution of the Earth" (B. Gutenberg, ed.) 2nd ed. pp. 340–361. Dover, New York.

Lindsay, R. B. [1957]. Astronomical data. *In* "American Institute of Physics Handbook" (D. E. Gray, ed.), pp. 2–90 to 2–91. McGraw-Hill, New York.

Radau, R. R. [1885]. Sur la loi des densités à l'interieur de la Terre. *Compt. rend.* **100**, 972.

Wiechert, E. [1897]. Ueber die Massenverteilung im Innern der Erde. *Nachr. Ges. Wiss. Göttingen Math.-physik. Kl.* **1897**, 221–243.

Williamson, E. D., and Adams, L. H. [1923]. Density distribution in the earth. *J. Wash. Acad. Sci.* **13**, 413–428.

8. Elastic Constants, and Elastic Processes in the Earth

8.1 Elastic Constants and Love's Numbers

The elastic properties of a perfectly elastic body are determined by any two of the following moduli: (1) the bulk modulus (coefficient of incompressibility) k, which controls the change in volume if an elastic body is compressed (positive or negative) by a small amount; (2) Lamé's constant λ which has no simple physical meaning; (3) Lamé's constant μ, the coefficient of rigidity, which controls the change of form if pure shear is applied; (4) Young's modulus E of elasticity which indicates the elongation of a column of unit cross section under tension or compression; and (5) Poisson's ratio σ which gives the ratio of the radial contraction of this column to the elongation. In a homogeneous, isotherm, and perfectly elastic body the functional relations between these moduli, the density ρ of the body, and the velocities V of longitudinal and v of transverse waves are given by the following equations

$$k = \tfrac{1}{3}\frac{E}{1 - 2\sigma} = \frac{2\mu(1 + \sigma)}{3(1 - 2\sigma)} = \lambda + \tfrac{2}{3}\mu = \rho(V^2 - \tfrac{4}{3}v^2) = \rho\Phi \quad (8.1)$$

$$\mu = \tfrac{1}{2}\frac{E}{1 + \sigma} = \frac{3k(1 - 2\sigma)}{2(1 + \sigma)} = \tfrac{3}{2}(k - \lambda) = \frac{\lambda(1 - 2\sigma)}{2\sigma} = \rho v^2 \quad (8.2)$$

$$\lambda = \frac{\sigma E}{(1 + \sigma)(1 - 2\sigma)} = 3k\frac{\sigma}{1 + \sigma} = k - \tfrac{2}{3}\mu = \frac{2\sigma\mu}{1 - 2\sigma} = \rho(V^2 - 2v^2)$$
$$(8.3)$$

$$E = 3k(1 - 2\sigma) = 2\mu(1 + \sigma) = \rho\frac{3V^2 - 4v^2}{(V/v)^2 - 1} \quad (8.4)$$

$$\sigma = \frac{\lambda}{2(\lambda + \mu)} = \tfrac{1}{2} - \frac{E}{6k} = \frac{1 - (2\mu/3k)}{2 + (2\mu/3k)} = \frac{E}{2\mu} - 1 = \tfrac{1}{2}\left[1 - \frac{1}{(V/v)^2 - 1}\right]$$
$$(8.5)$$

$$V^2 = \frac{k + \frac{4}{3}\mu}{\rho} = \frac{\lambda + 2\mu}{\rho} = \frac{3k}{\rho}\frac{1 - \sigma}{1 + \sigma} = \frac{2\mu}{\rho}\frac{1 - \sigma}{1 - 2\sigma} \qquad (8.6)$$

$$v^2 = \frac{\mu}{\rho} \qquad (8.7)$$

$$\left(\frac{V}{v}\right)^2 = 1 + \frac{1}{1 - 2\sigma}. \qquad (8.8)$$

For most portions of the earth's mantle, Poisson's ratio σ is close to $\frac{1}{4}$. If $\sigma = 0.2500$ the following equations hold

$$\mu = \lambda = 2E/5 = 3k/5 = \rho v^2 = \rho V^2/3 \qquad (8.9)$$

$$E = 3k/2 = 5\mu/2 = 5\rho v^2/2 = 5\rho V^2/6 \qquad (8.10)$$

$$k = 2E/3 = 5\mu/3 = 5\rho v^2/3 = 5\rho V^2/9 \qquad (8.11)$$

$$V^2 = 3\mu/\rho = 9k/5\rho \qquad v^2 = \mu/\rho = 3k/5\rho \qquad (8.12)$$

$$(V/v)^2 = 3 \qquad V = 1.732v. \qquad (8.13)$$

In perfect liquids, μ, E, and v are zero, $\sigma = \frac{1}{2}$, $\lambda = k = \rho V^2$.

During his investigation of the body tides of the earth, Love [1911, p. 53] introduced two constants, h and k^*. The quantity h defines the ratio of the height of the body tide of the earth at the surface to the height of the corresponding theoretical equilibrium oceanic tide, measured from the undeformed surface of the earth, and k^* the ratio of the additional potential, produced by the deformation of the earth, to the deforming potential. Usually, our number k^* is indicated by k, but this may lead to confusion with the bulk modulus, for which earlier the symbol k has been introduced. A third number, indicated by l, has been defined by Shida; it represents the ratio of the horizontal displacement in the terrestrial tide to that of the corresponding static ocean tide.

In a homogeneous fluid sphere, $h = 1$, $k^* = 0.6$, $l = 0.3$. In an absolutely rigid sphere all three numbers are zero. For a homogeneous solid sphere with the density ρ, the rigidity μ and the radius r, Kelvin found the following expressions for Love's numbers

$$h = \frac{5f}{2f + 1} \qquad (8.14)$$

$$k^* = \frac{3f}{2f + 1} \qquad (8.15)$$

$$l = \frac{3f}{2(2f + 1)} \qquad (8.16)$$

where

$$f = g\rho r/19\mu. \tag{8.17}$$

Thus, in a homogeneous solid sphere,

$$k^* = 0.6h = 2l. \tag{8.18}$$

For a nonhomogeneous solid sphere, k^*, h, and l are defined only for deformations of the free surface which are expressible by second-degree spherical harmonics. Fortunately, this includes all types of deformations that have been calculated from observations of tides, deflections of the vertical, changes in gravity, and variation of latitude.

The yielding of the earth produces a potential k^*W in addition to the potential W of the long-period tidal forces. The equilibrium height of the ocean tide is $(1 + k^*)W/g$. The tide in the earth's body is hW/g. Their difference which we observe in the free ocean from long-period tides is $(1 + k^* - h)W/g$. Since we know W/g from the theory,

$$\gamma = 1 + k^* - h \tag{8.19}$$

can be calculated. For details, see Lambert [1933], Melchior [1958, p. 401], or Tomaschek [1957b, p. 788].

A second combination of Love's numbers which can be calculated is

$$\delta = 1 + h - \tfrac{3}{2}k^*. \tag{8.20}$$

On the yielding earth the gravitational variation as a consequence of the solar–lunar action is modified by the factor δ compared with the theoretical equilibrium tide on a nonyielding earth. A third combination

$$\Lambda = 1 + k^* - l \tag{8.21}$$

is found from observed deflections of the vertical relative to the direction of the axis of rotation of the earth in space. Some authors prefer the letters D (for γ), G (for δ), and L (for Λ).

Two of Love's numbers can be found directly, k^* from the ratio of the "Euler period" of the movements of the earth's axis (Section 8.2) for an unyielding earth to the "Chandler period" of the actual earth, and l from records of the strain produced by the body tides (Section 8.3).

8.2 The Earth's Free Nutation. Latitude Variations

If the axis of the (undisturbed) rotation of the earth does not coincide with the main axis of inertia, it describes a circular cone about the axis of inertia with a period τ, which is called the "Chandler period" or the "New-comb period." The theoretical period τ_0 for an absolutely rigid sphere with the moments of inertia A and C is given by [see, e.g., Helmert, 1884, p. 400]

$$\tau_0 = \frac{A}{C - A} d_s \qquad (8.22)$$

where d_s is the time of one sidereal day in the units of time to be used for τ. The time τ_0 is called the "Eulerian period" of the free nutation. If we use the most probable values of A and C, we find $\tau_0 = 305$ sidereal days. The

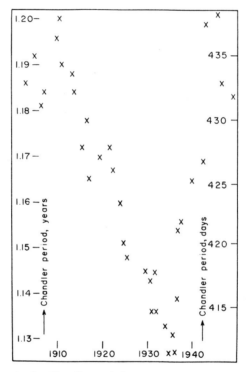

FIG. 8.1. Changes in the Chandler period 1900–1950, after Melchior [1957, p. 237].

smaller the rigidity is of a sphere, the greater is the actual period of nutation (for the earth, the Chandler period). As a consequence of the motion of the earth's axis with the period τ, the latitudes and longitudes of any point of the earth's surface are changing periodically by amounts of up to $\frac{1}{4}''$.

The earth's free nutation has been observed continuously since 1900 on several internationally organized stations in $39°8'$ north latitude. The extensive literature has been discussed, for example, by Lambert *et al.*, [1931] and by Melchior [1957].

Chandler recognized first the characteristics of the motion. It consists of a circular motion of the pole with the period τ which, since 1900, was between about 414 and 440 days (Fig. 8.1), and an elliptical motion with a period of one year. The combination of the two (Fig. 8.2) produces a kind of spiral with maximum amplitudes about every seven years.

Love [1911, p. 54] pointed out that

$$k^* = \left(\frac{2g\alpha}{a\omega^2} - 1\right)\left(1 - \frac{\tau_0}{\tau}\right) \tag{8.23}$$

where α is the ellipticity and a the equatorial axis of the earth and ω its angular velocity of rotation. Using the most recent data for the constants involved, Melchior [1957, p. 230] has calculated from Eq. (8.23) the following theoretical relationship between τ and k^*

τ	415	421	427	434	441	462 days
k^*	0.25	0.26	0.27	0.28	0.29	0.32

The problem of the energy balance of the nutational motion is complicated. Meteorological and oceanographic processes, including local differences in changes in sea level, disturb the equilibrium and give rise to the

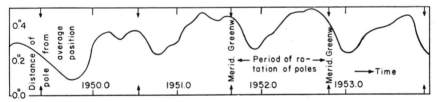

Fig. 8.2. Distance of the poles from their average position, 1949–1954. The arrows indicate the times when the deviation of the poles was toward the meridian of Greenwich. Based on Melchior [1957, Fig. 5b, p. 222].

free nutation of the earth with the period τ. Upon this motion is superposed the annual component which is produced by annual changes in the atmosphere and in the oceans. [For details, see e.g., Jeffreys, 1952, pp. 201–215; Melchior, 1957.] The question of the amount of damping of the motion connected with the nutation is still controversial (see Section 9.4). There are other controversial problems connected with the nutation [cf. Conference, 1958, pp. 140 ff.]. They are partly a consequence of insufficiently known numerical quantities, connected with the theoretical discussion, and partly of the fact that two major and perhaps several minor types of motion are superposed and have to be disentangled. Moreover, the period of the main term changes with time (Fig. 8.1).

8.3 Tides of the Solid Earth

The sun and the moon produce varying tidal forces on the earth which have been discussed in much detail [Bartels, 1957]. Curves for the tides of the earth's body (as well as those of the oceans) are usually treated by harmonic analysis and represented by terms with periods corresponding to the major terms of the forces [cf. Bartels, 1957, p. 754]. For many of these terms, international symbols have been selected.

The direction and relative amplitudes of the tidal forces produced by the sun and the moon at the earth's surface are indicated in Fig. 8.3. The

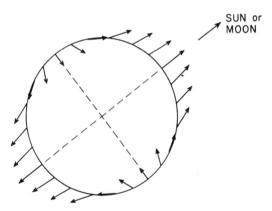

SUN or
MOON

Fig. 8.3. Relative tidal forces in the plane of the apparent path of the disturbing celestial body around the earth.

ratio of the solar to the lunar tidal forces is about 0.46. The ratio of the forces on opposite sides of the earth on the line towards the sun or moon is about 1.05 for the moon, 1.00013 for the sun.

There are three major effects of the tidal forces on the solid earth: a vertical displacement of the earth's surface, a change in gravity, and a tilt of the plumb line. For the measurement or recording of the body tides different types of pendulum instruments are used [Melchior, 1954, 1958, p. 404; Tomaschek, 1957b, p. 793; Colloquium, 1958, several papers]. Gravimeters give the change in gravity [Melchior, 1958, p. 426; Tomaschek,

1957b, p. 799]. Strain gauges record the change in strain. The records of tides of the earth's body are distorted by several types of disturbances; some of them are local, for example, effects of changes in air pressure distribution producing tilting of small and large blocks of the earth's crust, effects of wind, tilting of portions of the crust as a consequence of variations in heating by the sun (with a prevailing 24-hour period). Effects with prevailing periods similar to those under investigation are produced by the ocean tides; they are greatest near the ocean but are large enough to produce measurable effects on the records of body tides far into the continents. These effects may create the impression of a variation in the amplitudes of the body tides with the azimuth. During the early investigations these effects had been misinterpreted as an indication of different response of the crust to the tidal forces, depending on the azimuth. This "tide" which is superposed upon the actual lunar or solar tides is produced by the gravitational effect of the displaced water, by the deformation of the earth's crust by ocean tides, and by the change in potential [Tomaschek, 1956].

Observations of the body tides may be used directly in the calculation of Love's numbers (Section 8.5). Their amplitudes are of the order of 10 cm in latitude 50° and of 23 cm near the equator without the effect of the ocean tides, which may produce amplitudes of the same order of magnitude. Within the limits of error of a very few degrees, the body tides are in phase with the tidal forces [Melchior, 1958, p. 430; Tomaschek, 1957b, p. 810]. Markowitz [Colloquium, 1958, p. 137] concludes "that within the errors of observation the lunar tides in the crust of the earth are in phase with the theoretical." He estimates that the error in the phase calculated from observations of the monthly tide is ±1 day or less.

A large amount of data concerning body tides and conclusions based on these data are being published regularly under the auspices of the International Association of Geodesy, up to 1956 by W. D. Lambert, since then by P. J. Melchior.

8.4 Free Vibrations of the Earth

Another group of processes which depend on elastic constants in the earth are the free vibrations of the earth. There are several types. Love [1911, p. 216] has given some fundamental theory and has found a free period of the order of 60 min for spheroidal vibrations of the second degree. Recording of four successive waves with periods of 57 min, 3½ hours after the Kamchatka earthquake of November 4, 1952, by the Benioff strain seismograph at Pasadena, and the pointing out by Benioff [Benioff *et al.*, 1954, p. 985] that these may represent free vibrations of the earth, has aided in creating new interest in the problem of free vibrations of the earth. Pekeris and Jarosch [1958] have investigated in detail various types of free vibrations. By a variational method, they have found a period of 53 min for the spheroidal type of vibration. This is now being checked by an exact numerical solution. Jobert [1956, 1957] and Takeuchi [1959] have started additional calculations based on one of Bullen's models of the earth, and have found that the torsional oscillations of the earth of the spherical harmonic degree two should have a period of about $43\frac{1}{2}$ min. However, the findings do not aid much in any decision about the elastic constants in the earth. Pekeris [1958, p. 259] has pointed out that still longer oscillations may produce evidence in favor of one model for the earth's core over another.

8.5 Numerical Values of Love's Numbers

Selected values for γ (Eq. (8.19)) are listed in Table 8.1. Tomaschek

TABLE 8.1. VALUES OF $\gamma = 1 + k^* - h$ CALCULATED FROM VARIOUS OBSERVATIONS

Author	Year	Locality	γ
Shida	1912	Kyoto, Japan	0.78
Schweydar	1913	Freiberg, Saxony	0.84
Schweydar[1]	1913	Freiberg, Saxony	0.704
Michelson-Gale	1914	Yerkes Observatory	0.69
Doodson, Corkan[1]	1933	Bidston	0.703
Egedal	1936	Bergen, Norway	0.64
Picha[1]	1936/39	Brézové Hory (Pribram)	0.709
Tomaschek	1937	Eastern Germany	0.74
Tomaschek	1937	Bavarian Alps	0.60
Schaffernicht	1938	Central Germany	0.69
Corkan	1939	Liverpool	0.77
Corkan	1939	Bergen, Norway	0.65
Nisimura	1941	Manchuria	0.66
Zerbe	1949	Atlantic coast, USA	0.74
Melchior (Colloquium)	1958	Many ("most precise")	0.706

[1] Calculated by Melchior [1958, p. 416].

[1957b, p. 793] concludes that the value of $\gamma = 0.72$ (second decimal uncertain) can be regarded as a general result of observations of the type of experiment performed by Michelson-Gale, in which the change in water level in two buried tubes under the effect of the body tides is observed by an interference method. Tomaschek believes that $\gamma = 0.72$ is, in addition, the most probable value derived from observations with horizontal pendulums (loc. cit. p. 797). On the other hand, Melchior [1958, p. 416] believes that $\gamma = 0.706$ is the most probable value, "which should be very close to the true value of the coefficient γ."

Some findings for δ (Eq. (8.20)) are given in Table 8.2. Tomaschek [1957b, p. 810] points out, "that there exist individual variations which greatly exceed the purely experimental limits," but that $\delta = 1.20$ seems to be well founded.

TABLE 8.2. VALUES OF $\delta = 1 + h - \frac{3}{2}k^*$ FROM VARIOUS OBSERVATIONS

Observer	Reference	Remarks	δ
Many	Lambert [1951, p. 19]	Semidiurnal tide, many stations	1.198
Many	Lambert [1951, p. 19]	Diurnal tide, many stations	1.186
Lecolazet	Lecolazet [1957]	Diurnal tide, Strasbourg (K_1)	1.204 ± 0.006
Lecolazet	Lecolazet [1957]	Diurnal tide, Strasbourg, (O_2)	1.178 ± 0.006
Lecolazet	Lecolazet [1957]	Semidiurnal tide (M_2)	1.211 ± 0.005
Lecolazet	Lecolazet [1957]	Semidiurnal tide (S_2)	1.217 ± 0.013
Baars	Tomaschek [1957b, p. 810]	Average, world-wide	1.24
Lambert	Tomaschek [1957b, p. 810]	10 tropical stations	1.23
Tomaschek	Tomaschek [1957a]	Shetland Islands	1.23 ± 0.15
Stoyko	Melchior [1958, p. 431]	Pendulum clocks	1.21
Several	Melchior [1958, p. 426]	Latitude variation	1.13
Several	Melchior [Colloquium 1958]	Gravimeters, quartz clocks	1.20 ± 0.02

The third combination of Love's numbers, Λ is given by Eq. (8.21). According to Melchior [1958, p. 426], "it is generally accepted that Λ is between 1.1 and 1.2"; however, he points out that "it is difficult to decide a value for Λ, since the results are disparate." He finds [Melchior, 1958] $\Lambda = 1.13$ as a weighted mean of results obtained by analysis of observations of the latitude variations, and also [Colloquium, 1958] gives $\Lambda = 1.15 \pm 0.10$. Similarly, Nishimura [1950] calculates $\Lambda = 1.20 \pm 0.10$. Tomaschek [1957b, p. 814] concludes that "the problem of determining a definite value of Λ by latitude determinations cannot yet be regarded as solved."

Two of Love's numbers can be found directly, k^* from the ratio of the actual period of the free nutation to that for a rigid earth (Section 8.2), and l from measurements of strains produced by the body tides; according to Tomaschek [1957b, p. 815] such "observations indicate that probably

l = about 0.05." Melchior [Colloquium, 1958] gives l = 0.055 ±0.03. Tomaschek [1957b, p. 813] discusses direct calculations of k^* from the polar movement, and concludes that a value of k^* = 0.28, found in this way, should be regarded as reliable, especially since it is found "from the behavior of the integrated earth's globe as a whole."

Melchior [1958, p. 437] has pointed out that k^* is usually close to or slightly smaller than $\frac{1}{2}h$. This is confirmed by the values in Table 8.3, especially section B which contains k^* and h calculated on various assumptions. Jeffreys and Vicente [1957] have discussed theoretical difficulties in the calculation of Love's numbers, arising from effects of the liquidity of the core. This effect is different for short-period and long-period tides; the statical theory seems to be a sufficient approximation only for semidiurnal tides and those with longer periods.

In Table 8.3, results for the various quantities are summarized. The values found by Takeuchi [1950] are based on various assumptions, especially about the rigidity in the core. They are discussed in more detail in Section 8.6. Melchior [1958, p. 435] concludes "that the four methods of measuring earth tides give coherent results." On the other hand, Tomaschek [1957b, p. 818] points out that in considering the experimental values "the strange fact emerges that it is not easily possible to bring them into a consistent system from which conformable values for k^*, h, and l can be derived." However, the value k^* = 0.19 which Melchior finds as a common solution which fits Eqs. (8.19), (8.20), (8.21) on the basis of the observations for γ, δ, and Λ, is considered to be definitely too small by others. On the basis of Eq. (8.23) (Section 8.2) and assuming a Chandler period of 429.5 days, Melchior [Colloquium, 1958] finds k^* = 0.27, which disagrees with the solution from Eq. (8.19) to (8.21), given above. On the other hand, to k^* = 0.19 should correspond a Chandler period of only 382 days, which is definitely too small. If, however, k^* = 0.29 is regarded the best value, "then γ = 0.72 and δ = 1.20 yield different values of h, namely 0.57 and 0.635 respectively" [Tomaschek, 1957b, p. 818]. Tomaschek also points out (loc. cit. p. 818) that there seems "to exist some ambiguity as to the true value of Chandler's period." Figure 8.1 shows the basis for such doubts about the value of τ to be used for calculations. The various problems involved have also been investigated extensively by Jeffreys [1959, pp. 214–228]. No solution has been found which explains all contradictions.

The preceding discussion of Love's numbers is based mainly on observations. The connection of Love's numbers with the structure of the earth, especially with the rigidity in the earth's core, is discussed in more detail in Section 8.6.

TABLE 8.3. LOVE'S NUMBERS AND THEIR COMBINATIONS, (A) BASED ON OBSERVATIONS ACCORDING TO (a) MELCHIOR [1958, p. 435]; (b) TOMASCHEK [1957b, p. 817]; (c) NISHIMURA [1950, p. 366]; (B) BASED ON CALCULATIONS FOR SIX EARTH MODELS (1 TO 6) BY TAKEUCHI [1950]; μ IS THE (CONSTANT) RIGIDITY IN DYNES/CM^2 WHICH HE HAS ASSUMED FOR THE CORE

Author	μ	γ	δ	Λ	k^*	h	l
(A) (a)	—	0.706 ± 0.01	1.20 ± 0.02	1.13 ± 0.10	0.188 ± 0.06	0.482 ± 0.07	0.05 ± 0.03
(b)	—	0.72	1.20	1.22	0.29	0.46	0.08
(c)	—	0.66 ± 0.02	—	1.20 ± 0.10	—	—	—
(B) 1	0	0.703	1.152	1.22	0.290	0.597	0.068
2	0	0.675	1.188	1.20	0.281	0.606	0.082
3	10^7	0.674	1.189	1.19	0.275	0.601	0.081
4	10^9	0.675	1.188	1.19	0.275	0.600	0.081
5	10^{11}	0.713	1.167	1.16	0.243	0.530	0.083
6	10^{13}	0.946	1.127	0.96	0.055	0.109	0.092

8.6 The Rigidity in the Earth

The coefficient μ of rigidity is proportional to the tangential stress which is necessary to produce a given distortion (shear). It does not indicate the speed of flow or creep. Contrary to a widespread belief, rigidity is usually a minor factor in relatively slow continuous processes such as subcrustal currents or the motion of continents. Its main importance is in its connection with the velocity of elastic waves and with elastic movements of the whole earth.

Results of laboratory experiments [Adams, 1951; Hughes and Maurette, 1957] indicate that in the crust and in the upper mantle, μ should increase with increasing pressure and decrease with increasing temperature. Characteristic values at the surface are about $(2 \text{ to } 3) \times 10^{11}$ dynes/cm² for granites, $(3 \text{ to } 4) \times 10^{11}$ for gabbro, and $(5 \text{ to } 6) \times 10^{11}$ dynes/cm² for dunite. Representative values of the coefficient of the rigidity in the crust, calculated from Eq. (8.2), $\mu = v^2\rho$, are listed in Table 8.4.

TABLE 8.4. CHARACTERISTIC VALUES OF THE RIGIDITY μ IN THE EARTH'S CRUST, IN 10^{11} DYNES/CM²

Material	μ
Alluvium near the surface	0.1
Alluvium at a depth of 2 km	1
Tertiary sandstone at a depth of 2 km	2
Very old sediments at a depth of 2 km	4
Granitic layer in continents	3
Deeper continental layers	4

The values of the rigidity in the mantle can be found similarly from Eq. (8.2). Corresponding values for μ have been calculated from the most recent results [1958] for $v(r)$ and $\rho(r)$ and have been entered in Fig. 8.4. For the mantle, no large errors are to be expected since the velocity v of transverse waves as well as the density there (Figs. 7.1, 7.2) are fairly well known. Båth [1956] has investigated the rigidity in the suspected low-velocity layer in the upper mantle. Since the density increases slowly with depth throughout this layer, calculation of the rigidity depends mainly on the change of the velocity v of transverse waves with depth. If v has a minimum at a depth near 150 km, while ρ increases with depth, the rigidity could be practically constant in the uppermost portion of the mantle.

There is very little information about the rigidity in the core as a function of depth. Estimates have been based on the reflection of energy at the core boundary, on the rather rapid increase in longitudinal velocity in the transition zone from the outer to the inner core, and on Love's numbers.

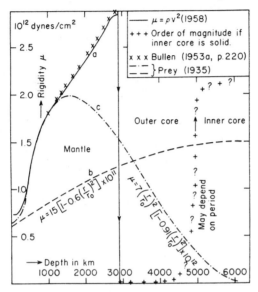

Fig. 8.4. Coefficient of rigidity (μ) in the earth. Curve a from the calculated velocity v of transverse waves and the calculated density ρ in the mantle. For the curves b and c, a continuous change of the rigidity with depth, given by the forms of the respective equations, had been assumed by Prey [1935].

The energy of transverse waves reflected at the boundary of the core (ScS) indicates that at least the outer core is not a usual solid [Honda *et al.*, 1956]. Press [1956] concludes similarly that the ratio of the rigidity to the bulk modulus in the outer core near the core boundary is smaller than 10^{-3} (i.e., that μ is not over 10^{10} dynes/cm^2), "indicating a state unlike that of a normal solid."

Bullen [1953b] has estimated the rigidity in the inner core on the basis of his hypothesis that the compressibility of a material at the pressures in the earth at depths below about 1000 km does not depend on the chemical composition of the material. On the assumptions that this hypothesis is correct, and that the increase in the velocity of longitudinal waves in the transition zone between the outer and inner core results from an increase in the rigidity, Bullen finds that the smallest possible value for the rigidity in the inner core would be 1.5×10^{12} dynes/cm^2.

If we assume that the increase in longitudinal velocity in the transition zone between outer and inner core (ratio a) results fully from the increase in the rigidity μ, and that at the pressure involved the bulk modulus k is not affected by the possible transition from the nonsolid to the solid state, μ inside the inner core is roughly given by

$$\mu = \tfrac{3}{4}k(a^2 - 1). \tag{8.24}$$

With $a = 1.1$ and $k = 13 \times 10^{12}$ dynes/cm², this would give an order of magnitude of 2×10^{12} dynes/cm² for μ inside the inner core near its boundary. It increases towards the center proportional to the density, if v, like V, does not change much with depth in the inner core. Corresponding values of μ in the core have been added with question marks in Fig. 8.4; they give the order of magnitude, at best.

Other rough estimates for the rigidity in the core have been based on Love's numbers. The first attempt along this line was made by Herglotz [1905] who had supposed a constant rigidity μ_1 in the mantle and another, μ_2, in the core. Schweydar [1916] developed a rather complicated system of equations which connect the rigidity in the earth with Love's numbers. He, and later Hoskins [1920] had introduced three boundary conditions and had assumed that the density ρ as well as the rigidity μ increase with depth throughout the earth following equations of the form

$$\rho = A - BR^2 \qquad \mu = C - DR^2 \tag{8.25}$$

where $R = r/r_0$ and A, B, C, D are constants. Prey [1929, 1935] has used the same forms (8.25) for μ and ρ in connection with equations based on improved boundary conditions. Moreover, he has supposed a different type of equation for μ of the form

$$\mu = ER^2(1 - FR^2) \tag{8.26}$$

where E and F are constants. Two of his solutions for μ, one for each form, have been entered in Fig. 8.4 as curves b and c. Considering that the form of the curve c in Fig. 8.4 is given, the curve is a good approximation to the curves found from the velocities v and the densities ρ for the rigidity in the mantle and its tentative values in the core.

A great step forward was made by Takeuchi [1950] when he developed more general equations than those of Prey to calculate Love's numbers for a given model of the earth. For the density and the elastic constants in the mantle, Takeuchi has used approximate values similar to those given in Figs. 7.1, 8.4, and 8.5 respectively, while he has made various assumptions for the mean rigidity of the core. He has calculated Love's numbers for six such models, five of which differ only in the mean rigidity of the core which he has assumed to be between zero and 10^{13} dynes/cm^2. His essential results which are based on tedious calculations are reproduced in portion (B) of Table 8.3. If we compare his calculated values for γ, δ, and Λ in section (B) of Table 8.3 with those found from observations in section (A), it appears that any rigidity in the core between zero and 10^{10} dynes/cm^2 is compatible with Love's numbers, calculated from observations. The results of Takeuchi's investigation in section (B) of Table 8.3 furthermore indicate that k^* is probably not less than 0.25. Calculations by Jeffreys and Vicente [1957, p. 169] on various assumptions give values for k^* of between 0.24 and 0.30.

We may conclude that the rigidity in the mantle is given with good approximation by curve a in Fig. 8.4, that it is probably less, possibly much less, than 10^{10} dynes/cm^2 in the outer core, but may be of the order of magnitude of 2×10^{12} dynes/cm^2 in the inner core.

8.7 The Bulk Modulus in the Earth

The bulk modulus k is the ratio of compressional stress to the volume strain. It is proportional to the change in pressure Δp which is needed to change a given volume w by a certain amount Δw; $k = -(\Delta p/\Delta w)w$. The larger the bulk modulus, the smaller the compressibility.

Laboratory data for the bulk modulus are more plentiful than those for the rigidity. The bulk modulus increases rather rapidly with an increase in pressure from 1 to roughly 1500 atm (depending on the material). This corresponds to the increase in pressure in the uppermost 5 km of the crust and is mainly a consequence of the closing of the pores in the rocks. With further increase in pressure, the increase in the bulk modulus k becomes much smaller, and in deep portions of the crust or in the upper portion of the mantle may be more than offset by a decrease in k as a consequence of the increasing temperature.

Characteristic values for the bulk modulus near the surface are roughly 4×10^{11} dynes/cm^2 for basalt, 8×10^{11} for gabbro and 12×10^{11} dynes/cm^2 for dunite; they show rather large variations in different samples of the same type of rock.

The bulk modulus in the earth may be found from Eq. (8.1), $k = \rho\Phi$. As may be seen from Fig. 8.5, there is little disagreement about the bulk modulus in the mantle. It is generally assumed that in the outer core the velocity v of transverse waves is too small to affect Φ, and that in the outer core with sufficient accuracy $k = \rho V^2$. The agreement between various results based on this assumption is good.

The values of k in the inner core are less certain. Bullard's curve in Fig. 8.5 gives an example of the values found on the assumption that the inner core is liquid, while the crosses are intended to indicate the order of magni-

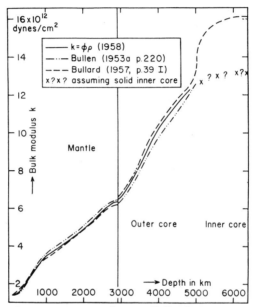

FIG. 8.5. Bulk modulus k as function of the depth in the earth.

tude of k in the inner core, if it is solid. However, in this connection we must consider the possibility of a vicious circle, as a major argument for a solid inner core is Bullen's [1949] hypothesis, that at pressures prevailing below a depth of the order of 1000 km, the bulk modulus is not noticeably affected by the material. There is no general agreement on this hypothesis [Ramsey, 1950]. In any case, Fig. 8.5 can be considered to give a good representation of the bulk modulus in the earth.

8.8 Poisson's Ratio in the Earth

If a cylinder is strained by stresses acting at both ends in opposite directions along the axis, the diameter d of the cylinder changes in the opposite direction to its length L. The ratio $-(\Delta d/d)/(\Delta L/L)$ is called Poisson's ratio. It is designated here by σ. Equation (8.5) shows that the maximum of σ is 0.5 for a material without rigidity ($\mu = 0$) as well as for an incompressible material (k very large). Poisson's ratio decreases as $2\mu/3k$ increases, and it approaches theoretically zero, if 2μ approaches $3k$. For σ smaller than zero, a cylinder stretched along its axis would expand simultaneously in all directions. For most rocks, σ is near 0.25, but values as small as 0.1 have been reported [Adams, 1951, p. 74].

For the interior of the earth, Poisson's ratio σ can be found from the ratio of the velocities V for longitudinal and v for transverse waves (Eq. (8.5), last term). This gives the following corresponding values of σ and V/v

σ	0.0	0.1	0.2	0.25	0.3	0.4	0.5
V/v	1.414	1.500	1.633	1.732	1.871	2.449	∞

In the crystalline layers of the earth's crust, σ seems to vary between about 0.22 and 0.27. Yoshiyama [1957] finds that in Japan V/v varies in the crust between about 1.66 and 1.70; this corresponds to σ between 0.217 and 0.235. Below the Mohorovičić discontinuity, he finds in the average 1.78 for V/v which corresponds to σ of about 0.27. Similar values had been found already by Zoeppritz and Geiger [1909] for the upper mantle.

Recent determinations [Gutenberg, 1953, p. 228] indicate that Poisson's ratio is about 0.27 at a depth of 100 km and that it increases to about 0.29 between 200 and 300 km depth. At a depth of about 2400 km, σ reaches about 0.30 and does not change noticeably in the deeper portion of the mantle down to the boundary of the core. In the outer core, Poisson's ratio is probably near 0.5, but may decrease in the transition zone from the outer to the inner core, perhaps to about 0.4, but even a smaller value is not excluded.

8.9 Young's Modulus and Lamé's Constant λ in the Earth

Young's modulus E is the ratio of tensile stress to linear strain. It is proportional to the force which must be applied at the end of a cylinder of given dimensions if it is assumed that the change in length is proportional to the force (Hooke's law). This assumption is correct within the limits of error in the treatment of many geophysical problems. Theoretically, the following values are expected for E for materials with a given Poisson's ratio

If $\sigma = 0.1$, $E = 2.4k = 2.2\mu$
    $\sigma = 0.2$ $E = 1.8k = 2.4\mu$
    $\sigma = 0.25$ $E = 1.5k = 2.5\mu$
    $\sigma = 0.3$ $E = 1.2k = 2.6\mu$
    $\sigma = 0.4$ $E = 0.6k = 2.8\mu$
    $\sigma = 0.5$ E $= 3.0\mu$, very small.

Consequently, E is about 2.5μ in the outer mantle, about 2.6μ in the deep portions of the mantle (Fig. 8.4), very small (about 3μ) in the outer core and probably near $2\frac{3}{4}\mu$ in the inner core.

Lamé's constant λ has been introduced as an abbreviation for the second term in Eq. (8.3). It is equal to μ if $\sigma = 0.250$, that is, approximately in the outer mantle; it increases to 1.5μ if σ is 0 3, that is, in the deeper portions of the mantle, and λ approximately equals k in the outer core where σ is nearly 0.50. If the inner core is solid, λ is there probably between $0.7k$ and $0.8k$.

References

Adams, L. H. [1951] Elastic properties of materials of the earth's crust. *In* "Internal Constitution of the Earth" (B. Gutenberg, ed.,) 2nd ed., pp. 50–80. Dover, New York.

Bartels, J. [1957]. Gezeitenkräfte. *In* "Encyclopedia of Physics" (S. Flügge, ed.), Vol. 48, pp. 734–774. Springer, Berlin.

Båth, M. [1956]. Some consequences of the existence of low-velocity layers. *Ann. geofis.* **9**, 411–450.

Benioff, H., Gutenberg, B., and Richter, C. F. [1954]. Progress report, seismological laboratory, California Institute of Technology, 1953. *Trans. Am. Geophys. Union* **35**, 979–987.

Bullard, E. C. [1957]. The density within the earth. *Verhandel. Ned. Geol. Mijnbouwk. Genoot. Geol. Ser.* **18**, 23–41.

Bullen, K. E. [1949]. Compressibility-pressure hypothesis and the earth's interior. *Monthly Notices Roy. Astron. Soc. Geophys. Suppl.* **5**, 355–368.

Bullen, K. E. [1953a]. "An Introduction to the Theory of Seismology," 296 pp. Cambridge Univ. Press, London and New York.

Bullen, K. E. [1953b]. The rigidity of the earth's inner core. *Ann. geofis.* **6**, 1–10.

Colloquium [1958]. Deuxième colloque international de la Commission du CSAGI pour l'étude des marées terrestres. *Communs. Observatoire Roy. Belg. No.* **142**, *Sér. Geophys. No.* **47**, 179 pp.

Conference [1958]. *Compt. rend. assoc. intern. seismol. et phys. interieur de la terre, Toronto, 1957, No.* **12**, 301 pp. and appendixes.

Gutenberg, B. [1953]. Wave velocities at depths between 50 and 600 kilometers. *Bull. Seismol. Soc. Am.* **43**, 223–232.

Helmert, F. R. [1884]. "Die mathematischen und physikalischen Theorieen der höheren Geodäsie," Vol. 2. Teubner, Leipzig.

Herglotz, G. [1905]. Ueber die Elastizität der Erde bei Berücksichtigung ihrer variablen Dichte. *Z. Math. Phys.* **52,** 275–299.

Honda, H., Sima, H., and Nakamura, K. [1956]. The ScS wave, the mechanism of deep earthquake and the rigidity of the earth's core. *Sci. Repts. Tôhoku Univ. Fifth Ser.* **7,** 169–179.

Hoskins, L. M. [1920]. The strain of a gravitating sphere of variable density and elasticity. *Trans. Am. Math. Soc.* **21,** 1–43.

Hughes, D. S., and Maurette, C. [1957]. Variation of elastic wave velocities in basic igneous rocks with pressure and temperature. *Geophysics* **22,** 23–31.

Jeffreys, H. [1952]. "The Earth," 3rd ed., 392 pp., 420 pp. Cambridge Univ. Press, London and New York.

Jeffreys, H. [1959]. "The Earth," 4th ed., 420 pp. Cambridge Univ. Press, London and New York.

Jeffreys, H., and Vicente, R. O. [1957]. The theory of nutation and the variation of latitude. *Monthly Notices Roy. Astron. Soc.* **117,** 142–173.

Jobert, N. [1956]. Évaluation de la période d'oscillation d'une sphère élastique hétérogène, par l'application du principe de Rayleigh. *Compt. rend.* **243,** 1230–1232.

Jobert, N. [1957]. Sur la période propre des oscillations sphéroidales de la Terre. *Compt. rend.* **244,** 921–922.

Lambert, W. D. [1933]. Rapport sur les marées de l'écorce terrestre. *Trav. Assoc. géodésie, Union géodés. géophys. intern. Lisbonne* 19 pp.

Lambert W. D. [1951]. Rapport général no. 10 sur les marées de l'écorce terrestre. *Trav. Assoc. géodésie intern. Assemblée Bruxelles* **1951** *Rappts. gen.* 42 pp.

Lambert, W. D., Schlesinger, F., and Brown E. W. [1931]. The variations of latitude. *Bull. Natl. Research Council (U.S.)* **78,** 245–277.

Lecolazet, R. [1957]. Enregistrement et analyse harmonique de la marée gravimétrique à Strasbourg. *Ann. géophys.* **13,** 186–202.

Love, A. E. H. [1911]. "Some Problems of Geodynamics," 180 pp. Cambridge Univ. Press, London and New York.

Melchior, P. J. [1954]. Les marées terrestres. *Observatoire Roy. Belg. Monograph* **4,** 134 pp.

Melchior, P. J. [1957]. Latitude variation. *In* "Physics and Chemistry of the Earth" (L. H. Ahrens, K. Rankama, and S. K. Runcorn, eds.), Vol. 2, pp. 212–243. Pergamon Press, New York.

Melchior, P. J. [1958]. Earth tides. *Advances in Geophys.* **4,** 392–443.

Nishimura, E. [1950]. On earth tides. *Trans. Am. Geophys. Union* **31,** 357–376.

Pekeris, C. L. [1958]. Geophysics, pure and applied. *Geophys. J.* **1,** 257–262.

Pekeris, C. L., and Jarosch, H. [1958]. The free oscillations of the earth. *In* "Contributions in Geophysics" (H. Benioff, M. Ewing, B. F. Howell, and F. Press, eds.), Vol. 1, pp. 171–192. Pergamon, New York.

Press, F. [1956]. Rigidity of the earth's core. *Science* **124,** 1204.

Prey, A. [1929, 1935]. Ueber die Elastizitätskonstante der Erde. *Gerlands Beitr. Geophys.* **23,** 379–429; **44,** 59–80.

Ramsey, W. H. [1950]. On the compressibility of the earth. *Monthly Notices Roy. Astron. Soc. Geophys. Suppl.* **6,** 42–49.

Schweydar, W. [1916]. Theorie der Deformation der Erde durch Gezeitenkräfte. *Veröffentl. Geodät. Inst. Potsdam* [N. F.] **66,** 51 pp.

Takeuchi, H. [1950]. On the earth tide of the compressible earth of variable density and elasticity. *Trans. Am. Geophys. Union* **31,** 651–689.

Takeuchi, H. [1959]. Torsional oscillations of the earth and some related problems. *Geophys. J.* **2**, 89–100.

Tomaschek, R. [1956]. "Probleme der Erdgezeitenforschung." Deutsche Geodät. Kommission, (A) Heft 23, Bayerische Akad., München, 16 pp.

Tomaschek, R. [1957a]. Measurements of tidal gravity and load deformations on Unst (Shetlands). *Geofis. pura e appl.* **37**, 55–78.

Tomaschek, R. [1957b]. Tides of the solid earth. *In* "Encyclopedia of Physics" (S. Flügge, ed.), Vol. 48, pp. 775–845, Springer, Berlin.

Yoshiyama, R. [1957]. The ratio of the velocity of P and S waves. *Bull. Earthquake Research Inst. Tokyo Univ.* **35**, 627–640.

Zoeppritz, K., and Geiger, L. [1909]. Ueber Erdbebenwellen. III. Berechnung von Weg und Geschwindigkeit der Vorläufer. Die Poissonsche Konstante in Erdinnern. *Nachr. Ges. Wiss. Göttingen Math. physik. Kl.* **1909**, 400–429.

9. Nonelastic Processes
in the Earth

9.1 Theoretical Treatment of Nonelastic Processes in the Earth

In early theoretical studies of geophysical phenomena it had usually been assumed that mechanical processes in the earth can be treated as purely elastic. Jeffreys was one of the first to consider nonelastic processes in geophysical investigations. Originally, he had represented "delayed elastic processes" (elastic afterworking, firmoviscosity, internal friction) by equations suggested by Larmor, while for time-dependent flow processes ("elasticoviscosity") he has followed suggestions of Maxwell. Jeffreys has introduced the following convenient, but frequently insufficient approximation for a shearing strain γ produced by a tangential stress S

$$\gamma = \frac{S}{\mu} - \lambda_r \frac{d\gamma}{dt} + \frac{1}{\eta} \int S \, dt \tag{9.1}$$

where

$$\eta = \mu\lambda \qquad \text{and} \qquad \nu = \mu\lambda_r \tag{9.2}$$

μ is the coefficient of rigidity, η the *coefficient of viscosity*, λ the *time of relaxation* in viscous flow; on the other hand, ν is the *coefficient of retarded elastic motion* or "coefficient of internal friction" in elastic processes which are delayed by firmoviscosity, for example, by internal friction; λ_r is the corresponding *time of retardation*, that is, the time in which in such processes the strain falls to $1/e$ of its value, if the stress is removed. Throughout Chapter 9, η and ν are expressed in poises ($=$g/cm sec), μ in g/cm sec^2 ($=$dynes/cm^2 $=$ baryes).

The first part of Eq. (9.1), $\gamma = S/\mu$, corresponds to Hooke's law; the following term is usually important only for short-period stresses and the

185

last term only for stresses lasting for intervals of at least a noticeable fraction of the time $\lambda = \eta/\mu$. Consequently, in most equations for nonelastic processes at least one of these two additional terms is insignificant. Jeffreys [1952, p. 7] suggests that to account to a first approximation for viscous flow (elasticoviscosity) in basic equations for elastic processes concerning the earth, the rigidity μ should be replaced by $\mu/[1 + (\Omega/\lambda)]$ where Ω is the operator of definite integration defined generally by

$$\Omega f(t) = \int_{-\infty}^{t} f(u) \, du. \tag{9.3}$$

For harmonic motion proportional to e^{iqt}, Eq. (9.3) can be evaluated, and it follows that μ is to be replaced by

$$\mu iq\lambda/(1 + iq\lambda). \tag{9.4}$$

In equations representing first-order approximations of processes in which the effect of *retarded elastic response* (e.g. internal friction) is significant, the product $\mu f(t)$ of the rigidity μ and any time-dependent function $f(t)$ should be replaced in the fundamental equations by

$$\mu f(t) + \nu \, \partial f(t)/\partial t \tag{9.5}$$

if Eq. (9.1) without the last term is a sufficient approximation. In such instances, terms containing only the bulk modulus k may be assumed to remain unchanged to a first approximation.

Even the greatly simplified equation (9.1) may lead to very complicated equations for which frequently no general solution can be given, though the equation is at best a rough approximation, and may be even useless for some problems. This has been pointed out already by Jeffreys. Other types of nonelastic processes which have been defined, among them creep, are not covered by Eq. (9.1). They are frequently represented by mechanical models, containing mainly springs and dashpots [Benioff, 1951a; Eirich, 1956; Reiner, 1958]. Moreover, many more or less complicated equations have been suggested for specific processes [see, e.g., Jeffreys, 1958].

It is sometimes overlooked that "firmoviscosity" (retarded elastic response) in solids frequently results in effects similar to those produced by "viscous flow" in true liquids. Following a suddenly starting constant stress, both processes result in a displacement which is smaller than that given by Hooke's law, but approaches it asymptotically. On the other hand, "viscous flow" in solids does not correspond to "viscous flow" in liquids. In solids, it results in a displacement which starts with the value given by Hooke's law but continues to increase beyond the amount produced by a purely elastic process, while in liquids it delays the displacement. Consequently, applications of the last term in Eq. (9.1) to equations for true liquids, or of equations containing ν or λ_r to equations for viscous flow of solids, lead to erroneous results. The following equations follow from Eq. (9.1) in special cases (t = time):

Assumed condition	Viscous response in solids	Retarded elastic response	
Short-period motion $(t \sim \lambda_r)$	Effect usually negligible	$\gamma = \dfrac{S}{\mu} - \lambda_r \dfrac{\partial \gamma}{\partial t}$	(9.6)
Long-period motion $(t \sim \lambda)$	$\gamma = \dfrac{S}{\mu} + \dfrac{1}{\eta} \displaystyle\int S\, dt$	Usually negligible	(9.7)
Long-period motion $(t \gg \lambda)$	S approaches $\eta(\partial \gamma / \partial t)$		
$\mu = 0$ and $\nu > 0$ (viscous fluid)		$S = \nu(\partial \gamma / \partial t)$	(9.8)

Thus, Eq. (9.1) leads to Eq. (9.6) for short-period motion with retarded response, but to Eq. (9.7) for long-lasting processes in solid material undergoing a type of viscous flow. In any case, the representation of nonelastic processes by Eq. (9.1) is limited by the form of the equation. Consequently, details of the theoretical results usually do not correspond to the details of the processes in nature. Especially, quantities assumed to be constant in Eq. (9.1), (9.6), (9.7), and (9.8) may actually change with time, with the frequency of vibrations involved in the process, with the amount of stress or of strain, etc.

Numerical values of quantities related to nonelastic processes which are assumed to be represented by Eq. (9.1) at selected depths in the interior of the earth are summarized in Tables 9.1a and 9.1b, a few corresponding data found in laboratory experiments and in processes at the earth's surface are added. Even the order of magnitude of most "constants" for nonelastic processes in Table 9.1 is doubtful, especially for those listed for the earth's interior. All these "constants" depend on the assumptions which have been made in calculating or estimating them.

A rather great variety of nonelastic processes are encountered in technical rheology, and many systems of equations have been developed to represent them [Eirich, 1956; Freudenthal and Geiringer, 1958; Reiner, 1958]. Unfortunately, most geophysicists are not sufficiently familiar with technical

TABLE 9.1a. ORDER OF MAGNITUDE OF NONELASTIC "CONSTANTS" (A) IN SOME
MATERIALS AT THE SURFACE OF THE EARTH, AND (B) AT SELECTED DEPTHS
IN THE INTERIOR OF THE EARTH AFTER GUTENBERG [1958b]
ON THE ASSUMPTION THAT EQ. (9.1) CAN BE APPLIED.

(A) Material	$\log \eta^1$	$\log \lambda$	$\log \nu$	$\log \lambda_r$
Shoemaker's pitch, 50°C	4	?	?	?
Shoemaker's pitch, 15°C	8	0	?	?
Rock salt, 18°C	18	7	?	?
Solenhofen limestone	$22 \pm$	$3 \pm$	$9 \pm$	$-2\frac{1}{2} \pm$
Gabbro	?	?	$9\frac{1}{4} \pm$	$-2\frac{1}{2} \pm$
Glacier ice	13 to 14	$-4 \pm$	?	?
Flowing lava	$\leq 5 \pm$	?	?	?

(B) Depth				
10 km (continent)	22 to 23	$4 \pm$	$9 \pm$	-2 to -3
100	$22 \pm$	$2 \pm$	$9 \pm$	-2 to -3?
700	$20 \pm$?	1?	9 to 10?	-3?
800 to 2900	<20?	≤ 0?	10?	-3?

[1] η = coefficient of viscosity, in poises; λ = corresponding time of relaxation in years;
ν = coefficient of retarded elastic response for elastic waves with periods of 0.1 to $20 \pm$
sec, in poises; λ_r = corresponding time of retardation, in seconds. It is very probable
that η and λ have minima at depths of the order of 100 to 150 km, where the temperature
is close to the melting point (Fig. 6.1 and Section 6.9).

TABLE 9.1b. ORDER OF MAGNITUDE OF NONELASTIC "CONSTANTS" IN THE
EARTH'S CRUST AFTER SCHEIDEGGER [1957a, P. 396].

Time interval	Applicable to	Behavior	Constants[1]
Up to 4 hours	Seismic wave transmission	Elastic solid with strength limit s	$\mu = 2 \times 10^{12}$ cgs $E = 5 \times 10^{12}$ cgs $s = 10^{10}$ cgs
4 hours to 15,000 years	Chandler wobble Earthquake aftershocks Faulting Earth's tides	Kelvin body with strength limit s	$\mu_K = 2 \times 10^{12}$ cgs $\eta_K = 3 \times 10^{17}$ cgs s unknown
Over 15,000 years	Large scale orogenesis Uplift of Fennoscandia Polar wandering	Bingham body [see, e.g., Eirich, 1956]	μ_M term possibly negligible $\eta_M = 10^{22}$ cgs $\vartheta = 4 \times 10^9$ cgs

[1] μ_K and μ_M are respectively the "Kelvin rigidity" and the "Maxwell rigidity," η_K
and η_M are the corresponding viscosities, ϑ is the yield stress at the surface.

rheology to apply these equations, and most rheologists do not have sufficient experience with geophysics to work out equations which are easily applicable to geophysical problems. Benioff [1951a] has applied some results of technical rheology to the relationship between earthquakes and rock creep. Hiersemann [1958] has discussed the importance of specific rheological models and equations for the investigations of problems of orogeny and subcrustal currents. Orowan [1958] has started to apply findings of technical rheology to various problems in geophysics, with very promising results. In his preliminary conclusions, Orowan points out that "the earth's crust shows viscosity; at the same time, it is probable that at greater depths . . . the rate of flow increases very slowly below a fairly distinct value of the shear stress, and much more rapidly above it. . . . In other words, it is likely to show non-Newtonian viscosity with a more or less distinct yield stress."

9.2 Attenuation of Elastic Waves in the Earth

Some phenomena which are connected with rapidly proceeding processes (time or period not over a few minutes) may be considered to be delayed elastic processes. They include internal friction and scattering in short-period waves. To a rough approximation they may be represented by Eq. (9.6). The attenuation of elastic waves by such processes is assumed to correspond to a factor e^{-kD}, where k is the coefficient of absorption and D is the distance along the wave path. If k varies in the body, kD is to be replaced by a corresponding integral. At the distance $D = 1/k$ the amplitude has decreased to $1/e$ by attenuation, at $D = 2.3/k$ it has decreased to 0.1.

Various assumptions [see, e.g., Gutenberg, 1958a; Knopoff and Mac-Donald, 1958] have been made to introduce attenuation effects into the theory for purely elastic waves. On the basis of several simple assumptions the theory indicates that single wavelets should be getting longer during their propagation. On another group of assumptions it follows theoretically that the absorption coefficient k should be proportional to $1/T^2V^3$ ($T =$ period, $V =$ velocity of the waves).

In laboratory experiments, k is usually not far from proportional to $1/T$. Förtsch [1956] has found that good agreement between theory and observations may be achieved if, in fundamental equations, to the expressions for purely elastic forces terms for frictional forces are added which he assumes to be proportional to the absolute value of all acting forces ("Coulomb-friction"). Knopoff [1956] has introduced a term, describing sinusoidal motion, into the differential equation of motion for a medium possessing solid friction. On his assumptions, the damping coefficient of sinusoidal waves is given by

$$k = \pi/QTV \qquad (9.9)$$

where Q is a constant of the material, T the wave period, and V the velocity. Empirical investigations related to Q have been discussed and extended by Birch [1942, p. 88]. If Eq. (9.9) holds, the logarithmic decrement δ of vibrations in a given material and the dimensionless constant $Q = \pi/\delta$ do not depend on the period, and

$$Q = \frac{\pi}{\delta} = \frac{\pi}{kTV} = \text{const.} \qquad (9.10)$$

Knopoff [1956] has found that in materials with $Q \gg 1$, the width T of a pulse increases proportional to the distance D.

Values of Q found from laboratory experiments [Birch, 1942, p. 92], especially Q of about 100 to 200 for granite under pressure of up to 200 atm in the frequency range 140 to 1600 cycles/sec, are of the same order of

TABLE 9.2. ABSORPTION COEFFICIENT k (PER 1000 KM) FOR AMPLITUDES, AND CORRESPONDING ORDER OF MAGNITUDE OF Q; (a) FOR SURFACE WAVES, (b) FOR BODY WAVES

Author	Wave type	Period, sec	k	Q
Surface waves				
Gutenberg [1924]	Love	100 ±	0.1	70
Gutenberg [1945a]	Rayleigh	20	0.2	200
Ewing and Press [1954]	Rayleigh	140	0.036	150
Ewing and Press [1954]	Rayleigh	215	0.022	150
Body waves				
Gutenberg [1945b, p. 58]	P, PKP	4 ±	0.06	1300
Gutenberg [1958a]	P, PP	2	0.06	2500
Gutenberg [1958a]	P, PP	12	0.06	400
Gutenberg [1958a]	S	12	0.06	700
Gutenberg [1958a]	S	24	0.06	400
Press [1956]	S	11	(0.09)	≤500

magnitude as those found for earthquake surface waves with periods of 20 to more than 200 sec (Table 9.2,a). This may indicate that at least in the earth's crust k is approximately proportional to $1/T$. On the other hand, Kárnik [1956] has combined data for Rayleigh waves with periods of between 0.001 ($k = 200$/km) and 200 sec ($k = 0.00002$/km) and has found that all data can be represented fairly well by

$$k = 0.017T^{-1.42}. \tag{9.11}$$

Investigations of records of nearby earthquakes indicate that the periods of body waves increase on paths through the upper portion of the crust. At distances beyond 20°, periods of a fraction of a second which exist in waves near the source have disappeared, and at distances between 25° and 110° transverse waves show rarely periods of less than 4 sec, while periods of 1 sec are recorded in direct longitudinal waves as far as they are observed, that is to distances of 100± degrees. Contrasting with waves through the crust and the upper portion of the mantle, there is no known indication of differences in the absorption coefficient of amplitudes, $k = 0.06\pm$/1000 km for longitudinal waves through the deeper portion of the mantle and for waves through the core, regardless of their period. Thus, the attenuation of longitudinal waves in the deep portions of the mantle and in the core cannot be represented by the same equations as the attenuation of those through the earth's crust nor of those used in laboratory experiments. Values for k are listed in Table 9.2.

If Eq. (9.9) holds, and if $Q \gg 1$, the time of retardation, λ_r is given by

$$\lambda_r = \frac{T}{2\pi Q} \tag{9.12}$$

which is a small fraction of T. If, on the other hand, we assume that Eq. (9.6) provides a sufficient approximation, λ_r is of the order of 0.003 sec (see, e.g., Jeffreys [1952], pp. 40, 107, from scattering of waves). All processes which could give information on the quantities involved are complicated, and usually it has to be assumed that only one type of mechanism is involved where the observations are actually affected by several such mechanisms. This is true, too, for the observed "lengthening of periods of waves with distance" [Gutenberg, 1958b], which may be either the result of greater absorption for waves with shorter than for those with longer periods or of an actual lengthening of the periods of single waves. On the other hand, longitudinal waves which have traveled repeatedly through the (liquid) outer core show prevailingly short periods, frequently less than 1 sec [Gutenberg, unpublished].

Knopoff and MacDonald [1958, p. 1192] conclude that "the dissipative characteristics of many solids cannot be accounted for by any linear mechanism of attenuation. One particular model which we [Knopoff and MacDonald] have explored in detail involves a nonlinear hysteresis loop resulting from a nonrecoverable deformation at small stresses. This model is by no means unique, and other models involving some frictional dissipation could also account for the observations."

9.3 The Strength Resisting Flow Processes (Yield Point)

The theoretical representation of flow processes is not only complicated by the difficulty in finding proper expressions to describe them, but also by the existence of a minimum stress, the yield point (often called "yield strength") which must be surpassed before flow may start. Unfortunately, the observational data as well as the definition of the yield point are rather vague. Daly [1940, p. 7] and others after him have tried to introduce respective definitions. The main difficulty arises from the fact that laboratory experiments indicate that, given enough time, materials may start flowing

TABLE 9.3. ORDER OF MAGNITUDE OF THE YIELD POINT FOR VARIOUS ROCK TYPES AT ABOUT 15°C, COMPILED FROM GRIGGS [1939a, 1940] AND FROM WEINBERG [1927]

Material	Confining pressure atmospheres	Yield point dynes/cm^2
Marble	1	10^9
Marble	10,000	10^{10}
Sandstone	1000	10^9
Granite	2000	10^{10}
Solenhofen limestone	1	10^{10}
Solenhofen limestone	10,000	10^{10}
Quartz	1	10^{10}
Quartz	20,000	10^{11}

at the smallest stresses available. On the other hand, it is believed that mountains up to 10 km high above the surrounding areas have not shown an observable decrease in height since observations exist. However, there seem to be no investigations about the accuracy of such statements. Moreover, the possibility exists that any actual changes in height of mountains may be interpreted as effects of geological processes of some other hypothetical origin.

It is usually assumed that in the upper portion of the crust the yield point is of the order of magnitude of 10^9 dynes/cm^2 [see, e.g., Jeffreys, 1952, p. 197; Scheidegger, 1957a, p. 394; Meinesz, in Heiskanen and Meinesz, 1958, p. 18]. A similar order of magnitude has been found for several rock types in laboratory experiments during short time intervals (Table 9.3). Unfortunately, the yield point depends, among other factors, on the history of the samples and on the duration of the experiments. Orowan [1958] believes that the tensile strength of the earth's crust under a horizontal tension rises from a low value of between zero and a few tens of bars (order of 10^7 dynes/cm^2) at the surface to several thousand bars (a few times 10^9 dynes/cm^2) at a depth of perhaps 10 or 20 km, and that below this depth it falls again to very low values.

We must conclude that the available data are not sufficient to provide definite statements and that a clarification of the whole problem is needed.

9.4 "Viscosity" of the Earth's Outer Layers. Postglacial Uplift

There is a variety of processes which may produce some kind of flow [see, e.g., Colloquium, 1951; Eirich, 1956, 1958; Scheidegger, 1957a; Orowan, 1958]. Unfortunately, there are very few generally accepted definitions for such gradual changes in the form of materials. Among them are creep, viscous flow, and plastic flow.

Creep is a non-Newtonian viscous flow. Below the more or less clearly defined "creep strength" the rate of deformation is very small. Above the creep strength, the rate of deformation increases rapidly with increasing stress.

In many investigations of gradual movements of material inside the earth it is assumed that it is permissible to suppose *Newtonian flow*, that is, to assume that the ratio of the stress to the shear rate D does not depend on D. This is a rather special assumption, but frequently it can be used as a first approximation since usually the available observations are scanty, and the processes are too complicated to permit the finding of precise quantities. In many geophysical and geological publications the expression "viscous" is used to indicate Newtonian flow, the expression "plastic" for more general types of flow, but in the earth-sciences there is appreciable confusion about the use of all terms connected with nonelastic gradual displacements.

The only phenomenon which has been believed to provide some data for the investigation of the order of magnitude of the speed of subcrustal flow is the "postglacial uplift." In portions of Fennoscandia (Fig. 9.1), as well as in the Great Lakes–Hudson Bay region (Fig. 9.2), the land is rising at a rate which, at present, has its maximum of the order of 1 m/century in the central region of the respective formerly glaciated area, decreases toward

zero near the boundary of the former ice sheet, and becomes slightly negative beyond [see, e.g., Gutenberg, 1941, 1954; Kääriäinen, 1953; Heiskanen
and Meinesz, 1958, p. 365].

Some geologists believe that most of the present uplift is a consequence
of tectonically produced stresses, and that there is no longer a noticeable
remainder of the gravity deficit which had been produced by the melting

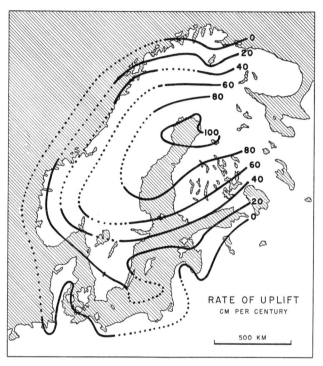

FIG. 9.1. Contemporary rate of uplift of Fennoscandia after Gutenberg [1958b, p. 414].

of the ice load deposited during the Ice Age. However, most geophysicists
and geologists agree that the past as well as the present uplift in formerly
glaciated areas is mainly a consequence of the removal of the ice, and that
the restoration of the equilibrium has not been completed. Otherwise, it
would be a peculiar coincidence that in Fennoscandia as well as in the Great
Lakes region of North America the area of maximum uplift throughout the
recent centuries agrees with the region of the largest former glaciation.

A serious objection to the assumption that Newtonian viscosity may be
supposed in a theoretical treatment of the postglacial uplift has been raised

by Orowan [1958]. He points out "that a significant part of the postglacial rise may be due to delayed-elastic strain recovery, not isostatic adjustment, and that it would be surprising, if the assumption of Newtonian viscosity was justified even as a crude approximation." The solution of the problem is further complicated by the probability that at depths of the order of 100 to 200 km the temperature approaches the melting point of the material

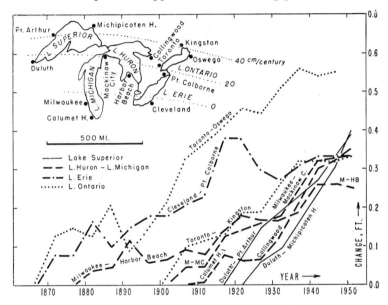

FIG. 9.2. Relative change in level (in feet) in the region of the Great Lakes, North America, at pairs of tide gauges. Insert: Location of the gauges and lines of equal uplift in cm/century. After Gutenberg [1958b, p. 416].

(Section 6.9) rather closely so that the numerical "constants" involved in these processes may differ appreciably at different depths and may depend on the region involved. Thus, the question must be raised, if the calculation of even the order of magnitude of the "coefficient of viscosity" and of the "time of retardation" in the earth's crust and in the upper portion of the mantle on the basis of the findings from the postglacial uplift is of much use. The answer is affirmative. We may assume that in the investigation of other problems and processes of similar types the assumption of Newtonian viscosity with the constants which have been found from the investigation of postglacial uplift may give useful answers, at least as far as the order of magnitude of the time scale for the decrease in strain from nonelastic movements is concerned. An example is the question, how fast the increase in strain from tectonic processes (in the widest sense) at depths of 100 or 200 km may be released in flow processes, on which conditions it may be expected to accumulate to some extent and, finally, may be partly reduced during deep-focus earthquakes.

The maximum thickness of the ice over the northern Baltic during the ice age is estimated to have been 2 to 3 km. The ice sheet began to melt about 40,000 years ago. About 9000 years ago, when in Fennoscandia the ice was reduced to patches northwest of the Baltic, the land near the former center of glaciation had risen between 250 and 300 m. An uplift of about 260 m has been added there since. The observed rates of uplift indicate that the flow in the crustal layers which has permitted the uplift corresponds to the rates required by Newtonian viscosity with a fair approximation. Calculations assuming a viscous process lead to the conclusion that the center of the area is still about 200 m below its equilibrium position. The absolute values of negative gravity anomalies increase to about 50 mgal [Heiskanen, 1951] as the center of the uplift is approached. However, the effects of the tectonic disturbances which are superposed upon the effects produced by the postglacial mass deficit result in irregularities in the distribution of gravity anomalies.

The phenomena related to the postglacial uplift in northern North America are similar to those observed in Fennoscandia. However, all data are less plentiful and do not provide results of the same accuracy as those found for Fennoscandia. The maximum thickness of the North American icecap is estimated to have been between 2 and 3 km, similar to that in Fennoscandia. The center of the uplift is probably in the southern portion of the Hudson Bay, and its maximum amount seems to exceed 300 m. The most reliable findings for the present uplift in northern North America are based on records of tide gauges in the Great Lakes. In Fig. 9.2 selected relative changes in sea level at pairs of tide gauge stations are reproduced. They are calculated from differences in five-year means of the observed water level at pairs of gauges. For each pair the difference in the first five-year period is taken as zero. Negative gravity anomalies near Hudson Bay may indicate that the uplift is incomplete. (*Can. Geophys. Bull.* **11**, 7 (1958).

Unfortunately, there is only one tide gauge in the Hudson Bay with records covering a time interval long enough for use in calculations of sea-level changes. It is at Churchill, Manitoba, and even there data are available at present for only 26 years. Moreover, adverse meteorological condition during most of the year, as well as ice which piles up during the winter and does not disappear until late in May or during June, make it advisable to use tide-gauge data for Churchill for the months July to September only. For the average during the months July, August, September 1928 to 1951 the observations give an average rate of 1.05 ± 0.18 m/century for the uplift at Churchill [Gutenberg, 1954]. Six-year averages give the following mean sea level in cm relative to the average for 1928–33

1928–33	1934–39	1940–45	1946–51	$\begin{pmatrix} 1952–54 \\ -21 \end{pmatrix}$
0 ± 4	-13 ± 5	-16 ± 4	-20 ± 6	

Other indications for uplift in the region of Churchill are controversial. A frequently quoted conclusion, that no appreciable uplift has occurred is based on the fact that on May 27, 1753, visitors cut their names into a bluff; these names were about 23 feet above sea level in 1934. The calculated amount of the uplift depends on the unknown fact whether the names have been cut from a boat or from the surface of usually high ice; either is possible at the end of May; (Compare Gutenberg [1941] p. 749.).

The changes of average sea level are rather irregular since the sea level (or lake level) at a given coast depends on meteorological conditions, especially precipitation and winds during a given year. In addition, the process called "postglacial uplift" does not only include uplift in the formerly glaciated area but also subcrustal flow from the surrounding regions which, correspondingly, show a sinking. Temporary blocking of the subcrustal currents which control the process must be expected to slow down or stop the uplift in portions of the affected area from time to time. Earthquakes prove the existence of occasional increase in strain in and about areas of postglacial uplift. The uplift in North America and in Fennoscandia proceed similarly in time and space, and in both areas the physical constants involved in the process are found to be of the same order of magnitude.

If the postglacial uplift is mainly a result of the decrease in the ice load, regions which at present are heavily loaded by ice, e.g., Antarctica and Greenland, should show a corresponding depression of the rock surface. Alfred Wegener had pointed out that the measurement of the ice thickness in Greenland by recording of explosion echoes from its bottom was one of the most important tasks for his expeditions to Greenland, which ended with his death there. His measurements indicate a rapid increase in ice thickness with increasing distance from the coast. About 40 km inland at points roughly 200 km northeast of Disko (Fig. 9.3, left top) with the ice surface about 1570 m above sea level, an ice thickness of 1200 m has been found on his expedition. His tentative result that in the central part of Greenland the rock surface is not far from sea level has been confirmed (Fig. 9.3) by a French expedition [Joset and Holtzscherer, 1954].

The fact that the rock surface in central Greenland forms a basin under the ice load furnishes a strong support for the theory of postglacial uplift. This uplift is probably connected with the flow process for which observations cover the longest time interval and the widest area, and the findings have been used repeatedly to calculate on various assumptions the "coeffi-

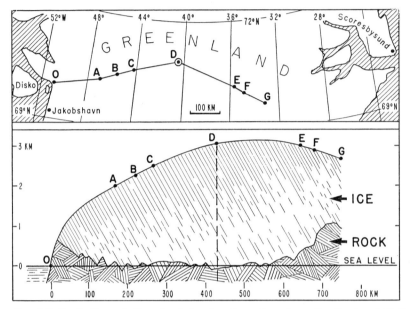

FIG. 9.3. Profile through Greenland showing the rock surface after Joset and Holtz-scherer [1954].

cient of viscosity" η, in the earth's upper few hundred kilometers. Usually it has been supposed for these calculations that η does not change with depth in the layers involved. Consequently, the results cannot be expected to give more than a rough approximation of the logarithm of the average "coefficient of viscosity."

Haskell [1935, 1936] has worked out a formal solution for the motion of a highly viscous fluid when a symmetrical pressure is applied at the surface. He starts with the problem of the motion of a semi-infinite, incompressible, viscous fluid (viscosity η, density ρ) under the action of a radially symmetrical load (radius r) applied at the time $t = 0$ upon a free surface. He neglects the curvature of the earth as well as inertial terms in the equations of motion in comparison with those arising from viscosity. The equations of motion (rate V, stress p, density ρ), in a gravitational field g are

$$\eta\Delta^2 V = \text{grad p} - (0, 0, \rho g) \qquad \text{and} \qquad \text{div } V = 0 \qquad (9.13)$$

with the positive z-axis directed downward. In cylindrical coordinates (r, z, Φ), setting $\bar{p} = p - \rho gz$, the components of stress in which we are interested are

$$p_{zz} = - (\bar{p} + \rho gz) + 2\eta \frac{\partial V_z}{\partial z} \qquad (9.14)$$

$$p_{rz} = \eta \left(\frac{\partial V_r}{\partial z} + \frac{\partial V_z}{\partial r} \right). \qquad (9.15)$$

At the free surface, $p_{rz} = 0$, and p_{zz} equals the applied stress; at infinity, stresses and velocities are zero. If the equation of the actual free surface is $z = \zeta(r,t)$, and if the plane $z = 0$ is taken at the undisturbed surface, the values of the quantities in Eqs. (9.14) and (9.15), except for ρgz, may be replaced by their values at $z = 0$. If the applied pressure is $-\sigma(r,t)$ the boundary conditions become

$$\bar{p}(r,0,t) + \rho g\zeta(r,t) - 2\eta \left(\frac{\partial V_z}{\partial z} \right)_{(r,0,t)} = \sigma(r,t) \qquad (9.16)$$

$$\left(\frac{\partial V_r}{\partial z} + \frac{\partial V_z}{\partial r} \right)_{z=0} = 0 \qquad \text{and} \qquad \frac{\partial \zeta}{\partial t} = V_z(r,0,t). \qquad (9.17)$$

Introduction of functions for V_r, V_z, and $\bar{p}$ leads to Bessel equations which are solved by Haskell. He has applied the resulting formal equations to the subsidence of a cylindric body. In this case $\sigma(r,t)$ is zero for all values of $r > r_0$ and at all times $t \leqslant 0$, and constant otherwise. He has then calculated the change in form of the viscous half space under the load of a cylindric body as well as under the load of an infinite long strip with parallel sides. Haskell also has applied his results to the viscous recoil of the earth after the disappearance of the Pleistocene ice on Fennoscandia. The most important result which Haskell finds is that such viscous type processes extend to unexpectedly great depths. As a consequence of the melting of the ice load, appreciable flow processes should affect most of the earth's mantle under the disturbed area. Specifically, on Haskell's assumptions, the vertical displacement should scarcely decrease within a depth equal to the radius of the original ice load (order of magnitude 500 km), and at twice this depth it should be about half that at the surface (many hundred meters). On the basis of Nansen's [1928] results for the uplift in Fennoscandia, and on the assumptions that Newtonian viscosity prevails and that the coefficient of viscosity η is constant throughout the mantle, Haskell finds the following values for η.

Starting year	5000 B.C.	4000 B.C.	3000 B.C.	2000 B.C.
η	2.6×10^{21}	3.2×10^{21}	3.0×10^{21}	2.9×10^{21} poises

There is general agreement between the findings of various authors that on the assumptions mentioned repeatedly the data for the postglacial uplift indicate a coefficient of viscosity η of 10^{22} or 10^{23} poises. Since the coefficient of rigidity μ is about 5×10^{11} dynes/cm^2, Eq. (9.2) gives a time of relaxation $\lambda = \eta/\mu$ of the order of many thousand years. However, we must keep in mind that the processes involved are certainly not an effect of pure Newtonian flow as we have assumed. Contrasting with our assumptions, they may include delayed-elastic strain recovery according to Orowan [1958], and the "coefficient of viscosity" changes with depth. Moreover, we cannot estimate the effect of tectonic processes which are superposed upon the postglacial uplift.

There are other methods to get information about the order of magnitude of log η in the earth. Effects of the viscosity in the earth on the Chandler period of the nutation (variation of latitude, Section 8.2) have been discussed by Prey [1942]. The greater the viscosity, the smaller would be its damping effect. However, the complication of the movement (Fig. 8.2) makes it very difficult to find the decay of the nutation from damping [Jeffreys, 1959, p. 255; Gutenberg, 1956a; Melchior, 1955, 1957; Anonymous, 1956], and there is considerable disagreement even about the order of magnitude of the time of relaxation of the nutation (10 years? 1000 years?).

Other information on the viscosity in the earth has been derived from the fact that for various terms of the body tides no phase difference between the tides and the tidal forces (Section 8.3) has been found within the limits of error of the observations. Schweydar [1912] has pointed out that the phases of both agree within ±5 min for the main half-day terms, and has concluded that in the mantle there can be no continuous layer of a thickness of even 100 km with a coefficient of viscosity η of 10^9 poises (more than that for pitch at normal temperature), nor a layer with a thickness of 600 km and a viscosity coefficient of 10^{13} poises (about as viscous as ice).

9.5 Flow in the Deep Portions of the Earth

As we go deeper into the earth the investigation of rheological problems must be based on an increasing number of assumptions (see Section 9.4). Doubt about the possibility of subcrustal flow across the mantle has been expressed by Birch [1951]. The rather rapid increase in seismic wave velocities at depths between about 200 and 900 km below the surface (Section 4.3) may indicate a zone of transition from a low-pressure form to a high-pressure form of the material and/or changes in chemical composition. In either case, a change in the viscosity is to be expected.

Others have expressed their opinion that noticeable flow processes in the upper portion of the mantle are not possible since otherwise earthquakes caused by rupture along fault surfaces down to a depth of about 700 km could not exist. However, the time of relaxation for viscous flow is of a higher order of magnitude than the time needed in active earthquake regions for accumulation of strain to the breaking point. In most active belts, relatively large shocks follow each other at intervals of the order of 100 or even 10 years. Consequently, the strain which accumulates in earthquake belts from tectonic processes should not be reduced appreciably by viscous flow during the time intervals between successive deep shocks in those portions of the earth's mantle where the breaking strength is reached in a time interval of the order of not over 100 years, while the time of relaxation during flow processes is of the order of 1000 years.

The fact that no deep-focus earthquakes have been observed below a depth of about 700 km since instrumental records made it possible to fix their depth—that is, since about 1905—may either result mainly from a rather rapid decrease in the accumulation of strain from disturbing processes below this depth, or mainly from an increase in speed of flow there great enough to prevent an accumulation of strain. In the latter case, the time of relaxation λ would be of smaller order of magnitude than 10^8 sec (about 30 years) below 700 km, and, correspondingly, η would decrease below an order of magnitude of 10^{20} poises at a depth of about 700 km. On the other hand, the existence of earthquakes in the upper 700 km of the mantle indicates that above a depth of $700\pm$ km η probably exceeds roughly 10^{20} poises. Since the energy of the largest shocks apparently decreases with depth (Fig. 9.4), it seems reasonable to assume that the same is true for the coefficient of viscosity (or similar coefficients in other types of flow processes), although we must keep in mind that the speed of strain accumulation also plays a role.

In the outer core, we may expect approximately "retarded elastic response" in a viscous fluid, Eq. (9.8), but there seems to be no indication of the order of magnitude of time constants in processes controlling the speed of flow in the outer or inner core. The hypothesis that the earth's magnetism results ultimately from mechanical currents (flow) in the core (Section 5.6) contains too many doubtful quantities to permit the finding of even the

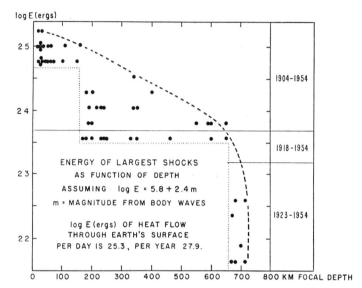

log E (ergs)

1904-1954

1918-1954

ENERGY OF LARGEST SHOCKS
AS FUNCTION OF DEPTH
ASSUMING   log E = 5.8 + 2.4 m
m = MAGNITUDE FROM BODY WAVES

log E (ergs) OF HEAT FLOW
THROUGH EARTH'S SURFACE
PER DAY IS 25.3, PER YEAR 27.9.

1923-1954

0   100   200   300   400   500   600   700   800 KM FOCAL DEPTH

FIG. 9.4. Logarithms of the energy E of the largest earthquakes 1904–1954 as a function of focal depth. All values of log E for which the calculation has given amounts greater than those indicated by the dotted lines have been plotted for the time intervals indicated at right. After Gutenberg [1956c, p. 12].

order of magnitude of time constants or coefficients of "viscosity" there beyond reasonable doubt.

9.6 Strain-Rebound Characteristics of Earthquake Series and Aftershocks

In recent years Benioff [1951a,b, 1954] has devised a procedure to determine the relative size of elastic strain-rebound increments from earthquake magnitudes and has applied it to series of aftershocks of earthquakes, as well as to series of earthquakes in certain regions and at certain depth ranges. He assumes that an earthquake is generated by the elastic rebound of a volume of rock having an average rigidity μ and an average elastic strain γ preceding the rupture. The energy stored in a unit volume of the rock is $\frac{1}{2}\mu g \gamma^2$. Benioff takes the conversion efficiency of strain energy into seismic waves as unity, so that the strain rebound S equals γ. The square root of the energy J is proportional to γ. For a sequence of shocks occurring on a given fault, a graph of the accumulated sum of the increments $J^{0.5}$ plotted against time represents the elastic strain-rebound characteristic (times a constant factor) of the sequence. Originally Benioff had derived values for $J^{0.5}$ from the instrumental earthquake magnitude M by means of the tentative equation [Gutenberg and Richter, 1942]

$$\log J^{0.5} = a + bM \tag{9.18}$$

with $a = 6$, $b = 0.9$. Later, Eq. (9.18) as well as the constants a and b have been revised repeatedly [e.g., Gutenberg, 1956c]. However, the result-

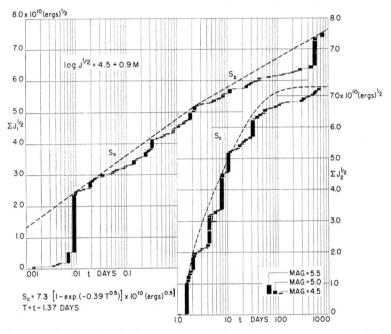

Fig. 9.5. Strain-rebound characteristics of the aftershock sequence of the Kern County, California, earthquake of 1952. From original by H. Benioff; t = time after main shock.

ing values of $\log J^{0.5}$ have not been changed much. In any case, the resulting value of $\log J^{0.5}$ may well be incorrect by one unit, especially in large shocks, but this does not seriously affect the following conclusions of Benioff.

Most strain-rebound characteristics of aftershock sequences show for certain time intervals t either a form

$$S_1 = l + m \log t \tag{9.19}$$

or

$$S_2 = O - Ne^{-P\sqrt{t}} \tag{9.20}$$

where l, m, O, N, P are constants of the process. S_1 corresponds to a form given by Griggs [1939a] for rocks, and by others for other materials under compressional elastic or recoverable creep strain. S_2 is of a form derived

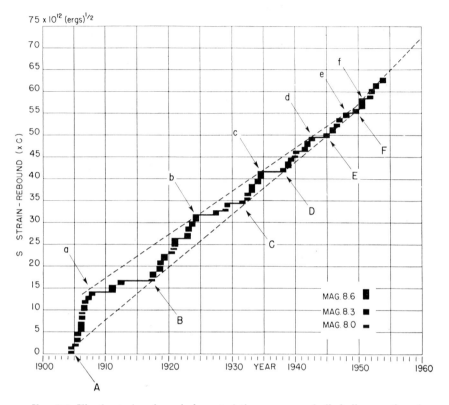

Fig. 9.6. Elastic strain-rebound characteristic; sequence of all shallow earthquakes magnitude $M \geq 8$ since 1904. Original by H. Benioff.

empirically by Michelson [1917, 1920] for shearing creep recovery. However, this form has not been verified by subsequent experiments. Creep tests by Lomnitz [1956] during shear have yielded only the form S_1. The occurrence of the form S_2 in aftershock sequences remains unexplained.

In aftershock sequences of the form S_1, activity followed for intervals varying from 100 days minimum to 600 days maximum. Sequences having the dual form came to definite terminations in intervals varying from 1 to 500 days. For example, Benioff [1955] has found that the aftershock series (Fig. 9.5) of the Kern County, California, earthquakes, 1952, exhibit one series of the form S_1, corresponding to shocks southeast of the fault and a second series of the form S_2 for aftershocks northwest of the fault.

Benioff [1951b, 1955] has applied the same method to series of earthquakes in various areas, and has found strain-rebound characteristics of forms similar to those discussed above. Figure 9.6 shows the strain-rebound characteristic of the sequence of all earthquakes of the world having magnitudes equal to or greater than 8.0, which have occurred since 1904. It has an approximately saw-tooth shape with amplitudes and periods decreasing linearly with time. Benioff points out that the initial points A, B, C, and D of the active intervals mark the times when the accumulated world strain

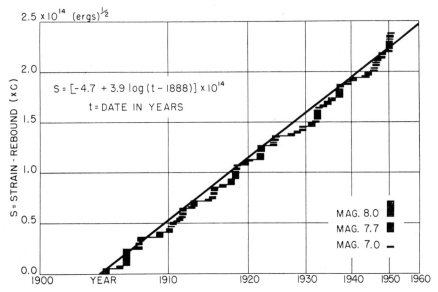

FIG. 9.7. Elastic strain-rebound characteristic; sequence of earthquakes with focal depths $h > 300$ km and magnitude $M \geq 7.0$ since 1905 (incomplete for magnitudes 7 to $7\frac{1}{2}$ for 1905 to 1917). After original by H. Benioff.

was maximum and that the end points a, b, c, d, e, and f mark the times at which the accumulated world strain passed through minima. The upper dashed line drawn through the points of minimum strain should therefore represent the total secular strain-generation (times a constant of the system). The small spread of points on this line indicates that the rate of strain-generation has been fairly constant from 1907 to 1951. Benioff [1955, p. 71] concludes from the regular alternation of high activity with periods of a relatively low activity that great shallow earthquakes are not independent events. However, "a world mechanism for locking and releasing the faults in accordance with the rebound characteristic is difficult to devise. Possibly it may involve changes in the radius of the earth."

The corresponding strain release in all large deep earthquakes (Fig. 9.7) fits a logarithmic curve so well that this may be interpreted as evidence that all great deep earthquakes, too, are related to a single stress system in which a compressional elastic creep strain has been accumulating or relaxing. There are indications in both curves that between 1950 and 1955 there may have been the beginning of a new cycle.

9.7 Convection Currents in the Earth

In a variety of geotectonic hypotheses the existence of subcrustal currents has been assumed [see, e.g., Colloquium, 1951, pp. 527–538]. From our present knowledge there is no reason why such currents should not be possible in near-homogeneous portions of the earth [see, e.g., Jardetzky, 1958, p. 130]. With increasing depth, the time of relaxation λ in flow processes seems to decrease (Table 9.1a) from the order of several thousand years in the upper $50\pm$ km of the mantle, perhaps to the order of 100 years at 700 km depth, and to still shorter time intervals below. However, changes in composition or in phase in the mantle (Section 4.3) may prevent or at least reduce such currents [Birch, 1951; Glangeaud, 1951]. Among many others, Meinesz [in Heiskanen and Meinesz, 1958, p. 401] discusses these difficulties and points out how the explanation of many tectonic problems is facilitated by the assumption of convection or other subcrustal currents.

The first comprehensive theoretical investigation of convection currents in the earth's mantle, as a consequence of the difference in temperature under ocean bottoms and under continents, has been made by Pekeris [1935] before possible difficulties produced by changes in phase or composition in the outer mantle had been pointed out. Pekeris has investigated six models and has found velocities of the currents of the order of 1 cm/year. "The crust is pushed upwards under the warmer (continental) regions and pulled downwards under colder (oceanic) regions." On the other hand, Lyustikh [1957] concludes that a world gravimetric survey provides no support for the convection hypothesis.

Griggs [1939b] has outlined a theory of mountain building by cyclic convection of thermal origin and has used mechanical models to support his ideas. Urey [1953] has discussed a variety of types of convection currents in all portions of the earth. Meinesz [in Heiskanen and Meinesz, 1958, p.

397] has shown theoretically that convection currents are possible on certain assumptions. Many others have based tectonic hypotheses on subcrustal currents of various types. Some of such hypotheses have been summarized, for example, by Gutenberg [1951, p. 186], and by Kraus [1958]. Usually, the possibility of subcrustal currents is postulated in such hypotheses, but neither the type nor other details of the nonelastic processes involved are discussed.

9.8 Movements of Large Crustal Blocks Relative to Each Other

Movements of extended blocks of the earth's crust relative to each other have been suggested in many geotectonic hypotheses. A detailed discussion could cover hundreds of pages. Only a few examples of such observed or hypothetical movements can be given here. Horizontal movements may be discovered by geological investigations, for example from displacements along faults. Vertical movements are often indicated, in addition, by changes of shore lines or by records of tide gauges. Finally, accurate data on present changes are provided by geodetic measurements, either triangulations or precise levelings [see, e.g., Tsuboi, 1939]. However, reliable data from any of these methods are scanty, and, even when the findings available from all are combined, there is no major region of the earth for which a fairly complete and reliable map showing recent displacements can be drawn.

Most observations of displacements concern crustal movements along faults in the circum-Pacific earthquake belts (Fig. 3.12). The San Andreas fault system is the longest belt which has been investigated in detail. In its central portion the displacements are so great that no corresponding rocks have been established beyond doubt on the two sides of the fault system. Rivers displaced at the faults show that the Pacific side has been and still is moving northwestward relative to the continental side. These rivers, flowing usually more or less southwestward, are diverted northwestward along the fault system and have broken through the respective features along the fault to the next river bed to the south as soon as the relative displacement along the fault had reached the distance of the two successive valleys. As this has happened an unknown number of times, the total displacement cannot be estimated from such information.

Hill and Dibblee [1953] have discussed some evidence that certain rock types on opposite sides of the San Andreas fault, which originally may have been deposited in the same locality, may now be hundreds of miles apart, depending on their age. Hill and Dibblee estimate that the speed of the average relative motion along the San Andreas fault system (southwest side moving towards northwest, relative to the northeast side) has been of the order of 1 cm/year, possibly since Cretaceous, hundred million years ago. Contemporary geodetic measurements indicate relative movements in the same direction, but a few times greater amounts of the relative displacements [Whitten, 1956].

In addition to the San Andreas fault system, running from northwest to southeast, there are in California fault systems extending more or less from northeast to southwest, with the northern side usually moving southwestward, relative to the southern. Moreover, Menard [1955] has investigated several "fracture zones" extending in the same general direction over 5000 km into the Pacific Ocean. He believes that "the sections of the crust between fracture zones have been deformed as blocks since the zones were formed."

Direction of faulting in Alaska has been studied by St. Amand [1957b]. He finds a type of motion similar to that along the San Andreas fault: The Pacific side moves counterclockwise (northwestward) relative to the continental side. He concludes that "seismic data and geologic observations indicate that the north Pacific Basin, from Baja California to the Kurile Islands at least, is and has been for a long time, rotating counterclockwise." On the other hand, Twenhofel and Sainsbury [1958, p. 1435] believe that "the geological data neither support nor deny St. Amand's hypothesis of major strike-slip movement" along the Denali fault in Alaska.

In Japan the conditions are more complicated as a consequence of the separation of the active zones in central Japan (Fig. 3.12). In northeastern Japan the motion seems to be southeastward on the oceanic side (counterclockwise) relative to the continental side, but in southeastern Japan in the fault zone towards the Marianas Islands the movement of the Pacific side is northwestward (clockwise). In some areas of Japan, geodetic measurements show even greater contemporary displacement than in California.

For the Philippines, Willis [1937, 1944] has concluded that along the southern portion of the Visayan Rift the oceanic side moves northward (clockwise) relative to the continental side. Similarly, Hess [1955, p. 398] indicates that along the east-westerly fault zone near the Fiji Islands the Pacific side is moving westward (clockwise) relative to the "continental" side.

There are well established data for New Zealand. Wellmann [1955] has found in detailed research that during movements along the main fault zone the "Pacific" southeast side has moved southwestward (counterclockwise) relative to the "continental" northwest side. Since Jurassic, the relative displacement may have reached 500 km; this indicates an average movement of the order of $\frac{1}{2}$cm/year. The average displacement along the main fault zone since the last glaciation is of the order of 1 cm/year; about four times this rate, in the same direction, has been found from geodetic measurements for the past 50 years. "The agreement in the order of magnitude is satisfactory and is as good as can be expected from the nature of the basic data . . . The total regional displacement . . . may be considerably greater" [Wellmann, 1955, p. 255].

In most areas which have been studied in detail, only a fraction of the displacement has occurred during earthquakes and the remainder during gradual flow-movement.

Apparently, it was pointed out first by Nakamura [1922] that, at least in Japan, compressions and dilatations recorded by the first onset of longitudinal waves in nearby earthquakes show distinct patterns of compressions and dilatations in an area within a radius of a few hundred kilometers around the source. Gherzi [1923] has found that in Zi-ka-wei (China) the type of the first motion in records of distant earthquakes depends on the azimuth of the epicenter at the recording station (more accurately, on the azimuth of the station from the epicenter). Somville [1925] has provided probably the first map showing (for Uccle, Belgium) areas with earthquakes which produce at a given station compressions, prevailing in the beginning of the longitudinal waves, and areas from which the first longitudinal wave arrives more frequently with a motion towards the source. Near the source there are frequently two approximately opposite sectors in which the first longitudinal impulse starts with a compression, and two where it begins with a dilatation.

Details of the distribution of these compressions and dilatations recorded over the earth after each major earthquake are now being studied increasingly to find the direction of the fault plane and the direction of the first motion in earthquakes. This kind of result will aid appreciably in the investigation of the prevailing motion along a given fault zone. The first motion in transverse waves is now also being studied, but conclusions are less reliable than those found from longitudinal waves, as the transverse waves begin in an already disturbed portion of the seismograms. Nevertheless, the findings may aid in the interpretation of the results from longitudinal waves which usually permit two solutions. The method is applicable to shallow and deep earthquakes.

Among the publications which have contributed to the development of these methods, are those by Byerly [1928], Gutenberg [1955], Hodgson

[1956, 1957], McIntyre and Christie [1957], and Keylis-Borok [1957]; see also Conference [1958, pp. 174–182]. Among the many publications giving discussions and interpretations of such data are those by Hodgson [1958], Hodgson and Cook [1958], Scheidegger [1957b] and Ritsema [1956, 1957a,b,c].

Even if we include in an investigation of crustal movements the best supported fault plane solutions, based on records of earthquakes, we find only relatively small portions of the earth's crust where the combined results of all available investigations seem to be sufficiently reliable for a deduction of movements of extended blocks of the earth's crust. Menard [1955] has concluded that the crustal movements along and across the northeastern Pacific indicate the existence of convection cells which are bounded by the San Andreas fault system, and the various fracture belts of the ocean bottom which are approximately perpendicular to the coast. On the other hand, Benioff [1957] and St. Amand [1957a] have concluded independently that the main circum-Pacific activity is probably the result of a tangential clockwise rotation of the continental margins relative to the suboceanic mass. On the assumption that the rate of this tangential slip is constant and equal to that along the San Andreas fault, Benioff estimates that the order of magnitude of the time for a complete revolution is 3×10^9 years. There is no definite information how deep into the earth's mantle such movements extend. The distribution of deep-focus earthquakes with depth (compare Figs. 3.13 and 3.14) indicates that the strain system covers at least the upper 800 km of the earth's mantle. Theoretical calculations by Haskell, which are based on Eqs. (9.13)–(9.17), point in the same direction.

Among the early hypotheses on movements of continents relative to each other is that of Taylor [1910; Symposium, 1928, pp. 158–177]. The most discussed hypothesis of this type [see, e.g., Symposium, 1928] is *Wegener's Theory*. Wegener [1912, 1915, 1929] has based his hypothesis originally on various types of arguments. In addition to the similarity of the figuration of the western and eastern Atlantic coasts, these include indications that several mountain ranges which are now interrupted by the Atlantic Ocean, originally may have continued without break from North or South America to Europe or Africa. Furthermore, Wegener presents paleontological as well as paleoclimatological evidence in support of his theory. According to Wegener's theory, originally all continents had been portions of one single continental block which had broken apart during Carboniferous. According to Wegener, the newly formed continents then drifted slowly in different directions through the substratum to their present positions, similar to icebergs drifting in the ocean.

Gutenberg [1927] has modified Wegener's hypothesis by replacing the breaking and drifting apart of the blocks by gradual flow in the upper portion of the earth's mantle (compare Fig. 9.10) which still continues. A spreading of the whole continental block towards the Pacific mass has been suggested repeatedly by geologists, for example, by Taylor [1910; Symposium, 1928, p. 165] and by Du Toit [1937], as well as by geophysicists.

One of the many objections against any theory of continental drift, the disbelief in the possibility of such large movements, can now be disregarded, since sufficient evidence of extensive movements of crustal blocks relative to each other has been found. The proof or disproof for specific assumed patterns of continental displacements as they have been outlined by Wegener and others has to be based, for example, on better geological, paleontological, and paleogeographic data [King, 1958]; on former connections between continents, or the lack of such connections; on improved evidence for changes in climate in one extensive area relative to others; on well substantiated data on gradual changes in the position of the two magnetic poles relative to the various continents during the earth's history (Section 9.9.2).

Doubts have been expressed if adequate *forces* exist to produce movements of large portions of the earth's crustal and deeper layers relative to each other. The answers of many authors of geotectonic hypotheses to this question are inadequate. Table 9.4 is a condensed summary of *some* suggestions which have been made for causes of movements in the earth, and corresponding possible results; both are changing rapidly as the pertinent investigations make progress.

The heat developed in disintegration of radioactive material is probably the largest original source of energy for many mechanical processes in the earth. It corresponds to an energy release of the order of magnitude of 10^{28} ergs/year, while the average annual release of energy in earthquakes is approximately of the order of 10^{25} ergs/year [Gutenberg, 1956c]. The depths at which some of the forces involved are acting are unknown. Some "results" are acting again as "cause," especially subcrustal currents. The investigations of Haskell [1935, 1936; see discussion following Eq. (9.15)] indicate that stress differences near the surface could be accompanied by not much smaller stress differences in the upper portion of the mantle, and vice versa.

The *mechanisms* in crustal and subcrustal movements offer other problems. As we have seen, our information about gradual movements in the earth is inadequate, and the question, to what extent and at what depths changes in phase or in material may be barriers to subcrustal flow, is still unsolved. Movements in the asthenosphere (Section 4.2), where the yield point is probably relatively close to zero, may not require great stress differences; but if the stress differences are relatively small, they must persist

TABLE 9.4. SOME SUGGESTED CAUSES FOR MOVEMENTS IN THE EARTH
AND THE CORRESPONDING POSSIBLE RESULTS

Cause	Result
1. Chemical processes Differentiation, combined with gravity Radioactivity	Layers in the crust Vulcanism Subcrustal currents
2. Radioactivity; heat radiation into space	Changes in temperature in the earth
3. Cooling of the earth's outer layers	Slight contraction of crust
4. Growing warmer of interior	Expansion of interior; subcrustal currents
5. Processes in the core	Terrestrial magnetism; effects on mantle
6. Differences in temperature and in thermal properties	Subcrustal currents
7. Sedimentation, erosion	Vertical movements; geosynclines; subcrustal currents; movements of the axis of the earth
8. Changes in astronomical elements of earth and moon	Changes in tidal stresses and of earth's figure; movements of earth's axis; changes in climate; transgressions, regressions.
9. Movements of continents	Movements of earth's axis; changes in climate
10. Differences in crustal structure	Movements of and in crustal blocks
11. Subcrustal currents	Changes in crust; mountains; earthquakes
12. Solar heat received by the earth and its changes	Melting and forming of ice
13. Melting and forming of ice	Vertical movements in the crust and upper portion of the mantle; movements of the earth's axis
14. Movements of the earth's axis	Changes in the rotational speed of portions of the crust and upper mantle, depending on the old and new latitude; movements of crustal blocks relative to each other.

for a long period of time to be effective. Moreover, the viscosity has probably a minimum at depths of the order of 100 to 150 km, where the temperature is probably near the melting point of the material (Section 6.9 and Fig. 6.1).

9.9 Secular Movements of the Poles

9.9.1 Movements of the Poles of Rotation

Kreichgauer [1902] apparently was the first to construct a reasonable hypothetical path of the North Pole of rotation relative to the continents

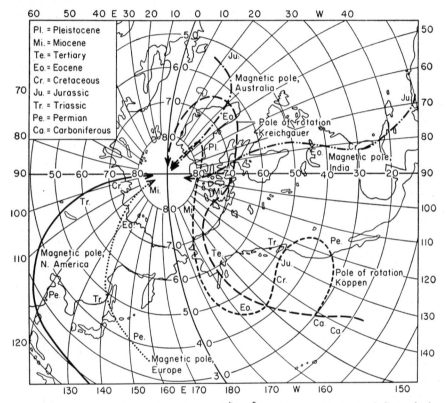

Fig. 9.8. Hypothetical paths of the North Pole of rotation on the basis of climatological evidence after Kreichgauer [1902] and after Köppen [1940] and of the magnetic North Pole on the basis of determinations of magnetic axes of rocks; data for North America and Europe according to Irving [1956], for Australia according to Irving and Green [1958], and for India according to Deutsch [1958]. All curves are smoothed and based on somewhat scattering data (compare Fig. 9.9), and it is assumed that the continents have not moved.

of the northern hemisphere during the geologic periods (see Fig. 9.8) on the basis of changes in climate. While some paleontologists, geologists, and climatologists do not believe that the paleoclimatological evidence indicates an appreciable shift of the poles of rotation relative to the continents (or vice versa), others have found independently that there is little difficulty in plotting climatological zones with different positions during the geological history. Nearly all such attempts have resulted in apparent paths of the poles of rotation, at least for the time since the Carboniferous, which differ relatively little between themselves. On Fig. 9.8, to be discussed in Section 9.9.2, two such curves, one suggested by Kreichgauer [1902] and another by Köppen [1940] are indicated.

For the geological periods preceding the Carboniferous the climatological data are scanty. Nevertheless, Kreichgauer had made an attempt to trace the movement of the North Pole back to pre-Cambrian times, to a position near the present South Pole. For periods starting with the Carboniferous, maps showing the position of the poles on the basis of more recent and more complete paleoclimatological data have been constructed by Köppen and Wegener [1924] and have been revised by Köppen [1940]. His result for the motion of the North Pole is indicated in Fig. 9.8. Köppen and Wegener place the North Pole of the Carboniferous in the Northern Pacific Ocean northeast of the present region of Hawaii. The corresponding position of the South Pole is between South Africa and Australia. According to Wegener's theory, these two continents were close together until the Carboniferous. In this way, all areas glaciated during the Permian–Carboniferous eras were brought together [cf. Köppen and Wegener, 1924, p. 22; Symposium, 1928, p. 11]. This result had been considered by Wegener as one of the arguments in favor of his theory of continental shift (Section 9.8).

If the poles of rotation have moved relative to the continents this may have been either the result of a shift of the earth's axis inside the earth, or of movements of large blocks of the crust plus portions of the outer mantle, relative to the main portion of the earth's body, or of both combined. The effect of motions in the core on displacements of the poles has been found to be negligible by Elsasser and Munk [1958].

Originally it had been calculated, especially by G. Darwin, that great energies are needed to shift the earth's axis inside the earth. However, Munk [1956a,b] has pointed out that the early theoretical equations contain errors, and that movements of the earth's axis may not require great energy. Munk [1956b] finds that the amount of polar displacement X may be calculated from

$$X = Q(1 + f\alpha t - e^{-\alpha t} \cos \omega t) \qquad (9.21)$$

where Q is a forcing function of the Heaviside step function type, representing the displacement of a mass relative to the crust;

$$f = \frac{\Delta h}{r_0}\left(1 - \frac{\bar{\rho}}{\rho_m}\right) \tag{9.22}$$

Δh = change in height, r_0 = radius of the earth, $\bar{\rho}$ = density of the added mass, ρ_m = mean density of the earth. Munk estimates that for a major geological movement f is of the order of 10^{-2}; α is the ratio μ/η of the rigidity to the viscosity of the earth. Munk suggests estimating η from the damping of the nutation with the angular frequency ω. For a rough estimate of X, Munk assumes that η is of the order of 2×10^{20} poises. To show the possible ease of movements of the earth's axis, Munk supposes that the second harmonic of the elevation of the earth's surface is a function of time, and he finds on the further assumption of a constant angular velocity of the poles of 90° in 5×10^8 years a value of the order of $\frac{1}{2}$m for the surface displacement which is necessary to produce this shift. These very rough estimates show that polar wandering of the observed order of magnitude may be produced by movements of the earth's axis inside the earth, if there are horizontally very extensive, though vertically relatively small changes in the earth's outer layers.

If movements of the continents relative to each other could be definitely proven, this could explain a portion of the observed "apparent" polar drift. At present there seems to be a preference for the assumption that blocks of the upper portion of the earth (down to a few hundred km?) move over the deeper portions, and that in addition the axis of rotation moves inside the whole earth, so that both processes are responsible for the hypothetical movements of the poles.

9.9.2 Movements of the Magnetic Poles Relative to the Continents

During recent years, extensive research has been undertaken to determine the positions of the magnetic poles during the geological past by use of observed directions of magnetic axes of rocks which have been deposited during a period of a given age. It is now widely believed that rocks become magnetized in the direction of the earth's field while they cool through the Curie point, and that the direction of their magnetic axis then remains fixed [Stott and Stacey, 1959] relative to the rock. Consequently, the direction of the magnetic axis of a rock *in situ* gives the direction of the magnetic pole at the time and at the point of the deposition of the rock, if effects of tectonic movements of the layer in which the rock is found since the time of its deposition are considered. Methods, to find this direction, have been summarized, e.g., by Runcorn [1956, p. 480] and by Collinson [1958].

Sometimes, reversals of the magnetic axis of rocks by 180° are observed. Possible explanations are still under discussion. Such reversals of the direction of the magnetic axis of the rocks are usually considered to be related to properties of the rock type. On the other hand, Creer [1958, p. 99] states that "world wide occurrence of reversals in geologically contemporaneous formations strongly suggests an origin closely connected with the main geomagnetic field."

The great majority of the increasing number of specialists who have studied paleomagnetism agree that the results of investigations of the magnetic axes of rock samples strongly indicate a gradual shift of the magnetic poles (Fig. 9.8) during the geological past [e.g., Einarsson, 1957; Runcorn, 1955a,b; Graham, 1955; Graham and Hales, 1957; Blackett, 1956; Howell and Martinez, 1957; Howell et al., 1958; Irving and Green, 1958; Creer, 1958; Collinson, 1958; Clegg et. al., 1956; see also Geophys. Abstr., 1957, No. 170, pp. 258–265]. Graham [1957] and others point out that great caution is required in the drawing of conclusions as the observations could be interpreted differently.

Several scientists point out, that the results obtained in North America while they agree fairly well with those found in Europe, show a systematic deviation from them well beyond the limits of error (Fig. 9.8); this they interpret as indicating a gradual shift in the distance between North America and Europe [see, e.g., DuBois, 1957; Bradley, 1957; Irving and Green, 1958, p. 70]. A noticeably larger relative shift is indicated between North America and South Africa [Graham and Hales, 1957, p. 195]: "The pole positions inferred from the measurements on the South African dolerites are not consistent with any of those found for rocks of the same age in Europe, North America and Australia. . . . The simplest way of reconciling the divergent pole positions is to postulate relative displacements of the continents, i.e., continental drift. . . . The displacements required are of the kind proposed by Wegener [1924]."

Irving and Green [1958] have investigated the movement of the magnetic poles relative to Australia (Fig. 9.9). They find that the positions of the paleomagnetic poles agree fairly well with the position of the earth's axis found from contemporary paleoclimatological evidence. However, the magnetic poles follow paths which differ completely from those found from the magnetic axes of rocks in Europe or from those in North America, if it is assumed that the continents have not changed their relative positions. The magnetic North Pole would have traveled northward through the Atlantic Ocean on the basis of the Australian data, while the European and North American data indicate paths through the western Pacific and East Asia respectively (Fig. 9.8). Moreover, "the form of the polar path from Australia prior to the Carboniferous is so different from that obtained from the northern continents . . . that the supposition of post-Carboniferous continental drift *only* is inadequate and it is necessary to suppose that

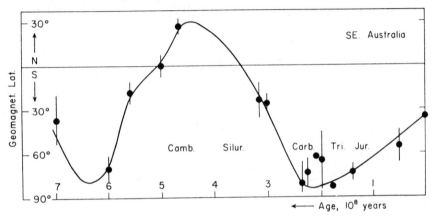

Fig. 9.9. Variations in geomagnetic latitude based on mean direction of magnetization of rock samples in southeastern Australia. The vertical lines represent errors, based on the limits within which the calculated latitude lay at $P = 0.95$; P is the probability as defined by Watson and Irving [1957]. After Irving and Green [1958, p. 69].

relative movements also occurred prior to the Carboniferous." This is also evident on maps reproduced by Collinson [1958, p. 208]. The path of the magnetic North Pole relative to India according to Deutsch [1958] follows roughly the present-day west coast of North America (Fig. 9.8) and lies between those based on Australian and those based on European data.

Gutenberg [1927] had tried to combine paleontological and paleoclimatological data with the findings of Wegener and had made an attempt to draft *sketches* of the earth's surface for different geological eras. Figure 9.10 is a reproduction of these maps of 1927 in which Gutenberg had used the positions of the poles and the equator considered by him the most probable for each map on the basis of climatological information. The hypothetical distribution of land and water after Ihering [1927] for each period had been added mainly to show the great changes which have occurred during the geological past. A more reliable drawing of details requires the

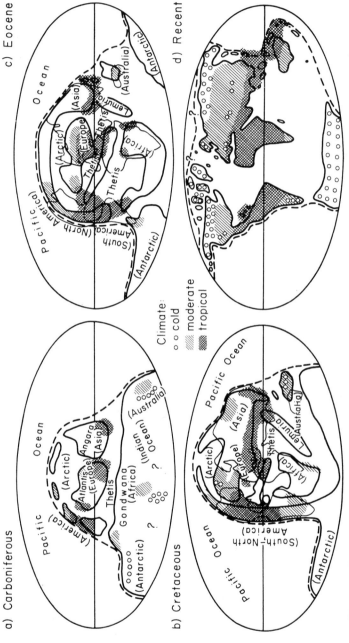

FIG. 9.10. Sketch of boundaries of continents and of their climates during the geological past after Gutenberg [1927]. The broken line indicates the hypothetical boundary of the Pacific Basin. The contours of the present continents are sketched with light lines in (b) and (c). Contours of land areas in the geological past after Ihering [1927].

use of more data to be compiled by specialists. Rough sketches of the contours of the present continents have been added in Fig. 9.10(b) and (c) on the basis of the original maps of Ihering to facilitate the comparison of the location of a given point during the geological past with respect to the poles and to other points on the earth's surface.

If we compare the paths of the magnetic poles which have been derived from paleomagnetic data (based, e.g., on Fig. 9.8) with the respective positions of the poles of rotation in Fig. 9.10, which have been based on paleoclimatological data, we find that in practically all instances both agree within the limits of error. For example, according to the recent paleomagnetic observations, central North America had been near the magnetic equator during Permian and Triassic, and has moved to about 30° north latitude during Cretaceous. All these results are in good agreement with Fig. 9.10, which was published over thirty years ago on the basis of paleoclimatological data. Similarly, Europe should have moved since Carboniferous from close to the equator to its present position according to the magnetic results as well as to Fig. 9.10. Both methods give roughly the same distances of South Africa from the respective South Poles since Jurassic. For Australia, the agreement may seem to be not quite so close; according to the paleomagnetic data, Australia was roughly 20° distant from the South Pole between Carboniferous and Jurassic, and afterwards its distance from the South Pole should have increased to its present value. Figure 9.10 gives a slightly greater distance from the South Pole for Carboniferous; however, according to Köppen–Wegener's figures [1924, pp. 22, 23; see also, Symposium, 1928, pp. 11, 17, 21] which are based on paleoclimatological data, the South Pole had been moving during Permian into West-Australia.

For the periods since and including Carboniferous, the curves for the path of the South Pole on the basis of Köppen–Wegener's data and that for the path of the magnetic South Pole in Fig. 9.9 are in excellent agreement. Finally, the magnetic data indicate that India has moved from a distance of about 45° from the South Pole during the Jurassic to about 10° south of the equator in Eocene, in reasonably good agreement with Fig. 9.10. Thus, there are now so many areas for which the findings derived from climatological evidence and those from paleomagnetic data are in good agreement that it is very difficult to consider this a coincidence [Gutenberg, 1956b].

The resulting locations of the magnetic as well as the geographic poles indicate that nearly the whole "continental block" had been located in the southern hemisphere during Carboniferous (Fig. 9.10). As has been mentioned, there are good indications that the poles of rotation as well as the magnetic poles had moved already considerably during pre-Carboniferous times. For example, Fig. 9.9 indicates that Australia, which was close to the South Pole during Permian and slightly more distant from it during Carboniferous, had crossed the magnetic equator twice before, once during Silurian and once in pre-Cambrian times.

The foregoing discussion [see also Irving, 1959] shows that the recent results concerning movements of the magnetic poles relative to the continents agree well with the older conception about continental movements based on paleontological data. This is an example of an hypothesis which has been strengthened by the addition of many new data of a type different from that on which it had been based originally. It seems to be more probable now than at the time when Wegener's theory had been formulated that, during the geological history, continents or portions of them have moved considerably relative to each other and relative to the earth's axis.

One of the many questions to be raised concerns the relationship between movements of the continental mass relative to the earth's axis on the one hand, and the movements of this mass relative to the Pacific mass on the other. The average velocities involved are of the same order of magnitude in both. If we compare the relative motions of the two systems in the few areas where we have data for both, we find no obvious answer. For example, the North American continent has moved northward since Carboniferous according to Fig. 9.10, but the movement of its westernmost portion east of the San Andreas fault system has been southward relative to the borderland of the Pacific mass. On the other hand, the movements observed in New Zealand, with the "continental side" west of the Alpine fault moving northward relative to the "Pacific" eastern side, are in the same direction as those following from Fig. 9.10. Thus, at present, it is difficult to decide, if, or how much, the movements of portions of the earth's crust relative to each other are related to the movements of the earth's axis inside the earth. It also has not been possible to determine whether or not the Pacific mass has a movement relative to the deep interior of the earth. Thus, we cannot yet decide if the "movements of the poles" are mainly a consequence of movements of the earth's axis relative to the earth's body, nor how far they result from movements of the earth's crust, including possibly portions of the mantle, relative to the main body of the earth.

Observations of polar shift by astronomical means during the present century indicate movements of the poles at a rate of a much smaller order of magnitude than those found for shifts which, for the geological past, have been based on paleontological and paleomagnetic data. The problem has been discussed, e.g., by Elsasser and Munk [1958]. However, there are indications from the paleoclimatological data that during the Recent era the direction of the motion of the North Pole has almost reversed itself [e.g., Köppen, 1940; see also Fig. 9.8]. On the other hand, movements of crustal blocks relative to each other, changes in the distribution of water and land, which we find (Fig. 9.10), and changes in the mass of ice and of water resulting from changes in the climate of large portions of the earth (ice ages) seem to produce great enough changes in weight distribution in the earth's crustal layers to fulfil those requirements for changes in the position of the earth's axis, which have been found by Munk [1956a,b] and to which we have referred on p. 215.

Finally, we must realize that all the findings and hypotheses to which we have referred in this section are only rough qualitative outlines which certainly will change considerably in the future. As Graham [1956] and others have pointed out, the data are consistent with various versions of polar wandering and continental drift, but they do not reveal which processes have actually taken place. To find a better and more reliable approximation to the history of the earth during the last few hundred million years and to its present structure

THE DATA "MUST BE GREATLY AMPLIFIED AND STRENGTHENED."

This might be called the motto of this book.

References

Anonymous [1956]. Geophysical discussion. *Observatory* **76,** 96–100.

Benioff, H. [1951a]. Earthquakes and rock creep. *Bull. Seismol. Soc. Am.* **41,** 31–62.

Benioff, H. [1951b]. Crustal strain characteristics derived from earthquake sequences. *Trans. Am. Geophys. Union* **32,** 508–514.

Benioff, H. [1954]. Orogenesis and deep crustal structure. *Bull. Geol. Soc. Am.* **65,** 385–400.

Benioff, H. [1955]. Seismic evidence for crustal structure and tectonic activity. *Geol. Soc. Am. Spec. Papers* **62,** 61–73.

Benioff, H. [1957]. Circumpacific tectonics. *Compt. rend. assoc. séismol. et phys. intérieur de la terre, Toronto, 1957, Resumé* **120;** *Publs. Dominion Astrophys. Observatory Ottawa* **20,** 395–402.

Birch, F. [1942]. Internal friction in vibrating solids. "Handbook of Physical Constants." *Geol. Soc. Am. Spec. Papers* **36,** 89–92.

Birch, F. [1951]. Remarks on the structure of the mantle, and its bearing upon the possibility of convection currents. *Trans. Am. Geophys. Union* **32,** 533–534.

Blackett, P. M. S. [1956]. "Lectures on Rock Magnetism," 131 pp. Weizmann Sci. Press, Jerusalem and Interscience, New York.

Bradley, J. [1957]. The meaning of paleographic pole. *New Zealand J. Sci. Technol.* **B38,** 354–365.

Byerly, P. [1928]. The nature of the first motion in the Chilean earthquake of November 11, 1922. *Am. J. Sci.* (5) **16,** 232–236.

Clegg, J. A., Deutsch, E. R., and Griffith, D. H. [1956]. Rock magnetism in India. *Phil. Mag.* [8] **1,** 419–431.

Collinson, D. W. [1958]. Rock magnetism. *Roy. Astron. Soc. London, Occasional Notes* **3,** 203–210.

Colloquium [1951]. Colloquium on plastic flow and deformation within the earth. *Trans. Am. Geophys. Union* **32,** 494–543.

Conference [1958]. *Compt. rend assoc. intern. séismol. et phys. intérieur de la terre, Toronto, 1957, No.* **12,** 301 pp. and appendixes.

Creer, K. M. [1958]. Symposium on palaeomagnetism and secular variation. *Geophys. J.* **1,** 99–105.

Daly, R. A. [1940]. "Strength and Structure of the Earth," 434 pp. Prentice-Hall, New York.

Deutsch, E. R. [1958]. Recent palaeomagnetic evidence for the northward movement of India. *J. Alberta Soc. Petrol. Geol.* **6,** 155–162.

DuBois, P. M. [1957]. Comparison of palaeomagnetic results for selected rocks of Great Britain and North America. *Advances in Phys.* **6,** 177–186.

Du Toit, A. L. [1937]. "Our Wandering Continents," 356 pp. Hafner, New York (reprinted 1957).

Einarsson, T. [1957]. Der Paläomagnetismus der isländischen Basalte und seine stratigraphische Bedeutung. *Neues Jahrb. Geol. u. Paläontol.* **4,** 159–175.

Eirich, F. R., ed. [1956]. "Rheology: Theory and Applications," Vol. 1, 761 pp. Academic Press, New York.

Eirich, F. R., ed. [1958]. "Rheology: Theory and Applications," Vol. 2, 591 pp. Academic Press, New York.

Elsasser, W., and Munk, W. [1958]. Geomagnetic drift and the rotation of the earth. *In* "Contributions in Geophysics" (H. Benioff, M. Ewing, B. F. Howell, and F. Press, eds.), Vol. 1, pp. 228–236, Pergamon, New York.

Ewing, M., and Press, F. [1954]. An investigation of mantle Rayleigh waves. *Bull. Seismol. Soc. Am.* **44,** 127–147.

Förtsch, O. [1956]. Die Ursachen der Absorption elastischer Wellen. *Ann. geofis.* **9,** 469–524.

Freudenthal, A. M., and Geiringer, H. [1958]. The mathematical theories of the inelastic continuum. *In* "Encyclopedia of Physics" (S. Flügge, ed.), Vol. 6, pp. 229–433. Springer, Berlin.

Gherzi, E. (1923). *Note Sismol. Observatoire Zi-Ka-Wei No.* **4,** 5.

Glangeaud, M. L. [1951]. Thermodynamic theory of peri-continental liminary zones. *Trans. Am. Geophys. Union* **32,** 521–523.

Graham, J. W. [1955]. Evidence of polar shift since Triassic Time. *J. Geophys. Research* **60,** 329–347.

Graham, J. W. [1956]. Palaeomagnetism and Magnetostriction. *J. Geophys. Research* **61,** 735–739.

Graham, J. W. [1957]. Rock magnetism. *Carnegie Inst. Wash. Yearbook 1956–57* **56,** 97–100.

Graham, K. T. W., and Hales, A. L. [1957]. Palaeomagnetic measurements on Karroo dolerites. *Phil. Mag. Suppl.* **6**, 149–161.

Griggs, D. T. [1939a]. Creep of rocks. *J. Geol.* **47**, 225–251.

Griggs, D. T. [1939b]. A theory of mountain-building. *Am. J. Sci.* **237**, 611–650.

Griggs, D. T. [1940]. Experimental flow of rocks under conditions favoring recrystallization. *Bull. Geol. Soc. Am.* **51**, 1001–1022.

Gutenberg, B. [1924]. Dispersion und Extinktion von seismischen Oberflächenwellen und der Aufbau der obersten Erdschichten. *Phys. Z.* **25**, 377–381.

Gutenberg, B. [1927]. Die Veränderungen der Erdkruste durch Fliessbewegungen der Kontinentalscholle. *Gerlands Beitr. Geophys.* **16**, 239–247; **18**, 281–291; [1936]. Structure of the earth's crust and spreading of the continents. *Bull. Geol. Soc. Am.* **47**, 1587–1610.

Gutenberg, B. [1941]. Changes in sea level, postglacial uplift, and mobility of the earth's interior. *Bull. Geol. Soc. Am.* **52**, 721–772.

Gutenberg, B. [1945a]. Amplitudes of surface waves and magnitudes of shallow earthquakes. *Bull. Seismol. Soc. Am.* **35**, 3–12.

Gutenberg, B. [1945b]. Amplitudes of P, PP, and S and magnitudes of shallow earthquakes. *Bull. Seismol. Soc. Am.* **35**, 57–69.

Gutenberg, B. [1951]. Hypotheses on the development of the earth. *In* "Internal Constitution of the Earth" (B. Gutenberg, ed.), 2nd ed., pp. 178–226. Dover, New York.

Gutenberg, B. [1954]. Postglacial uplift in the Great Lakes region. *Arch. Meteorol. Geophys. u. Bioklimatol.* **A7**, 243–251.

Gutenberg, B. [1955]. The first motion in longitudinal and transverse waves of the main shock and the direction of the slip. *In* "Earthquakes in Kern County, California during 1952." *Div. of Mines, San Francisco, Bull.* **171**, 165–170.

Gutenberg, B. [1956a]. Damping of the earth's free nutation. *Nature* **177**, 887–888.

Gutenberg, B. [1956b]. Verschiebung der Kontinente, eine kritische Betrachtung. *In* "Geotektonisches Symposium Zu Ehren von Hans Stille" (F. Lotze, ed.), pp. 411–421. F. Enke, Stuttgart.

Gutenberg, B. [1956c]. The energy of earthquakes. *Quart. J. Geol. Soc. London* **112**, 1–14.

Gutenberg, B. [1958a]. Attenuation of seismic waves in the earth's mantle. *Bull. Seismol. Soc. Am.* **48**, 269–282.

Gutenberg, B. [1958b]. Rheological problems of the earth's interior. *In* "Rheology: Theory and Applications" (F. R. Eirich, ed.), Vol. 2, pp. 401–431. Academic Press, New York.

Gutenberg, B., and Richter, C. F. [1942]. Earthquake magnitude, intensity, energy and acceleration. *Bull. Seismol. Soc. Am.* **32**, 163–191.

Haskell, N. A. [1935, 1936]. The motion of a viscous fluid under a surface load. *Physics* **6**, 265–269; **7**, 56–61.

Heiskanen, W. [1951]. On the postglacial uplift of land in Fennoscandia. *Trans. Am. Geophys. Union* **32**, 524–525.

Heiskanen, W. A., and Meinesz, F. A. V. [1958]. "The Earth and its Gravity Field," 470 pp. McGraw-Hill, New York.

Hess, H. H. [1955]. Serpentines, orogeny, and epeirogeny. *Geol. Soc. Am. Spec. Papers* **62**, 391–408.

Hiersemann, L. [1958]. Die rheologischen Eigenschaften der Erdkruste vom Standpunkt der neuen Erkenntnisse über den Herdvorgang bei grossen Erdbeben. *Ann. geofis.* **11**, 113–123.

Hill, M. L., and Dibblee, T. W. [1953]. San Andreas, Garlock and Big Pine faults, California. *Bull. Geol. Soc. Am.* **64**, 443–458.

Hodgson, J. H. [1956]. Direction of faulting in some of the larger earthquakes of the Southwest Pacific, 1950–1954. *Publs. Dominion Astrophys. Observatory Ottawa* **18**, 171–216.

Hodgson, J. H. [1957]. Nature of faulting in large earthquakes. *Bull. Geol. Soc. Am.* **68**, 611–643.

Hodgson, J. H. [1958]. Direction of displacement in western Pacific earthquakes. *In* "Contributions in Geophysics" (H. Benioff, M. Ewing, B. F. Howell, and F. Press, eds.), Vol. 1, pp. 69–86. Pergamon, New York.

Hodgson, J. H., and Cock, J. T. [1958]. Direction of faulting in some of the larger earthquakes of 1954–1955. *Publs. Dominion Astrophys. Observatory Ottawa* **19**, 223–258.

Howell, L. G., and Martinez, J. D. [1957]. Polar movement as indicated by rock magnetism. *Geophysics* **22**, 384–397.

Howell, L. G., Martinez, J. D., and Statham, E. H. [1958]. Some observations on rock magnetism. *Geophysics* **23**, 285–298.

Ihering, H. V. [1927]. "Die Geschichte des atlantischen Ozeans," 237 pp. Fischer, Jena.

Irving, E. [1956]. Palaeomagnetic and palaeoclimatological aspects of polar wandering. *Geofis. pura e appl.* **33**, 23–41.

Irving, E. [1959]. Palaeomagnetic pole positions: a survey and analysis. *Geophys. J.* **2**, 51–79.

Irving, E., and Green, R. [1958]. Polar movement relative to Australia. *Geophys. J.* **1**, 64–72.

Jardetzky, W. S. [1958]. "Theories of Figures of Celestial Bodies," 186 pp. Interscience, New York.

Jeffreys, H. [1952]. "The Earth," 3rd ed., 392 pp. Macmillan, New York.

Jeffreys, H. [1958]. On a modification of Lomnitz's law of creep in rocks and on rock creep and thermal instability. Summary. *Observatory* **78**, 188–190.

Jeffreys, H. [1959]. "The Earth," 4th ed., 420 pp. Macmillan, New York.

Joset, A., and Holtzscherer, J. J. [1954]. Sondages séismiques au Groenland. *Ann. géophys.* **10**, 351–381.

Kääriäinen, E. [1953]. On the recent uplift of the earth's crust in Finland. *Fennia* **77** (2), 106 pp.

Kárnik, V. [1956]. Magnitudenbestimmung europäischer Nahbeben. *Trav. Inst. Geophys. Acad. Tchecoslov. Sci. No.* **47**, 124 pp.

Keylis-Borok, V. I. [1957]. The determination of earthquake mechanism using both longitudinal and transverse waves. *Ann. geofis.* **10**, 105–128.

King, L. C. [1958]. Basic palaeogeography of Gondwanaland during the Late Palaeozoic and Mesozoic eras. *Quart. J. Geolog. Soc. London* **114**, 47–77.

Knopoff, L. [1956]. The seismic pulse in materials possessing solid friction. *Bull. Seismol. Soc. Am.* **46**, 175–183.

Knopoff, L., and MacDonald, G. J. F. [1958]. Attenuation of small amplitude stress waves in solids. *Revs. Modern Phys.* **30**, 1178–1192.

Köppen, W. [1940]. Die Wanderung des Nordpols seit der Steinkohlenzeit. *Meteorol. Z.* 1940, 106–110.

Köppen, W., and Wegener, A. [1924]. "Die Klimate der geologischen Vorzeit," 255 pp. Borntraeger, Berlin.

Kraus, E. G. [1958]. Fünfzig Jahre Unterströmungs-Theorie. *Geologie* **7**, 261–283.

Kreichgauer, D. [1902]. "Die Aequatorfrage in der Geologie," 394 pp. Steyl.

Lomnitz, C. [1956]. Creep measurements in igneous rocks. *J. Geol.* **64**, 473–479.

Lyustikh, E. N. [1957]. Convection in the earth's envelope according to the calculations of Pekeris. *Bull. acad. sci. U.R.S.S., Geophys. Ser. No.* **5**, 63–75.

McIntyre, D. B., and Christie, J. M. [1957]. Nature of the faulting in large earthquakes. *Bull. Geol. Soc. Am.* **68**, 645–652.

Melchior, P. [1955]. Sur l'amortissement du mouvement libre du pôle instanté de rotation à la surface de la Terre. *Atti accad. nazl. Lincei Rend. Classe sci. fis. mat. e nat.* [8] **19**, 137.

Melchior, P. J. [1957]. Latitude variation. "Physics and Chemistry of the Earth" (L. H. Ahrens, K. Rankama, and S. K. Runcorn, eds.), Vol. 2, pp. 212–243. Pergamon Press, New York.

Menard, H. W. [1955]. Deformation of the northeastern Pacific Basin and the west coast of North America. *Bull. Geol. Soc. Am.* **66**, 1149–1198.

Michelson, A. A. [1917, 1920]. Laws of elastic viscous flow. *J. Geol.* **25**, 405–410; **28**, 18–24.

Munk, W. H. [1956a]. Polar wandering: A marathon of errors. *Nature* **177**, 551–554.

Munk, W. H. [1956b]. Polar wandering. Geophysical discussion. *Observatory* **76**, 98–99.

Nakamura, S. [1922]. On the direction of the first movement of the earthquake. *J. Meteorol. Soc. Japan,* **41**.

Nansen, F. [1928]. The earth's crust, its surface forms, and isostatic adjustment. *Avhandl. Norske Videnskaps-Akad. Oslo I Mat. Naturv. Kl.* **12**.

Orowan, E. [1958]. Lectures on "Mechanical Problems of Geology" given at the California Institute of Technology; to be published.

Pekeris, C. L. [1935]. Thermal convection in the interior of the earth. *Monthly Notices Roy. Astron. Soc. Geophys. Suppl.* **3**, 343–367.

Press, F. [1956]. Rigidity of the earth's core. *Science* **124**, 1204.

Prey, A. [1942]. Über Polschwankung und Polwanderung. *Gerlands Beitr. Geophys.* **56**, 155–202.

Reiner, M. [1958]. Rheology. *In* "Encyclopedia of Physics" (S. Flügge, ed.), Vol. 6, pp. 434–550. Springer, Berlin.

Ritsema, A. R. [1956, 1957a]. "The mechanism in the focus of 28 South-East Asian earthquakes." Lembaga Meteor. dan Geofisik, Verh. 50, 76 pp.; Verh. 52, 31 pp. Djakarta, Indonesia.

Ritsema, A. R. [1957b]. Pacific and "Mediterranean" earthquake mechanisms. *Trans. Am. Geophys. Union* **38**, 349–353.

Ritsema, A. R. [1957c]. Stress distributions in the case of 150 earthquakes. *Geol. en Mijnbouw* **19**, 36–40.

Runcorn, S. K. [1955a]. Palaeomagnetism of sediments from the Colorado Plateau. *Nature* **176**, 505.

Runcorn, S. K. [1955b]. Rock magnetism-geophysical aspects. *Phil. Mag. Suppl.* **4**, 244–291.

Runcorn, S. K. [1956]. Magnetization of rocks. *In* "Encyclopedia of Physics" (S. Flügge, ed.), Vol. 47, pp. 470–497. Springer, Berlin.

St. Amand, P. [1957a]. Circum-Pacific orogeny. *Compt. rend. assoc. intern. séismol. et phys. intérieur de la terre, Toronto, 1957, Resumé* **121,**

St. Amand, P. [1957b]. Geological and geophysical synthesis of the tectonics of portions of British Columbia, the Yukon Territory, and Alaska. *Bull. Geol. Soc. Am.* **68,** 1343–1370.

Scheidegger, A. E. [1957a]. Rheology of the earth: the basic problem of geodynamics. *Can. J. Phys.* **35,** 383–397.

Scheidegger, A. E. [1957b]. Table of Russian fault plane solutions. *Publs. Dominion Astrophys. Observatory Ottawa* **19,** 99–109.

Schweydar, W. [1912]. "Untersuchungen über die Gezeiten der festen Erde und die hypothetische Magmaschicht." *Veröffentl. Preuss. Geodät. Inst. Potsdam* **54.**

Somville, O. [1925]. Sur la nature de l'onde initiale des téléséismes enregistrés à Uccle de 1910 à 1924. *Publs. Bur. Central Séismol. Intern. Trav. Sci.* (A) **2,** 65–88.

Stott, P. M., and Stacey, F. D. [1959]. Magnetostriction and Palaeomagnetism of igneous rocks. *Nature* **183,** 384–385.

Symposium [1928]. "Theory of Continental Drift." 240 pp. Am. Assoc. Petrol. Geologists, Tulsa, Oklahoma.

Taylor, F. B. [1910]. Bearing of the Tertiary mountain belt on the origin of the earth's plan. *Bull. Geol. Soc. Am.* **21,** 179–226.

Tsuboi, C. [1939]. Deformations of the earth's crust as disclosed by geodetic measurements. *Ergeb. kosmischen Phys.* **4,** 106–168.

Twenhofel, W. S., and Sainsbury, C. L. [1958]. Fault patterns in southeastern Alaska. *Bull. Geol. Soc. Am.* **69,** 1431–1442.

Urey, H. C. [1953]. On the origin of continents and mountains. *Proc. Natl. Acad. Sci. U. S.* **39,** 933–945.

Watson, G. S., and Irving, E. [1957]. Statistical methods in rock magnetism. *Monthly Notices Roy. Astron. Soc. Geophys. Suppl.* **7,** 289–300.

Wegener, A. [1912]. Die Entstehung der Kontinente. *Geol. Rundschau* **3,** 276–292.

Wegener, A. [1915, 1929]. "Die Entstehung der Kontinente und Ozeane," 1st ed. [1915], 94 pp.; 4th ed. [1929], 231 pp. Vieweg, Braunschweig; (English translation of 3rd ed. [1924]. "The Origin of Continents and Oceans." Dutton, London).

Weinberg, B. [1927]. Some results of experimental study of substances having considerable internal friction. *Indian J. Phys.* **1,** 279–310.

Wellmann, H. W. [1955]. New Zealand Quaternary tectonics. *Geol. Rundschau* **43,** 248–257.

Whitten, C. A. [1956]. Crustal movement in California and Nevada. *Trans. Am. Geophys. Union* **37,** 393–398.

Willis, B. [1937]. Geologic observations in the Philippine archipelago. *Bull. Natl. Research Council Philippine Isl.* **13,** 108 pp.

Willis, B. [1944]. Philippine earthquakes and structure. *Bull. Seismol. Soc. Am.* **34,** 69–81.

AUTHOR INDEX

Numbers in italics refer to the page on which the reference is listed.

SUBJECT INDEX

A

Absorption coefficient, 189–191
Accuracy of results, 1, 3, 4, 6, 94, 221
Airy anomalies, 52, 53, 54, 58
  hypothesis, 48, 49, 55
Amplitudes of seismic waves, 16, 36–38,
  76–79, 85, 95, 96, 111, 156
Andesite line, 59, 60
Anomalies of gravity, 51–58, 61, 64, 65
Approximations, 2, 5
Asthenosphere, 21, 76, 145, 146
  channel, 77–89
  movements in, 145, 146, 212
Astronomical data, 10
Astronomical elements, secular changes,
  212
Atlantic structure, 59
Attenuation, elastic waves, 189–192
Australia, geomagnetic latitude, 217
Axis, magnetic, shift, 211–220
Axis of rotation, energy for shift, 212,
  214, 215
  shift relative to crust, 214, 220
    to interior, 214, 215, 220

B

Basalt, 26, 29, 65, 134, 179
Basaltic layer, 21, 30, 31–35, 51, 55–59,
  64, 133, 134
Bingham body, 188
Body tides, 115, 166, 170, 171, 188
  amplitudes, 171
  disturbances, 171
  no phase lag, 171, 200
  recording, 170
  strain, 171
Body waves, 3, 14, 15, 165, 166
  attenuation, 190, 191
  dispersion, 111, 112
  periods, 191

shadow zones, 25, 76–79, 81, 83–85,
  96
velocity, 15, 16, 26, 29, 32–35, 41,
  76–81, 108–113
Bouguer anomalies, 51, 52
  correction, 47
Boundaries in earth, 17
Breaking strength, 201
Bulk modulus, 91, 94, 151, 165, 166,
  179, 180, 186
  change in transition solid-liquid,
    112, 113
  effect of pressure, 180
  in earth, 180
  in rock, 179
Bullen's regions in earth, 17, 18, 75, 82,
  95

C

Caustics of travel time curves, 102–109,
  111, 112
Chandler period, 167–169, 173–200
  accuracy, 174
  variable value, 168
Channel, low-velocity, 39, 40, 77, 86, 87
  waves, 39, 40, 41, 77, 78, 86, 87
Clapeyron equation, 136
Clairaut's differential equation, 161
  equation, 150
Climate, changes, 211, 212, 213
Composition of earth, 115
Compressibility, 165, 179, 180
Compressions and dilatations, 209, 210
Conductivity, electric in earth, 126, 143
  thermal, 124–129, 139–142
Conrad discontinuity, 30, 32–34, 41, 50,
  57, 64
Continental block, 210, 218, 219
  drift, 210–212, 216, 218, 220, 221
  movement relative to Pacific, 208–210,
    218, 220
  reflections, 36, 37